The Open

Science Short Course

Empire of the microbes

Charles Cockell and Audrey Brown

This publication forms part of the Open University course S171 *Empire of the microbes*. Details of this and other Open University courses can be obtained from the Student Registration and Enquiry Service, The Open University, PO Box 197, Milton Keynes MK7 6BJ, United Kingdom (tel. +44 (0)845 300 60 90; email general-enquiries@open.ac.uk).

Alternatively, you may visit the Open University website at www.open.ac.uk where you can learn more about the wide range of courses and packs offered at all levels by The Open University.

To purchase a selection of Open University course materials visit www.ouw.co.uk, or contact Open University Worldwide, Walton Hall, Milton Keynes MK7 6AA, United Kingdom for a brochure (tel. +44 (0)1908 858793; fax +44 (0)1908 858787; email ouw-customer-services@open.ac.uk).

The Open University
Walton Hall, Milton Keynes
MK7 6AA

First published 2009.

Edited and designed by The Open University.

Typeset by SR Nova, Bangalore, India.

Printed and bound in the United Kingdom by Latimer Trend & Company Ltd, Plymouth.

The paper used in this publication is procured from forests independently certified to the level of Forest Stewardship Council (FSC) principles and criteria. Chain of custody certification allows the tracing of this paper back to specific forest-management units (see www.fsc.org).

ISBN 9781848 73008 3

1.1

Contents

The S171 Course Team

Chair
Charles Cockell

Authors
Audrey Brown
Charles Cockell

Course Manager
Isla McTaggart

Course Coordinator
Nick Adams

Consultant authors
Aaron Gronstal
Karen Olsson-Francis
Annika Simpson
Paul Wilkinson

Critical Readers
Hilary MacQueen
David Pearce

External Course Assessor
Dr Trudy Hartford

Production Team
Martin Chiverton (*Producer*)
Nicky Farmer (*Course assistant*)
Michael Francis (*Media developer*)
Emily Fuller (*Media assistant*)
Sara Hack (*Graphic artist*)
Rafael Hidalgo (*Media Project Manager*)
Chris Hough (*Graphic designer*)
Jenny Hudson (*Course Team assistant*)
Martin Keeling (*Media assistant, Rights*)
Will Rawes (*Media developer*)
Brian Richardson (*Media developer*)
Andy Sutton (*Media developer*)
Peter Twomey (*Editor*)

Chapter 1
Introduction to microbes

1.1   What is a microbe?

The Microbe is so very small
You cannot make him out at all,
But many sanguine people hope
To see him through a microscope

From *The Microbe* by Hilaire Belloc, 1900

The empire of the microbes reaches into almost every environment on Earth. Because of their small size, microbes are also called micro-organisms and their study is called microbiology. Microbes have been a pervasive influence in the lives of people from ancient times to the present day. They are beneficial to us in many ways; they help to recycle nutrients in the environment, as well as being used in a variety of processes such as making bread and brewing beer. At the same time, however, they have been a scourge to human society; they are responsible for many diseases, some of which have wiped out millions of people. Understanding microbes is therefore vital to scientists such as health professionals and environmentalists. But even the general public, concerned with such problems as hospital 'superbugs', can gain a great deal of understanding about many challenges in society by knowing something about microbiology. In this course you will learn about the amazing diversity and roles of microbes.

Apart from being so small that you need a microscope to see them, many people think of microbes as 'germs' or 'bugs'. The word 'germ' is usually used to refer to a disease-causing microbe. You may have seen advertisements for bleach, boasting that a particular brand kills 'all known germs'. The word 'germ' tends to give the false impression that all microbes are bad for humans. Calling them germs is inaccurate and probably not very fair to them, so the term will not be used again in the course. Calling microbes 'bugs' also suggests that they are harmful, and worse still, from a biological point of view, the word bug actually refers to a group of insects. Although some microbiologists occasionally refer to disease-causing microbes as bugs, as the term is technically incorrect, it will not be used again either.

Many microbes play vital roles in our health and environment and most do no harm or have no direct impact on humans at all. However, because diseases are so important to human society a great deal of attention has been focused on the microbes responsible for causing them and so you will find, as you go through the course, that many of the examples used are disease-causing microbes.

■ From your general knowledge, can you think of any useful roles that microbes play in our lives?

☐ Microbes are used in producing some types of food and drink. Yeast makes bread rise, while other microbes are used in the production of yoghurt and cheese. Antibiotics are made by microbes. Other microbes play vital roles in turning garden waste into compost and in digesting sewage. They also play an important role in our own digestive systems.

The term microbe includes various different groups of organisms. Bacteria (singular bacterium) are the most common microbe. In fact, bacteria are probably the most abundant group of organisms on the Earth; almost all surfaces which have not been specially sterilised harbour bacteria. But also included in the term microbes are: fungi, such as yeast; microscopic algae, such as those which form the powdery green coating on the shady side of tree trunks; and some less well-known groups called Archaea, which can be found in many environments including extreme environments such as hot springs in volcanic areas. The term microbe could also include the viruses, such as those that cause influenza (flu) and the common cold. The viruses are very different from most microbes because they cannot reproduce on their own so they tend to be viewed as a special group of microbes; you will learn more about them in Chapters 3 and 5. In general in this course the term microbe refers to bacteria, Archaea and fungi.

Question 1.1

Individual pollen grains from plants, sperms (spermatozoa) from animals and red blood cells are too small to see without a microscope. Why are these not classified as microbes?

1.2   The bubonic plague bacterium

A microbe which has played an influential part in the history of society, and was one of the first to be studied by early microbiologists, is the bacterium responsible for the bubonic plague. This provides a startling example of the profound influence that a tiny organism can have on our lives and society. About one-third of the population of Europe was wiped out by the plague in the 14th century. In Box 1.1 you can read more about this epidemic – a disease which appears in unexpectedly large numbers in a population. The plague microbe is carried around in the saliva of fleas and as the fleas jump from rats to people they spread the fatal disease around. The plague bacterium gives you some idea of why microbiology is such an important field. Until humans understand these microbes, how they function and how they cause disease, we are at their mercy.

Box 1.1 The Black Death

The bubonic plague has been a constant threat to people throughout history. It appeared without warning and caused rapid devastation. The most infamous outbreak, to which the term 'Black Death' is usually applied, was in the 14th century. Sometime during 1348 a ship arrived in England carrying, among other things, bubonic plague microbes, either in people or in fleas carried by rats. Historical accounts suggest that the ship arrived either in Bristol or Dorset. By November 1348, 30 000 of London's 70 000 population had died from bubonic plague. Within three years 30 to 40% of the whole population of England was dead.

Although little is heard about them these days, plague bacteria still live naturally in the environment. In parts of Asia they are to be found associated with marmots. In 2003 there was an outbreak of plague in Algeria and more recently there have been outbreaks in Madagascar.

When the plague bacterium enters the body, usually by flea bites but also by being breathed in, it reproduces and spreads into the body and produces poisonous substances called toxins that then circulate through the blood. As the toxins spread, they cause the formation of lesions (ulcers), and swellings called buboes (hence 'bubonic'). It takes between 2 and 6 days from infection for the microbe to start causing disease symptoms, and it can kill within a few days more. The microbe itself was isolated by microbiologists in 1894 during an outbreak of the disease in Hong Kong. Nowadays a considerable amount is known about the microbe and how it works, leading to intensive efforts to make better vaccines to protect against the disease. You will learn about vaccines in Chapter 5.

1.3   Naming microbes

■ What problems can you think of with using the name 'plague microbe' for this particular organism?

☐ Here are three problems you might have thought of:

(i)   In other languages, the disease will have a different name, so then the microbe would have a different name too and scientists discussing it might not realise they were talking about the same organism.

(ii)   The same microbe might cause a different disease in a species other than humans, and that could cause confusion about which microbe was being discussed too.

(iii)   The name tells us nothing about the microbe itself and gives no indication of how this particular microbe is related to other ones.

So microbes, like all other forms of life on Earth, are identified scientifically by being given two names, which scientists throughout the world use, and which identify them as belonging to a particular species. The exact meaning of the word species will be considered in more detail in Chapter 2, but, for now, it is sufficient to take species to refer to different types of living things.

■ Identify, or hazard an educated guess at, the common name of the species of animal, plant or microbe which have the following names: *Homo sapiens*, *Marmota himalayana*, *Rattus rattus*, *Bacillus anthracis*, *Panthera leo*, *Vibrio cholerae* and *Nicotiana tabacum*.

☐ *Homo sapiens* is the modern human. (*Homo* and *sapiens* are Latin for 'man' and 'wise', respectively.)

Marmota himalayana is the Himalayan marmot, as mentioned in Box 1.1.

Rattus rattus is the black rat which may have brought the plague to England.

Bacillus anthracis is the microbe that causes the disease anthrax.

Panthera leo is the lion (the tiger is *Panthera tigris*).

Vibrio cholerae is the microbe that causes the disease cholera.

Nicotiana tabacum is the tobacco plant. (The drug nicotine is present in the leaves and was named after the plant.)

■ What do you notice about the way that the scientific names of the species are written?

☐ Scientific names are always given in italics and typically have two words. The first word always starts with a capital letter and the second word with a small (lower case) letter.

■ Considering the scientific names for the lion and tiger, which of the two words would you say is the more general name for the group to which they both belong, and which is the name that identifies the particular species?

☐ The second word identifies the particular species: *leo* for lion and *tigris* for tiger. The name *Panthera* is for the group of closely related big cats. These closely related big cats are said to belong to the same genus (plural genera).

In these examples, it was relatively easy to identify the species from the scientific name, but often that is not the case. For example, it is not at all obvious that *Xenopsylla cheopis* is the rat flea that carries the plague microbe in its saliva or that *Yersinia pestis* is the plague microbe itself, except that an organism with the species name *pestis* sounds as though it might be the cause of pestilence or plague, in this case bubonic plague.

When scientists are communicating amongst themselves about organisms with which they are familiar, they often refer to the first name (genus) of the organism simply by the initial letter. So, wildlife experts might talk about *P. leo* and *P. tigris* and dinosaur experts often abbreviate *Tyrannosaurus rex* to *T. rex*. Microbiologists do it too. They talk about *Y. pestis* or *V. cholerae*.

■ You will almost certainly have heard in the news of two microbes harmful to health, which are commonly referred to by the initial letter of their genus name and then their species name. What are they?

☐ *E. coli* (*Escherichia coli*) is a microbe that is usually harmless and found naturally in the gut. However, some strains, notably one called *E. coli* O157, cause food poisoning. (A strain is a subset of microbes belonging to the same species but which differ in some minor characteristics; they are often identified by a number.)

There is also the so-called 'hospital superbug' *C. difficile*, where *C.* stands for *Clostridium*. In fact this one is often abbreviated yet further and just called *C. diff*. The microbe *C. diff* causes diarrhoea and fever and in rare cases can be fatal.

You will see in Chapter 2 how closely related genera are put together into larger groupings called families, and these families are eventually grouped into phyla (the plural of phylum).

1.4   The sizes and shapes of microbes

Figure 1.1 shows two pictures of a group of the bacterium that causes plague, greatly enlarged but to different sizes. A group of microbes like this is often referred to as a colony. In Figure 1.1a the bacteria have been stained to make them easier to see under the microscope. You will find out more about how images like this are taken in *Laboratory methods 1.1*, later in this section. The image in Figure 1.1b was taken by an 'electron' microscope rather than a light microscope and gives much greater detail which is also enhanced by the use of colour – a so-called false-colour image. In Chapter 5 you will learn more about how an electron microscope is used by microbiologists.

Figure 1.1b shows the size of one of the bacteria indicated as about one micrometre, 1 μm. One micrometre, 1 μm, also known as a micron, is one-thousandth of a millimetre, and this is a typical size for a microbe. If you are not familiar with these very small units of measurement, you should now work carefully through Box 1.2 before continuing with this text.

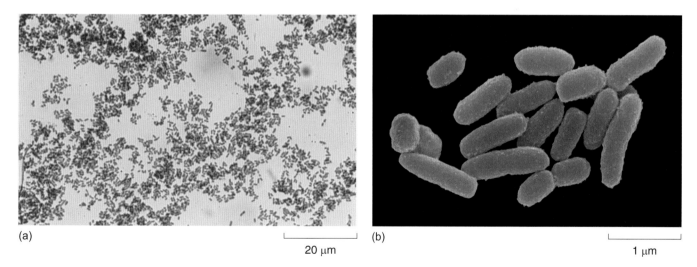

(a)   20 μm   (b)   1 μm

Figure 1.1   The bacteria *Yersinia pestis* that cause bubonic plague: (a) seen under a (visible) light microscope having been stained with a dye to make them easier to see (you will learn more about this staining method later); (b) a high-powered electron microscope image that has been artificially coloured – called a false-colour electron micrograph (see text).

Box 1.2 Measuring the size of microbes

Because microbes are so small they need to be measured in much smaller units than those with which you may be familiar, such as millimetres. In science, the units used are known as SI units, which is an abbreviation for Système Internationale d'Unités (International System of Units). The basic SI unit for length is the metre (abbreviated to m). Different words are placed in front of metre to designate different magnitudes. So, for example, a kilometre (kilo-metre or km) is one thousand metres, as kilo means one thousand. A centi-metre is one hundredth of a metre, so there are one hundred centimetres (cm) in a metre and a milli-metre (mm) is a thousandth of a metre.

■ How many millimetres are there in one centimetre?

□ Since a metre is made up of 100 cm, and 1000 mm, there must be 10 mm in 1 cm

To get down to the scale of microbes a unit is needed which is one thousandth of a millimetre – the micrometre, abbreviated to μm, where μ is the Greek letter mu.

■ How many micrometres (μm) are there in one metre, 1 m?

□ If there are 1000 μm in 1 mm, and then 1000 mm in 1 m, there will be $1000 \times 1000 = 1\,000\,000$ μm in 1 m. So there are 1 million μm in 1 m. 'Micro' means small, and it is also used more generally, as in words like micro-organisms, to mean very small. Sometimes the unit μm is referred to as a micron, rather than a micrometre.

There is an even smaller unit, called a nanometre, and abbreviated to nm. One nanometre is one-thousandth of a micrometre or one-millionth of a millimetre.

In summary,

$$1 \text{ km} = 1000 \text{ m}$$
$$1 \text{ m} = 100 \text{ cm} = 1000 \text{ mm}$$
$$1 \text{ mm} = 1000 \text{ μm}$$
$$1 \text{ μm} = 1000 \text{ nm}$$

Question 1.2

If a chain of 400 microbes of a particular species measured 0.8 mm, how long would each microbe be?

■ How would you describe the shape of *Yersinia pestis*, as shown in Figure 1.1b?

□ *Y. pestis* is an elongated oval shape. In three-dimensions it would be a tiny cylinder with rounded ends. Microbiologists refer to microbes like this as being 'rod-shaped' and call them bacilli.

Many microbes are spherical like those in Figure 1.2, and these are called 'cocci' (singular coccus). One of the more unusual shapes to be discovered is a square microbe, found in extremely salty environments, with distinctive sharp edges and corners, in contrast to the much more common cylindrical or spherical forms. This microbe (Figure 1.3) has been named *Haloquadratum walsbyi*, where *Halo* is salt and *quadratum* is square. The species name *walsbyi* is in honour of the British microbiologist Anthony Walsby who first described this microbe in 1980 in brine collected in the Red Sea.

■ Use the scale bar in Figure 1.3 to calculate the approximate size of one individual of *Haloquadratum walsbyi*.

☐ The scale bar represents 5 μm. The long rectangular microbes are almost as long as the scale bar – about 4 μm. The square ones are 2–3 μm in each direction.

Perhaps the prize for the largest microbe should go to one found growing on the sea floor off the coast of Namibia in Africa. This giant microbe, known as *Thiomargarita namibiensis* (translated as 'the sulfur pearl of Namibia'), is shown in Figure 1.4 and can grow to over 600 μm in diameter. Section 1.9 will discuss the factors that limit the size to which a microbe can grow.

■ Measure the size in millimetres of *Thiomargarita namibiensis* in Figure 1.4. If the microbe is actually 600 μm across, how many times has the picture been magnified? How does the actual size of the microbe compare with the dot at the bottom of this question mark?

☐ The microbe appears around 40 mm across on the figure, which is 40 × 1000 μm = 40 000 μm. If it is actually 600 μm in diameter, then it has been magnified 40 000/600 times, which is nearly 70 times.

The dot under the question mark appears to be just less than 0.5 mm. Since there are 1000 μm in 1 mm, then the dot is about 500 μm wide, which is slightly less than the size of one individual of *Thiomargarita namibiensis*.

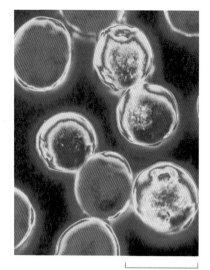

1 μm

Figure 1.2 A false-colour light micrograph of *Halococcus*, a coccoid bacterium that lives in salt water.

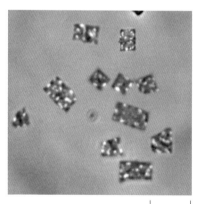

5 μm

Figure 1.3 A light micrograph of the square microbe, *Haloquadratum walsbyi*.

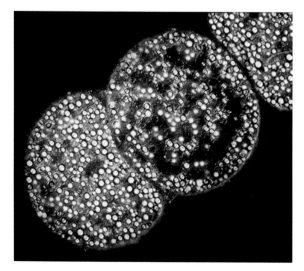

Figure 1.4 A light micrograph of two individuals and part of a third of the largest known microbe *Thiomargarita namibiensis* (see text for scale).

Question 1.3

By measuring the microbe in the bottom left-hand corner of Figure 1.1b, work out how many times the image has been magnified.

A good magnifying glass would enable you to magnify an object about 20 times at the most. For greater magnifications, it is necessary to use a microscope. *Laboratory methods 1.1* is the first of a number of descriptions of microbiological laboratory methods and techniques that you will meet throughout this course. You should read this now.

Laboratory methods 1.1   Using a light microscope

Although the light microscope was first developed in the 17th century, it still remains an important tool for studying micro-organisms in the laboratory. In Chapter 3 you will explore in more detail the history of microbiology and the important role that light microscopes have played in the discovery of microbes.

As you read through the following text, use Figure 1.5, which shows a labelled photograph of a simple light microscope, to identify the parts. Most light microscopes work by passing (transmitting) a focused beam of light upwards through the sample being observed and then focusing that light via a series of lenses, so that the enlarged image of the sample can be viewed via an eyepiece. Alternatively, a camera can be attached to the top of the microscope to record the image as a micrograph.

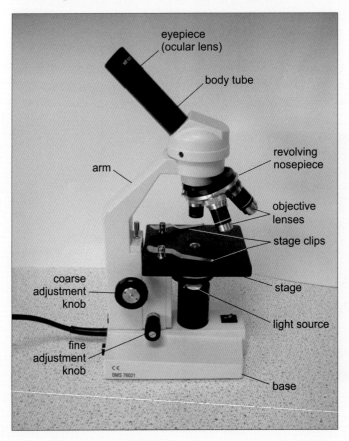

Figure 1.5 A simple light microscope (see text for description).

So that the light can be transmitted through the object, for example a sample consisting of yeast growing in a drop of sugary liquid, the drop needs to be placed on a glass microscope slide (about 70 mm × 25 mm, with a thickness of 2 mm). Often it is necessary to add a drop of coloured staining solution (dye) to the microbes being observed, to make them show up more clearly and to help with identification (see Activity 2.2). To prevent the liquid from evaporating, a very thin glass coverslip (20 mm × 20 mm, with a thickness of 0.25 mm) is carefully lowered onto the droplet (Figure 1.6). This complete assembly (slide, prepared sample and coverslip) is then placed on the microscope stage which has a central hole to allow the light to shine up from below. It is held in place with stage clips. The coarse and fine adjustment knobs are used to focus the image, which is then visible in the eyepiece (ocular lens).

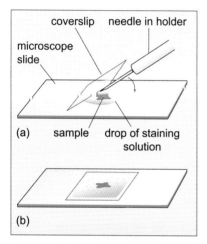

Figure 1.6   The preparation of a microscope slide. (a) Using a needle set into a holder, the coverslip is lowered onto the prepared sample. (b) The sample spreads out thinly under the coverslip and the complete slide is now ready to be placed under the microscope for examination.

The amount by which the image is magnified is the product of the magnification of the eyepiece (usually 10 times, written as ×10 or 10×) and the magnification of the chosen objective lens on the revolving nosepiece. The nosepiece typically carries three objectives with different magnifications, say ×10, ×40 and ×100.

■ What are the maximum and minimum magnifications possible from the microscope just described? How do these compare with a magnifying glass?

☐ The minimum magnification with the microscope is ×100 (= ×10 objective multiplied by ×10 eyepiece) and the maximum is ×1000 (= ×100 objective multiplied by ×10 eyepiece). Since a good magnifying glass would only give a magnification of ×20, the microscope gives magnification of between 5 and 50 times that of the magnifying glass.

■ The diameter (thickness) of a human hair is about 100 µm. How thick would it appear to be if magnified 100 times?

☐ If magnified 100 times, the hair would appear to be 100 × 100 µm = 10 000 µm thick. Since there are 1000 µm in 1 mm, this is 10 mm or 1 cm.

■ How big would *Yersinia pestis* appear if magnified 1000 times?

☐ *Y. pestis* is about 1 μm in size, which magnified by 1000 would give an image 1000 μm or 1 mm across, so it would be about the size of an elongated full stop.

The best light microscopes can magnify up to about 1500 times (i.e. ×1500) and with this, it is possible to see objects down to about 0.2 μm in size. So a light microscope enables the shape and colouration of microbes to be seen, but little of the internal detail. To see more detail, an electron microscope is used. Viruses are too small to be seen with a light microscope so must be studied with an electron microscope.

In this course you will use a digital light microscope to observe many different microbes so that you can gain first-hand experience of how a microscope works and what its limitations and possibilities are.

Question 1.4

(a) Calculate the size of the microbes depicted in Figure 1.7a and in Figure 1.7b, using the information about size given in the picture and the caption.

(b) How do the sizes compare?

(c) What would be the advantage of using a scale bar, rather than stating the magnification, if you wanted to copy the image for use in another publication?

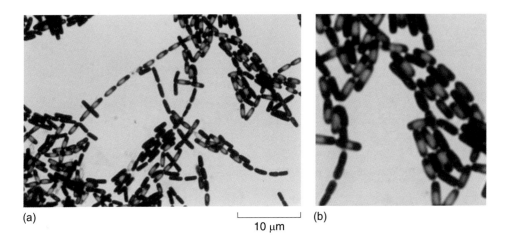

(a)   10 μm   (b)

Figure 1.7 Enlarged light micrographs of stained bacilli: (a) with a scale bar to indicate size; (b) magnified about 3000 times.

1.5 The structure of bacteria

You may already know that larger organisms, including ourselves, are made up of millions of tiny components called cells. The human body contains cells of many different types – skin cells, liver cells, muscle cells, blood cells, etc. Human cells are typically between about 10 μm and 30 μm across, that is much larger than most microbes. However, despite their small size, microbial cells contain all that is necessary for them to live, grow and reproduce.

Figure 1.8 shows the structural features of a generalised bacterium, though not all bacteria have all of these features.

■ Working from the outside towards the inside, what layers are shown surrounding the bacterium in Figure 1.8?

☐ The outermost layer is labelled the capsule. Inside that is the outer membrane, then the cell wall and then the plasma membrane.

The capsule, outer membrane and cell wall act as protection around the bacterium and will generally be grouped together and referred to as the 'cell wall' in later chapters. In different bacteria, these components are made of different chemicals and these differences have been used as a quick way of identifying two main groups of bacteria, using a test called Gram staining, as you will see in Activity 2.2. The plasma membrane has the ability to control which substances enter and leave the bacterium (there will be more about these in Section 1.8). It is said to be selectively permeable because it lets some substances through and others not.

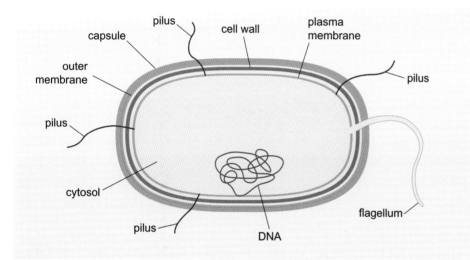

Figure 1.8   The structural features of a generalised bacterium. The features marked pilus and flagellum will be discussed in Chapter 2.

The internal contents of the cell are in a fluid called cytosol, which is a complex mixture of carbohydrates (including sugars), proteins and other substances dissolved in water. Most of the life processes of the bacterium take place here.

■ Look back to the image of the square microbe, *Haloquadratum walsbyi* in Figure 1.3. Not all the bacteria in this image appear to be square, or even approximately square. What shape are the others and can you suggest why this might be?

☐ Some of them appear to be rectangular. Some are almost twice as long as the square ones. This could be because they have grown up to their maximum size and are about to divide in half to form two square cells again.

In fact, most cells, not just microbial cells, grow up to a maximum size and then divide into two smaller cells, which then grow up to their maximum size and divide into two, and so on. When a cell divides, the two new cells must each have a share of the vital components from inside the cell. In particular, they must have a copy of the DNA (deoxyribose nucleic acid). DNA is the genetic material which carries the instructions for making all the proteins in the bacterium. Some of these proteins help to build all the other molecules needed for the microbe to grow and repair itself. So without DNA, a cell cannot survive and grow. In bacteria, most of the DNA is in the form of one very long thin strand, the bacterial chromosome. The strand is joined at its two ends to make a circular loop, which is attached to the plasma membrane (Figure 1.8). Because DNA is so important, not only to microbes but to all life on Earth, it is considered in more detail in the next section.

1.6   The structure and function of DNA

In 1953 James Watson and Francis Crick, working in the UK, deduced and published the three-dimensional structure of DNA in collaboration with Maurice Wilkins and Rosalind Franklin. Their fundamental discovery was that the DNA molecule is in the form of a double helix. There are two strands coiled around one another, and they are held together across the strands like a spiral staircase, as shown in Figure 1.9. This intricate structure makes the molecule very stable and resistant to being damaged.

Now imagine unwinding the DNA structure. This would give a ladder with rungs as shown in Figure 1.10. The sides of the ladder are made up of alternating chemicals, represented by the pentagons and the circles. Look carefully at the coloured blocks, which represent chemicals called bases, making up the rungs of the ladder.

■ Describe the arrangement of the bases shown in Figure 1.10.

☐ Altogether there appear to be four different kinds of bases, which are represented by differently sized coloured blocks. They are labelled A, C, T and G. They do not appear to be in any particular sequence. Each base can appear on either side of the ladder. However, the sequence on one side of the ladder determines the sequence on the other side because they always go together in the same pairs. Base A always appears opposite T, with two red lines holding them together, and C always appears opposite G, with three red lines holding them together. (The red lines represent a type of chemical bond called a hydrogen bond.)

Watson and Crick, in their famous 1953 paper published in the scientific journal *Nature*, wrote:

> 'We wish to suggest a structure for … deoxyribose nucleic acid (DNA). This structure has novel features which are of considerable biological interest… It has not escaped our notice that the specific pairing we have postulated immediately suggests a possible copying mechanism for the genetic material.'

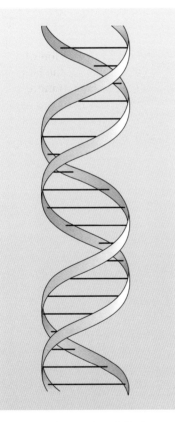

Figure 1.9   A simplified model of part of a hugely magnified molecule of DNA, showing the double helical structure.

■ Why is it so important to be able to copy the DNA (genetic material)?

☐ DNA is the molecule that carries the instructions for making all the proteins in the cell and these proteins help to make all the other parts of the cell. So, it is essential that when a cell divides into two, there is some way of copying the DNA so that each of the new cells produced contains the same DNA as the original cell.

■ Can you see how the structure identified by Watson and Crick 'suggests a possible copying mechanism'? Think about breaking the red bonds and pulling the two sides of the ladder apart.

☐ If the two sides of the DNA ladder are pulled apart, then it would be possible to use each half-ladder to reconstruct a new half-ladder based on the pairing between the pairs A and T, and C and G. This would generate two complete ladders, each identical to the original one, and one of these could be put into each of the new cells produced when the microbe divides.

This process is shown in more detail in Figure 1.11. Work carefully through this figure and its caption now.

So you have now seen in principle how DNA can be copied. The next aspect is to consider how it can carry the code for making all the proteins, though the process itself will not be described in any detail here. Proteins are composed of very long chains of smaller molecules called amino acids, like a row of beads. About 20 different sorts of amino acid are used by all life on Earth. Any particular protein consists of hundreds or even thousands of these amino acids, attached together in a particular order. It is the order of the bases along one strand of the DNA molecule that determines the sequence of amino acids in the protein. The length of DNA that codes for one protein, or a distinct part of a protein, is called a gene and the whole set of genes carried by an organism is called its genome.

If each amino acid was represented by one base – A or T or C or G – then there would only be four possible amino acids.

■ If two bases represented each amino acid, how many possible codes would there be?

☐ Each code could start with one of the letters, followed either by another letter the same, or one of the other three letters. The possible codes are AA, AT, AC, AG; TT, TA, TC, TG; CC, CA, CT, CG; and GG, GA, GT and GC. There are 4 possible start letters, so there are 16 (i.e. 4^2 or 4×4) two-letter codes in all.

That is not enough codes for 20 amino acids. So, assuming that each code consists of the same number of bases, the minimum number needed to code for 20 amino acids is 3.

■ How many possible codes would there be if there were 3 bases in each code?

☐ Based on the same logic, there would be a total of 4^3 or $4 \times 4 \times 4 = 64$ possible codes (which you can list for yourself if you have the time and energy).

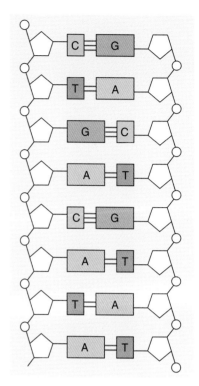

Figure 1.10 A portion of a DNA molecule with the helix unwound, showing in more detail how the strands are held together by hydrogen bonds between pairs of bases.

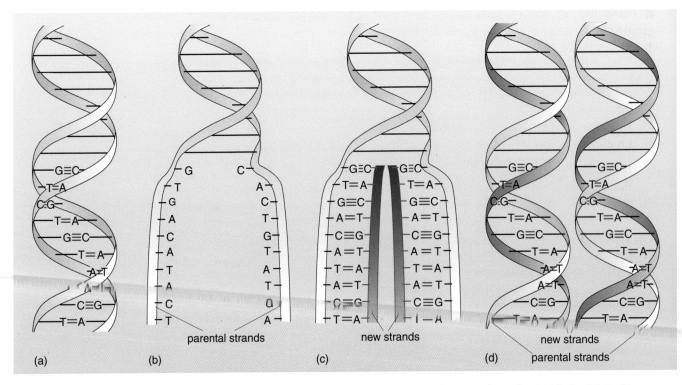

Figure 1.11 The process of copying DNA, known as DNA replication. (a) A portion of a DNA double helix showing 10 bases on one strand, paired with their partners on the other strand. (b) Part of the double helix has unwound and come apart at one end, with the base pairs separated. (c) Two new strands have been produced using molecules in the cytosol, with each base paired correctly with a new partner. (d) The whole of the DNA has been copied and the new pairs of strands have wound into two new double helices, each identical to the original.

In fact, this is the case in microbes, in humans and in all other living organisms discovered so far. The code for each amino acid consists of a sequence of three adjacent bases. In fact, several of these different triplets of bases code for the same amino acid, and a few of them act as 'stop' sequences to indicate the end of the protein molecule. So all 64 have a role.

Question 1.5

How many bases would be needed in a DNA molecule, to code for a protein which consisted of a sequence of 120 amino acids?

The number and sequence of bases in the whole of the *Yersinia pestis* genome has been worked out; the genome has been sequenced. There are over 4600 000 bases, though it is not yet clear now many genes these represent. Although *Y. pestis* reproduces simply by one individual dividing into two, a process called binary fission, there must be a way of passing on the genes from the parent to the 'daughter' bacterium. Each new bacterium must contain the complete *Y. pestis* genome. Differences in the sequence of bases in the DNA is the major factor that separates different species of microbes. You will look at species in more detail in Chapter 2. The more different the genes are in the genome of two microbes, the more likely that the microbes will belong to different species.

1.7   Binary fission in microbes

■   Before a microbe divides, so that one individual becomes two, what vital process must happen?

☐   It must copy its circular loop of DNA or chromosome (see Section 1.5), so that there is a complete version ready to be put into each of the new daughter microbes.

The process by which a microbe divides in two is called binary fission. It is depicted in Figure 1.12. During binary fission, the chromosome makes a copy of itself, the copies separate and the cell elongates. A division begins to develop in the middle of the elongated cell and eventually the two cells split apart, producing two identical daughter cells.

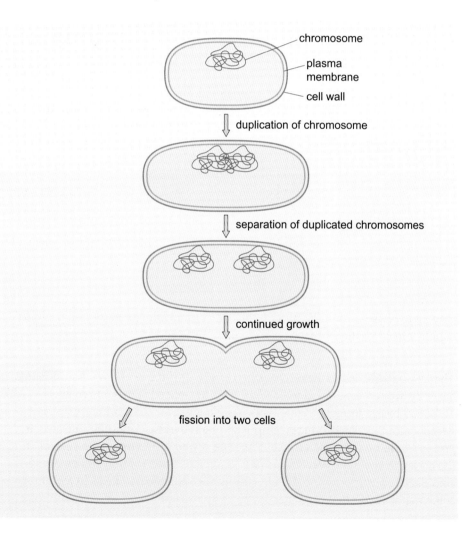

Figure 1.12   The stages in the process of binary fission in a microbe.

■ In ideal conditions, a *Yersinia pestis* individual can divide into two every 2 hours. Starting with one bacterium, how many bacteria would be produced after 12 hours?

☐ After 2 hours, the bacterium would have divided once to give 2 bacteria. After 4 hours, each of those two would have divided and there would be a total of 4, and after 6 hours there would be 8. The 8 would double to 16 after 8 hours, 32 after 10 hours and 64 after 12 hours.

After one day (24 hours) there would be a very impressive 4096 bacteria from just one parent.

Question 1.6

(a) Assuming that these 4096 *Y. pestis* microbes arranged themselves in a single row, how long in millimetres, would the row be? You may need to go back to Section 1.4 to check on the size of the *Y. pestis* microbe.

(b) About how long would it take to get enough microbes to form a line 32 mm (3.2 cm) long?

In fact, the reproducing microbes would tend to stick together to form a blob, not a single row. When the conditions are right and microbes have enough nutrients and energy a visible mass of microbes can form. Figure 1.13 shows microbes growing at the edge of hot springs in Yellowstone National Park in Wyoming, USA. The stunning yellows and oranges that you can see are vast numbers of different species of microbe. There will be more about microbes like this, which live in extreme environments, in Chapter 6.

(a) (b)

Figure 1.13 (a) A hot spring in the Yellowstone National Park. The bright yellow and orange colours around the periphery of the spring are microbes growing on the rock surface. The blue colour in the middle is caused by the mineral-rich water. The nobbly surface is formed of minerals deposited from the hot spring water. (b) A microbiologist sampling water containing microbes around a hot spring at Yellowstone. The whitish mounds are minerals that are deposited by the hot spring water.

■ Can you think of a reason why the microbes shown in Figure 1.13a don't grow and reproduce to cover the whole area of Yellowstone National Park?

☐ These microbes need specific temperature and water conditions, which are only available beside the hot springs. They cannot live and grow and reproduce in cooler, drier conditions.

In theory by dividing by binary fission, microbes could continue dividing until they covered the Earth in a thick layer. However, this does not happen because their growth is always restricted by some limiting factor in their environment, such as insufficient raw materials to build the components of new microbes, or unsuitable environmental conditions. For each species of microbe, there are conditions where it can grow and reproduce at the maximum rate. If these optimal conditions are not met, then the growth rate slows down, and often stops completely. There will be more on how microbes survive adverse conditions in Chapters 2 and 6.

■ How does the reproduction of bacteria, as described so far, differ fundamentally from the kind of reproduction that takes place in most animals?

☐ Most animals do not simply divide in half because their bodies are too complex for that to happen. Instead, there are two sexes, with each producing special reproductive cells. They mate and eggs from the female are fertilised by sperm from the male. Each fertilised egg can grow into a new individual. This is called sexual reproduction. Binary fission is an example of asexual reproduction because it does not involve two individuals coming together.

The advantage of sexual reproduction is that, because DNA from both parents is present, some aspects of the genetic characteristics of those two individuals are combined. Thus the offspring has some characteristics of one parent, and some of the other, but is not identical to either parent, nor (usually) to any of its siblings. This can be a significant advantage.

Think back to the Black Death referred to in Box 1.1. Although bubonic plague was a terrible disease, many people survived and this was partly because each individual human being has a slightly different genetic make-up. So, in any human population infected, some individuals will be resistant to the disease and so will survive. Other individuals, unless they receive medical treatment, will sadly die. If all the individuals had carried identical genetic information, then the whole population in the area could have succumbed to the plague. So mixing up the genes by sexual reproduction enables some individuals in a population to survive a newly occurring disease, whereas without the mixing up of genes, they might all die. A similar argument can be applied to other species and to other changes in the environment, such as the disappearance of the usual type of food, say due to an area being flooded. Some individuals in sexually reproducing populations will have the appropriate mix of genes that allows them to make use of a new type of food in a flooded environment; thus the whole population does not die of starvation.

When microbes divide by binary fission, there is no mixing of genes from two parents. This form of asexual reproduction works well if conditions remain the same.

■ Consider a species of microbe living in damp soil. What might happen if, due to a river changing its course, the soil suddenly became waterlogged all year round?

☐ If the individuals of a species were all genetically identical in terms of their requirement for living in damp, but not waterlogged soil, then they would not be able to survive in the new conditions and they would all die.

So, though binary fission can be extremely quick and does not involve the time-consuming activity of finding a mate, it has the disadvantage that it reduces flexibility if conditions change. However, things cannot be this simple, since microbes do, from time to time, appear with the ability to live under new conditions. For example, about one-third of us carry in our noses a common bacterium *Staphylococcus aureus* which normally causes no problems. However, if *S. aureus* enters a wound, it can cause a severe infection. This infection used to be relatively easily treated with a type of antibiotic called methicillin, but over time, some *S. aureus* have developed resistance and are now termed methicillin-resistant *S. aureus* or, more commonly, MRSA. (You will learn more about MRSA in Chapter 5.) It seems most likely that this happened because the original *S. aureus* picked up a gene or genes from other bacteria which were resistant to methicillin and incorporated that DNA into its own. In Chapter 5 you will find out more about how this exchange of DNA can occur, and see that binary fission is not the only way in which DNA can be passed on from one microbial cell to another.

In addition, microbes can change by a process called mutation. The replication of DNA, like any biological process, is never 100% efficient and as it is copied in each generation there may be errors introduced in the sequence of base pairs. These errors can produce different characteristics in microbes and may improve their ability to adapt to new conditions. Often mutations can be detrimental, however, and result in the death of those microbes carrying them.

1.8   The requirements for life

All living organisms on Earth, from humans to microbes, share some common basic requirements.

■ What are the requirements for human life to survive?

☐ You probably thought first of food and water and then also that we need to breathe in oxygen from the air around us. We also need our surroundings to be at a suitable temperature. There are places on Earth where it is too hot or too cold for humans to live without making special adaptations, in terms of clothing and shelter, which, of course, other species are not able to do.

■ Why do we need food?

☐ We need food to grow and to maintain and repair our bodies. We also need it to provide energy for moving.

Microbes similarly need a source of energy and they need raw materials with which to carry out repairs, and to grow and reproduce. However, many of them do not get their energy by taking in substances that you might think of as food, nor do they get their raw materials from food either. Many of them do not even need oxygen to survive; in fact, oxygen may kill them. However, the essentials of water, some source of raw materials for constructing their components and a source of energy are common to all. They also need appropriate environmental conditions, though some of them live in the most extreme environments found anywhere on Earth.

1.8.1   Raw materials and energy

All living things need a similar set of raw materials for building up the DNA, proteins, and all the other chemical components of their cells. If you are not familiar with the ideas of atoms, elements and molecules, you should now read Box 1.3.

Box 1.3 Some basic chemistry

All the substances in the Universe, from stars to *Staphylococcus aureus*, from yachts to *Yersinia pestis* are made up of atoms of about 100 basic different types. These different types of atom are called elements. Each of them is given a symbol, which can usually be matched up easily with the element.

■ Draw lines across the page to link the following 10 elements, commonly found in living things, with their symbols, then check the answer below.

Element	Symbol
calcium	N
carbon	K
hydrogen	Na
iron	H
oxygen	S
nitrogen	Ca
phosphorus	Fe
potassium	C
sodium	O
sulfur	P

☐ The elements and symbols are: calcium Ca, carbon C, hydrogen H, iron Fe (from the Latin *ferrum*), oxygen O, nitrogen N, phosphorus P, potassium K (from the Latin *kalium*), sodium Na (from the Latin *natrium*), and sulfur S.

The elements can bind together in a myriad of ways to form an inexhaustible list of compounds. When elements are combined, the compound they form often has properties entirely different from the elements that go into it.

■ When carbon (coal) is burned completely in oxygen from the air, what compound is formed and how do its properties differ from the original elements?

☐ Carbon, a black solid, combines with oxygen (a colourless gas) to form carbon dioxide (another colourless gas). Carbon dioxide has the formula CO_2 (spoken as C, O, 2), which means that it is made up of one atom of carbon and two atoms of oxygen.

■ You have probably heard that water is H_2O (spoken as H, 2, O). Which elements are these and how many atoms of each are used?

☐ Water (which is a liquid at normal temperatures) is formed by two atoms of hydrogen and one of oxygen. (Both hydrogen and oxygen are colourless gases.)

The formula for the simplest amino acid is NH_2CH_2COOH and the sugar, ribose, is $C_5H_{10}O_5$.

■ In which molecules do you find (i) amino acids and (ii) ribose?

☐ (i) Amino acids are found in proteins and (ii) ribose is found in DNA deoxy*ribose* nucleic acid (see Section 1.6). In fact the ribose molecules are represented by the pentagons in the sides of the ladder in the DNA structure (Figure 1.10), with four of the carbon atoms and one of the oxygen atoms at the corners of the pentagon.

You will notice that amino acids and the sugar, ribose, both contain carbon and, in fact, carbon is the most important element needed by all living things to make up the vast majority of the molecules in their cells. These molecules containing carbon are given the general name of organic compounds. So, all organisms need a source of carbon atoms with which to produce their own organic compounds.

■ How do (i) animals and (ii) plants obtain their carbon?

☐ (i) Since animals eat food which contains molecules such as proteins and sugars, they obtain their carbon from that food. (ii) Plants obtain their carbon by absorbing carbon dioxide from the air.

Amongst the microbes are species which do both of these things. Some obtain their carbon by taking in organic compounds made by other living organisms, while others take in carbon dioxide gas from the atmosphere and use that to make their own organic compounds.

■ Apart from a source of carbon, what are the other essential requirements for life?

☐ All living things require energy and water.

■ How do (i) animals and (ii) plants obtain the energy that they need to stay alive?

☐ (i) Animals obtain their energy from food. Carbohydrates (particularly sugars), fats and, to a lesser extent, proteins in the diet, can all be used to generate energy. Oxygen, which animals obtain by breathing it in from the environment around them, is involved in that process and most animals cannot survive for more than a few minutes without oxygen. (ii) Plants obtain their energy from sunlight, using a process called photosynthesis. The light is trapped by a coloured pigment in the cells. Commonly this is the green pigment, chlorophyll.

Although this looks like a clear distinction, it is a bit more complicated than this. Plants actually use the Sun's energy to help to build up their own organic compounds, some of which they then break down in a process identical to that used by animals, to produce the energy that they need for their life processes. The process of breaking down organic compounds to produce energy is called (cellular) respiration. Respiration can proceed using oxygen, which is the sort of respiration that occurs in animals, and is called aerobic respiration, or it can proceed without oxygen, which is anaerobic respiration. The latter is a very common process in microbes that live underground, where there is very little oxygen. Anaerobic respiration uses a compound other than oxygen to carry out respiration; such a compound might be a sulfate, i.e. a sulfur-containing compound, but there are many other possibilities. You will learn more about anaerobic respiration in Chapter 7 when you look at the vital role of microbes in the environment. Yet another way of getting energy in oxygen-free environments is called fermentation, the process used to make beer and wine. Chapter 4 will introduce you to the immense importance of this reaction in many industrial and food-making processes. Anaerobic respiration and fermentation are often treated as the same, but they are not; they involve different pathways for releasing energy.

Examples of these processes can be summarised as word equations as follows:

* Aerobic respiration:
  organic compounds + oxygen ⟶
  carbon dioxide + water + energy for life   (Equation 1.1)

* Anaerobic respiration:
  organic compounds + sulfate ⟶
  carbon dioxide + sulfide + energy for life   (Equation 1.2)

* Fermentation:
  organic compounds ⟶
  carbon dioxide + alcohol (or acid)
  + energy for life (less than in aerobic respiration)   (Equation 1.3)

* Photosynthesis:
  carbon dioxide + water + energy from Sun ⟶
  organic compounds + oxygen   (Equation 1.4)

■ Look carefully at Equations 1.1 and 1.4. What is the similarity between them?

☐ Equation 1.4 is effectively the same as Equation 1.1, but with the arrow going in the opposite direction. In photosynthesis the energy involved is the energy being collected from sunlight, and in aerobic respiration the energy involved is the energy for life processes being produced by the reaction.

■ Which of the processes shown in Equations 1.1 to 1.4 could occur in daylight and which could occur at night?

☐ Photosynthesis is the only process which depends on light so will only occur in daylight. The other three processes can occur at any time of the day or night.

There are microbes whose chemical processes are similar to animals and other microbes whose processes resemble those of plants. So there are some microbes which take in organic compounds and break them down by respiration to produce energy, like animals and plants do. Some use oxygen for aerobic respiration (Equation 1.1) and others do not use oxygen but instead respire anaerobically (Equation 1.2). While there are some microbes which are actually killed if oxygen is present, many of them can respire either aerobically or anaerobically, depending on the environmental conditions. Like plants, some microbes contain appropriate pigments, often a version of chlorophyll, which can capture the energy of sunlight by photosynthesis (Equation 1.4) and they build up their own organic compounds, which they then use in respiration. The main groups of microbes that photosynthesise are cyanobacteria and algae. All these processes that go on in living things are called metabolism.

Thus microbes have tapped into almost every available energy supply on Earth and it is this versatility in acquiring energy for growth and reproduction that has contributed to their presence in almost every habitat on the Earth.

1.9 What limits the size of a microbe?

Although microbes are found all over the Earth, above and below the surface of land and water, they are all very small.

■ What are the approximate shapes and sizes of the plague microbe *Yersinia pestis* and the microbe *Haloquadratum walsbyi*? Look back to Section 1.4 if you need to check.

☐ *Y. pestis* is rod-shaped (cylindrical) and about 1 μm long. *H. walsbyi* is the square microbe, which is 3–5 μm across.

Let us assume, for the sake of this argument, that our two microbes are actually little cubes, with sides 1 μm and 5 μm, respectively. This is not true in either case, but it makes the maths easier!

■ What is the area of one face of the smaller microbe?

☐ Area of a rectangle = length × width. So the area of one face of the microbe, a square with sides of 1 μm in each direction would be 1 μm × 1 μm = 1 μm^2.

■ How do you calculate the volume of a cube?

☐ The volume of a cube = length × width × height.

If you need more help with understanding areas and volumes, and their units, you should access Section 6 of the Maths Skills ebook from the course website.

Question 1.7

(a) Calculate the volume of each cubic microbe (with sides of 1 μm and 5 μm), giving your answer in μm^3.

(b) Now calculate the total area of the surface of each cubic microbe in μm^2 (*Hint*: calculate the area of one face of the cube, and then multiply by the number of faces.)

(c) Now compare the surface area of each cubic microbe with its volume and express that as a ratio. Ignore the units here. (Ratios are explained in Section 3.2 of the Maths Skills ebook.)

It is important that you complete this question and check your answer at the back of the book before continuing.

The ratio of surface area to volume is much bigger for a small microbe than for a large one. So, as a microbe gets larger, it has relatively less surface area, compared with the volume inside the microbe. The molecules which a microbe needs have to be absorbed across its surface, and then move through the cytosol. Similarly, waste products have to move from the cytosol to the surface, and then to the surrounding environment. In a large bacterium, there is relatively less surface through which molecules can move and relatively more cytosol. So microbes can only reach a certain size before their surface area becomes too small for the amount of material that needs to pass through. There is therefore a limit to the size to which microbes can grow. In fact, if the microbe is long and thin (rod-shaped), rather than being a cube, then its surface area is larger.

■ Look back to *Haloquadratum walsbyi* in Figure 1.3. Do you think these cells are cubes?

☐ Although the cells appear roughly square or rectangular, they are not like the cubes in Question 1.7. They are quite flat squares (like minute tiles). Because of that, they have a large surface area, top and bottom, and a very thin layer of cytosol between.

There seems little doubt that the ratio of surface area to volume is one reason for microbes remaining so small. Another reason might be the fragility of very large cells. However, their small size has not prevented them from living in almost all the habitats you can think of on Earth, including some that are very surprising. Chapter 2 starts by looking at the diversity of microbes.

Activity 1.1   Introduction to the digital microscope

The estimated time for this activity is two hours. There is a closely-related activity near the start of Chapter 2 that you may wish to do at the same time.

In this activity you will learn to use the digital microscope, and get familiar with it by looking at the different shapes of microbe mentioned in the chapter.

You will find the detailed instructions for this activity in the Activities section of the course website.

Question 1.8

Complete Table 1.1 about the microbes that you have met in Chapter 1 that cause disease and illness.

Table 1.1 Disease/illness-causing microbes. To be completed in Question 1.8.

Disease/illness caused	Name of microbe
anthrax	
	Clostridium difficile
food poisoning	
	Staphylococcus aureus
bubonic plague	

Question 1.9

List three differences between binary fission and sexual reproduction.

Question 1.10

Use ticks in Table 1.2 to indicate which processes apply to which groups of living organisms.

Table 1.2 For use in Question 1.10.

	Photosynthesis	Aerobic respiration	Anaerobic respiration
green plants			
animals			
microbes			

Question 1.11

Which of the following statements about microbes are true, and which are false? Explain the errors in the false statements.

(a) All microbes are either bugs or germs.

(b) *Yersinia pestis* is carried in the saliva of *Xenopsylla cheopis*.

(c) A bacillus is a round microbe, a coccus is a square one.

(d) Bacteria have their DNA packaged into several chromosomes.

Summary of Chapter 1

- Microbes are involved in many environmental processes and play an important role in health science. Very few of them are dangerous to humans, but because they are important to human health, this small percentage is probably the best studied.

- Microbes are small and most are invisible to the unaided eye. It is necessary to use a microscope for the study of microbes in the laboratory.

- Although microbes have tremendous variations, they all share some common cell structures – cell membranes, DNA and cytosol. DNA is the code for life which is copied and passed on in the process of microbial division known as binary fission.

- Microbes use a variety of methods to get energy to grow. Some of these methods share features with those found in humans – using organic compounds respired in oxygen. Many microbes can use sunlight for photosynthesis like plants and some anaerobic microbes can grow in environments without any oxygen.

Chapter 2
The diversity of microbes

2.1 What is a species?

Section 1.3 introduced the way that species of microbes, and all other living organisms, are named. As this is so important for the rest of the course, this chapter begins with a little more discussion about how species are classified.

Scientific names consist of two words, a genus name followed by a species name. But how do scientists know when they have found a new species? What *is* a species?

The idea of a species is much more blurred in the microbes than in animals and plants because many microbes exchange DNA between each other, making it difficult to find out exactly what species they belong to. Having said that, many of them do have sufficient differences that they can be assigned species names like plants and animals. Before delving into the complex world of microbes, it is useful to explore the idea of species in more familiar animals.

■ Consider the pairs of animals shown in Figure 2.1. Do you think the members of each pair belong to the same species or different species – and why?

☐ (a) Lion and tiger belong to different species – *Panthera leo* and *Panthera tigris*. But why? – apart from the fact that it said so in Chapter 1! They are both big cats, but they look different. Lions are honey-coloured and the males have impressive manes; tigers are striped and do not have manes.

(b) The African elephant and Indian elephant are both elephants and look very similar, though the African elephant has relatively bigger ears and has a concave back. It is also bigger overall, though this is not clear from the photographs. These differences are characteristics of different species.

(c) Humans and chimpanzees look very different too, and belong to different species, *Homo sapiens* and *Pan troglodytes* respectively, though analysis of their DNA shows that more than 98% of it is common to both species.

(d) Horse and donkey. These animals look rather similar, though donkeys have bigger ears, and the sounds made by the animals are different. But horses and donkeys can breed together to produce mules, though normally mules cannot themselves breed. Horses and donkeys are different species.

(e) Chihuahua and Great Dane. Despite Chihuahuas being only 15–25 cm tall and Great Danes being at least 75 cm tall, they are both dogs and belong to the same species. They could produce puppies together which could themselves breed. In fact, they both also belong to the same species, *Canis lupus*, as the grey wolf (dogs are a domesticated sub-species).

Figure 2.1 Some species of animals: (a) lion and tiger; (b) African elephant and Indian elephants; (c) humans and chimpanzees; (d) horses and donkeys; (e) Chihuahua and Great Dane.

■ Based on the answer above, summarise three ways in which different species can be distinguished.

□ (i) Different species may look different (they are said to have different morphology, where 'morph' means 'shape'), though looking different is not a sufficient criterion to distinguish species, as with the dogs. On the other hand, organisms which superficially look rather similar, like the African and Indian elephants, may not belong to the same species.

(ii) DNA analysis can be used to distinguish species, though the differences may be quite small.

(iii) From the information given, it appears that if individuals can breed together and produce offspring that can themselves breed, then the individuals belong to the same species, as with dogs. However, if offspring can be produced that cannot themselves breed, then the parents belong to different species, as with horses and donkeys.

■ Which of these three ways could definitely not be used to identify species of microbe?

□ The breeding criterion [(iii) in the answer above] is not useful for microbes because most microbes reproduce asexually (Section 1.7).

Activity 2.1 Using the digital microscope to examine different species of microbe

The estimated time for this activity is one hour.

In this activity you will use the digital microscope to examine a variety of microbes at different magnifications and to develop your skills in identifying important features to enable you to compare microbes. It is important that you do this activity before moving on with the text.

You will find the detailed instructions for this activity in the Activities section of the course website.

Activity 2.1 has shown that the morphology (shape and external appearance) of microbes is not particularly helpful for identifying different species. Many of them look very similar, but have quite different environmental requirements or cause quite different diseases. Although morphology has been used in the past, the identification of microbial species is now based on differences in their DNA and RNA. RNA also occurs in the cell and resembles half of a DNA molecule, just one strand of the double helix. It is another part of the system used to produce proteins. Differences in both DNA and RNA are used to allocate microbes to families and various other groupings according to how closely they are related.

2.2 Classification of microbes

■ Which of the disease-causing microbes in the following list are most closely related, and why?

Bacillus anthracis – causes anthrax in humans.

Bacillus thuringiensis – kills insects, and can be used to control insect pests.

Escherichia coli – causes food poisoning in humans.

Bacillus cereus – causes a food poisoning illness in humans very similar to that of *Escherichia coli*.

☐ The three species – *Bacillus anthracis*, *Bacillus thuringiensis* and *Bacillus cereus* all belong to the same genus (*Bacillus*) and so are closely related, despite having very different effects in quite different species. Although *Escherichia coli* and *Bacillus cereus* cause very similar food poisoning illnesses in humans, they are less closely related to each other.

It is possible to group genera into larger groupings called families. To take a more familiar example, the wild cats, including lynxes, snow leopards, and ocelots, as well as lions, tigers, leopards, jaguars and cheetahs, all belong to the cat family, scientifically called Felidae. The same sort of scheme can be applied to the microbes. Bacterial genera can also be grouped into families. So, the plague microbe, *Yersinia pestis*, *Escherichia coli* and *Salmonella enterica*, which also causes a form of food poisoning, all belong to the family Enterobacteriacaea.

Digital Microscope (DM) Slides 1.1 and 2.3

Note that the names of families are not written in italics but start with a capital letter.

Depending on how closely they are related, the families are grouped into orders, the orders into classes and the classes into phyla (singular phylum). However, the intermediate groupings are less commonly used for bacteria than phyla and families, and these latter two are the groupings that will be used in this course. The Enterobacteriacaea is one of the families in the phylum Proteobacteria. Figure 2.2 shows how a strain of *E. coli* can be classified within the domain Bacteria.

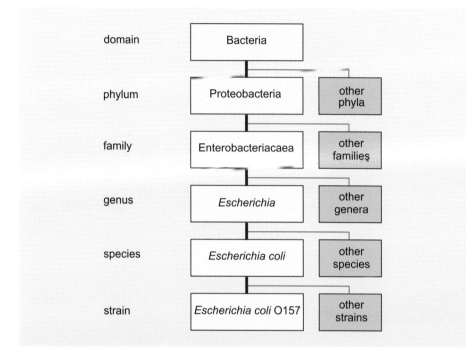

Figure 2.2   Classification of *Escherichia coli* O157.

The relationships between various groups of organisms can be shown in a type of diagram called an evolutionary or phylogenetic tree. One example of such a tree is shown in Figure 2.3, where the bacteria are shown in blue. The different branches of the tree depict the way that microbes have evolved so that ones further away from each other are presumed to be more distantly related.

In Figure 2.3, in red, are another group of microbes, called the Archaea, which includes many of those that live in extreme environments, and which you will be meeting in Chapter 6. The large groups – Bacteria, Archaea and Eukaryotes – are often referred to as 'domains'. The Bacteria and Archaea together form the prokaryotes. Prokaryotes are those organisms which have their DNA in the cytosol of the cell attached to the plasma membrane. In eukaryotes the DNA is present in a group of chromosomes which are stored in a special part of the cell called the nucleus, surrounded by the nuclear membrane. The name prokaryotes comes from the Greek words 'pro' meaning before and 'karyon' meaning kernel or nut. So these are cells without a kernel, i.e. without a cell nucleus.

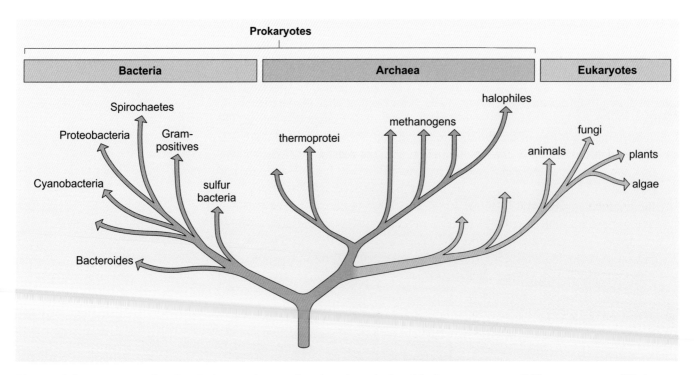

Figure 2.3   An example of a phylogenetic tree showing the relationship between some different groups of living organisms, particularly microbes, encountered in the course. Some groups of organisms are not shown (denoted by unlabelled arrows).

■ What shape is the DNA molecule of bacteria? (You may need to look back to Section 1.5 for a reminder.)

☐ Every DNA molecule is a double helix, two strands wound around one another. In bacteria, the two ends of the helix are joined so that the DNA forms a circular loop.

The remaining living things, which include other microbes and all plants and animals, are called eukaryotes (meaning 'true kernel'), where the DNA exists as a series of individual double helix molecules, each one packaged up into a chromosome, with all the chromosomes stored in the cell nucleus.

■ From Figure 2.3, which of the eukaryotes are microbes? (You may wish to refer to Section 1.1.)

☐ The fungi and some algae are microbes. The rest of the eukaryotes are organisms whose bodies are made up of more than one cell, usually, like ourselves, with a large number of different kinds of cell.

Look carefully at Figure 2.3 and make sure you can identify the groups mentioned in this section and their relationship to each other. You will notice that viruses, which were mentioned in Section 1.1 as microbes, are not included in Figure 2.3. That is because they cannot be considered to be related to the three domains because they are an entirely different group of organisms, as you will learn in the next chapter.

2.3   Culturing microbes

Microbiologists need to breed, or grow, microbes in the laboratory. This is called 'culturing' microbes.

■   For what reasons might it be necessary to culture microbes either in the laboratory or on an industrial scale?

☐   If the microbes are used in food production, such as yeast for making bread, then they will need to be cultured on an industrial scale. If someone is in hospital suffering from an infection, then it may be necessary to culture the microbe causing that infection to see which antibiotics would be most appropriate to administer to the patient. In fact, antibiotics themselves are produced from microbes, and so those microbes need to be grown on an industrial scale too. Additionally, scientists may need to culture all sorts of different microbes for research purposes.

■   If microbes are to be successfully cultured, what will need to be provided? You might find it useful to refer back to Section 1.8.

☐   They will need appropriate sources of water, raw materials (nutrients) and energy, and they will need appropriate environmental conditions.

These requirements can only be determined for a particular new microbe species by comparison with other closely related species (if there are any) or by replicating as far as possible the conditions under which the microbe was found to be living. So, if a microbe was found living at a depth of about 20 cm in uncultivated soil in the north of the UK, it would be sensible to try to grow it in cool, damp conditions in the dark. If a microbe caused blood poisoning in humans, then it would be best to try to grow it at body temperature (37 °C) and to supply it with blood, or a blood substitute, in which to grow. Once a species of microbe has been successfully cultured, then microbiologists will record the conditions and communicate them to others via scientific books and articles (often called 'scientific papers'). Probably less than 1% of known species of microbes have currently been cultured in the laboratory. You should now read *Laboratory methods 2.1*.

Laboratory methods 2.1   Culturing microbes

In the laboratory microbes can either be cultured in a liquid medium, called a broth, or the liquid can be solidified as a firm gel using agar (extracted from seaweed) on the surface of which the microbes can be grown. The medium contains the nutrients and energy sources for the microbes to grow. The usual container for the gel is a small plastic dish with a lid called a Petri dish and a dish of agar is often referred to as an 'agar plate'. The shape and colour of the microbial colonies that grow on the surface of the gel can then be examined under a microscope. Figure 2.4 shows an example of colonies of fungi with a characteristically furry appearance growing on a Petri dish and the fungal filaments that cause this growth habit.

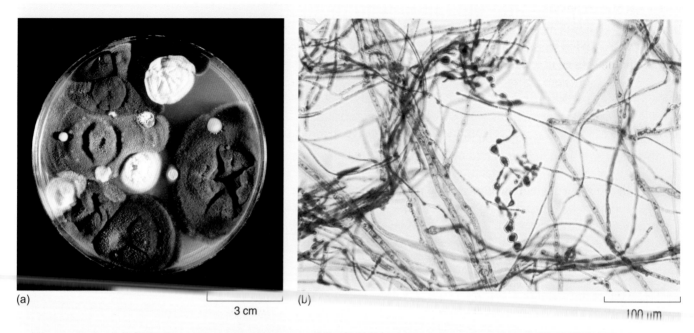

(a)
3 cm
(b)
100 µm

Figure 2.4 (a) Colonies of fungi growing on solid agar gel in a Petri dish. (b) A light micrograph showing filaments of fungi that have been stained blue.

In addition to chemicals containing the elements listed in Box 1.3, in order to grow, microbes may also need very small quantities of other elements (trace elements), such as copper (Cu) and zinc (Zn) and they may need some other special molecules, such as vitamins. These can all be added to the initial liquid medium in appropriate amounts.

One of the major challenges of microbiology is to find the right culture medium to encourage particular species to grow. Often a wide range of chemicals is used, in the hope that the ones needed by a particular microbe will be present. For example, to culture soil microbes which use sugars as their energy source, a medium rich in a number of different sugars would be used. Growth conditions such as temperature and light must be carefully controlled too. Different microbes reproduce at different rates, and so sufficient time, sometimes several months, needs to be allowed for a visible colony to develop. It is particularly important that cultures of microbes are not contaminated by unwanted species, which might be present in the air, on the equipment being used, on the hands of the person setting up the culture, etc.

The techniques for culturing microbes in the laboratory are shown in detail in the video sequence used in Activity 2.2, which you should do now.

Activity 2.2 Culturing microbes in the laboratory

The estimated time for this activity is one hour.

In this activity, you will watch a 15-minute video sequence showing microbiologists at work in a laboratory. When you watch the video, you may find it useful to pause the sequence at the end of each part, to read the relevant text and answer the relevant questions.

Part 1 Aseptic technique

In this part, you hear a mention of 'culture collections' of microbes. Major collections are held in the UK, the US and Germany. Pure cultures of many different species are maintained at each site and made available to microbiologists on request, together with instructions for their continued culture in the lab to which they are being sent. New microbes which are discovered can be deposited in one of the collections, so that they become available for other researchers to use. The cultures are also used as a way of conserving important representative species from the wild.

Question 2.1

(a) Why is the aseptic technique essential in microbiological labs?

(b) How are culture media sterilised before use?

Part 2 Pouring plates

In this part, the technique of flaming is demonstrated. It involves passing the neck of a bottle through the flame of a Bunsen burner. This heats the air close to the neck of the bottle, causing it to expand and rise away from the bottle into the flame, taking any airborne microbes with it, so preventing them entering the bottle and potentially contaminating the culture.

Part 3 Streak plates

Question 2.2

(a) What is an inoculum?

(b) Why are the microbes streaked out with the loop on the surface of the agar?

(c) What characteristics are used to distinguish colonies from one another?

Part 4 Inoculating broths

Question 2.3

(a) Thinking back to the bottles of culture medium shown in Part 1 of the video, what might produce the red colour in the agar shown in this part?

(b) How is it possible to identify whether there are any microbes growing in a broth, where colonies cannot be seen?

Part 5 Gram staining

Different species of bacteria have cell walls with different chemical compositions. In the early days of microbiology, it was discovered that this could be used as a means of identification. An ingenious staining method was developed by microbiologist Hans Christian Gram in 1884. One type of cell wall stains purple using Gram staining, and the other does not stain at all, in the first stage, but can then be stained a pale pink in a subsequent step. These different groups of bacteria are known as Gram-positive (purple or blue) and Gram-negative (pink) (see Figure 2.5). In general, the Gram-negative microbes are the more pathogenic ones (more likely to cause serious illness). You do not need to know the details of the staining process, but you should have a general idea of how a slide is stained.

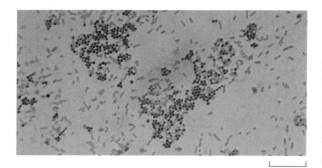

Figure 2.5 A light micrograph showing a mixture of rod-shaped Gram-negative bacteria (pink) and round Gram-positive bacteria (purple). These microbes have been Gram stained to show the two different species.

10 μm

Question 2.4

(a) How are the microbes fixed to the microscope slide before staining?

(b) What are the general names for rod-shaped and round bacteria, respectively?

Part 6 Serial dilution

In this part, a method of diluting a culture by ten-fold serial dilution is demonstrated. The dye (or bacteria) in each tube is 10 times more dilute than the previous one. (If you are not familiar with values expressed as 10^{-2}, etc., you should access Section 7 of the Maths Skills ebook from the course website.) Note that the liquid volume referred to as a 'mil' is in fact a millilitre (one-thousandth of a litre). It is the same as a cubic centimetre. The long tube which the microbiologist is using to suck up the liquid is called a pipette. A buffer is a solution which remains at a constant pH (level of acidity). You will meet pH in more detail in Box 4.2.

Part 7 Spread plates

Question 2.5

What is the difference between spread plates and streak plates?

Part 8 Pour plates

Here the microbial culture is added to the agar while it is warm and then it is allowed to solidify. This means that microbes which cannot grow in the presence of oxygen – called obligate anaerobes – and so would not survive on the surface of the agar, can live in the body of the agar where there is no oxygen. On the other hand, aerobic microbes, which need oxygen, can only grow on the surface and will not grow within the agar.

Part 9 Bacterial lawns

Question 2.6

How is a bacterial lawn used to test the effectiveness of different antibiotics on the growth of a species of microbe?

■ Can you suggest two additional precautions that the microbiologist in the later part of the video sequence might have used, to assist in preventing contamination of the bacterial cultures?

☐ She could have had her hair covered, which the first microbiologist you saw did have. She could also have been wearing disposable gloves. These would protect the cultures from possible contamination from microbes on her hands, and protect her hands too from pathogenic bacteria in the cultures. In some laboratories, microbiologists would also wear face masks.

2.4   Moving around

Microbes can be moved around in the air and by water currents, such as in rivers. Many microbes are transported from one continent to another in air currents after they have been picked up from the ground by wind. You might have been assuming so far that microbes once placed in position on the surface of an agar plate, for example, stay put. This is true for many microbes. However, for some of them the ability to move is a crucial part of their existence and they have some remarkable ways of doing so. It allows them to colonise many varied environments.

■ Why might microbes need to move around?

☐ There are many possible reasons. A microbe which uses light as its energy source – a photosynthetic microbe – might find itself in the dark. A microbe which uses sugars for energy might be in a region where the sugars had been used up. A microbe might find itself in a region where a toxic substance, perhaps an antibiotic, is present. All these microbes would benefit by being able to move to a new area, even if that area was only a few micrometres away.

2.4.1   The flagellum

Movement is most commonly achieved in microbes with the use of a flagellum (plural flagella), a remarkable and exquisite cell structure that works by spinning round. Figure 1.8 showed a generalised bacterium with just one flagellum. Figure 2.6 shows the bacterium *Salmonella* which has a number

DM Slide 5.1

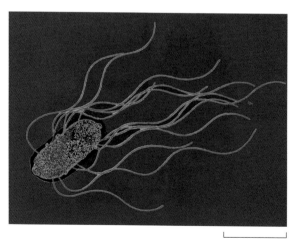

1 μm

Figure 2.6   A false-colour electron micrograph of the bacterium *Salmonella* with flagella.

of flagella. Swimming speeds in the range 2 µm–200 µm per second in water have been reported in microbes using flagella which are typically about 15 µm–20 µm long.

Activity 2.3   Movement of microbes – Part I

The estimated time for this activity is 10 minutes.

You will find it helpful to watch the short video sequence on the movement of microbes (microbial 'motility' as it is called by specialists in the field) on the DVD at this point. The detailed notes for the activity, including some questions, are in the Activities section of the course website.

A flagellum is rotated by a structure within the cell membrane, which turns it at over 200 revolutions per second. In the simplest situation, there is one flagellum, or a group of flagella, at the back of the microbe. As they rotate in one direction the microbe rotates in the other direction and is propelled forwards. To change direction, the flagella briefly rotate in the opposite direction, which causes the microbe to tumble and so change the direction in which it is facing. When the original direction of rotation resumes, the microbe moves off in a new direction. If the conditions are improving, the microbe stops tumbling and continues in the same direction. If conditions are getting worse, the amount of tumbling increases until a direction is found in which conditions are improving. In Figure 2.7, the zigzag path shows how a microbe might be tumbling in adverse conditions.

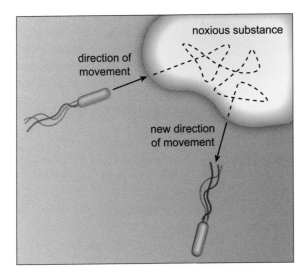

Figure 2.7   A possible track of a microbe which encounters a noxious substance in a fluid.

Question 2.7

Assume that a photosynthetic microbe was buried by a gardener turning over the soil, to a depth of 50 mm. If this microbe could move at 100 μm per second, what is the minimum length of time that it would take to reach the surface again?

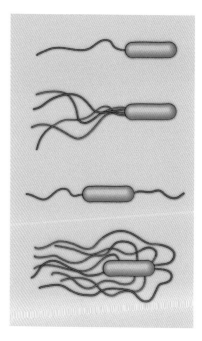

Figure 2.8   Sketch showing some different arrangements of flagella.

DM Slides 5.2 and 5.3

Microbes have flagella arranged in a variety of ways. Some members of the family Vibrionaceae (in the phylum Proteobacteria – see Figure 2.3), which are widely found in the environment and include *Vibrio cholerae* that causes the disease cholera, can either have flagella at one end of the cell or they can be all over the outside surface of the microbe, depending on whether the microbes are attached to a surface or are free-swimming. Some of the different arrangements are shown in Figure 2.8.

The detailed structure of a flagellum, as shown diagrammatically in Figure 2.9, is remarkable. The main filament of the flagellum is composed of a hollow cylindrical structure, about 20 nm (nanometres) in diameter, which is anchored to a rotating mechanism by a specialised structure called the hook. The chemical motor that rotates the flagellum is made up of over 20 different proteins. To build the flagellum, new proteins are passed from the base, up through the hollow core, and added to the end of the filament, just underneath the tip of the filament. The flagellum is probably one of the most exquisite microbial structures evolved by Nature.

Question 2.8

Based on the length of the flagellum given at the start of this section, how many times longer is the length of a typical flagellum than its diameter?

2.4.2   Other methods of movement

Although flagella on the outside of cells are by far the most common means of achieving locomotion, it is by no means the only way microbes are able to move. A bacterium belonging to the phylum Spirochaetes (see Figure 2.3) is shown in Figure 2.10. In this phylum are species responsible for Lyme disease and syphilis. A microbe that has a corkscrew shape, such as the spirochaetes, is referred to as a spirillum, joining the cocci, bacilli and square-shaped microbes as yet another microbial shape. Spirochaetes have numerous flagella located between the plasma membrane and the cell wall and can move using these internal flagella. However, to be able to move forwards, the flagella at both ends of the cell must move in opposite directions; if they moved in the same direction, the actions would cancel each other out and the cells would be stationary. How this is accomplished is not understood, but the flagella in spirochaetes are known to be more complex than in most microbes.

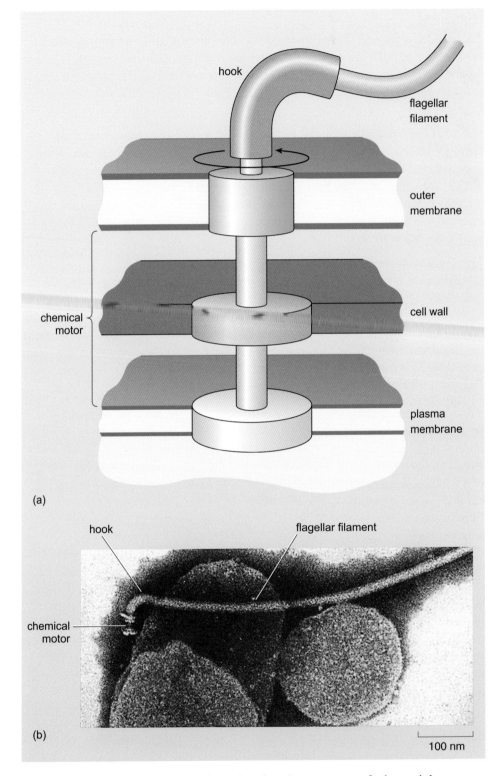

Figure 2.9 (a) Schematic diagram showing the structure of a bacterial flagellum. (b) Electron micrograph of *Rhodospirillum molischianum*, showing the structure of an isolated flagellum.

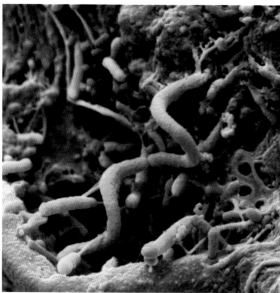

Figure 2.10   A false-colour scanning electron micrograph of bacteria from soil, including, in the centre and coloured green, a corkscrew-shaped spirochaete.

1 µm

Pseudomonas aeruginosa is a common and well-studied bacterium, found in soil, water and other moist locations. This species moves using much shorter structures than flagella, called pili (singular pilus, see Figure 1.8), which are just a few micrometres long. Less dramatic than the flagella, pili can be extended from the cell surface and they achieve movement by twitching; short jerks can be observed as a slow movement of organisms when viewed down a microscope. *Pseudomonas aeruginosa* can also cause human infections. It can take advantage of a weakened immune system and become a risk to human health, causing eye, ear and wound infections and it commonly causes infections in people with cystic fibrosis, so understanding how it moves around might help to explain how it behaves inside the human body.

DM Slide 2.4

2.5   When the going gets tough

Whether or not microbes can move over small distances, they sometimes find themselves in environmental conditions which are wholly unsuitable for their survival. On these occasions, the only way of surviving is to shut down most of their life processes and become dormant. The most common way in which microbes do this is to form spores. Not all bacteria form spores, but of those that do, the process has been particularly well studied in the bacilli.

When a bacillus detects that environmental conditions are deteriorating to the extent that normal survival is impossible, the spore-forming process is initiated, as shown in Figure 2.11. The first step is that a copy of the DNA is made.

■   On what other occasions do microbes copy their DNA?

☐   The DNA is copied just before the microbe is going to divide by binary fission (Figure 1.12), so that each of the two new 'daughter' cells contains the complete set of genetic information (genome).

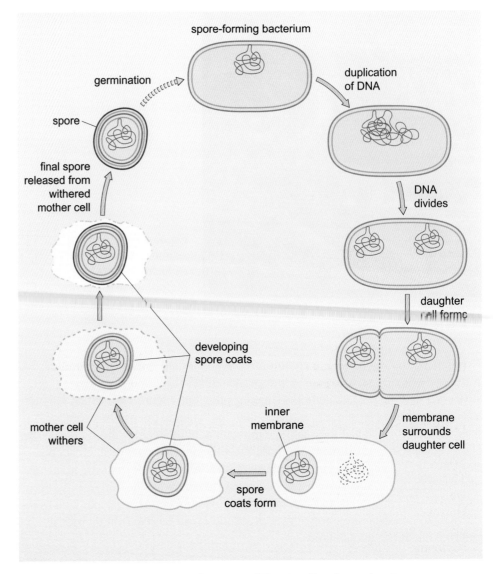

Figure 2.11 The formation of a spore. (The details of germination are not shown.)

DM Slide 1.4

In spore formation, only one of the DNA copies is used. A membrane develops around that copy, while the other copy and the rest of the microbe eventually wither away. Over a period of about 8 hours, more coats develop around the core containing the DNA, eventually forming a spore with a multi-layered coat, as shown in Figure 2.12. This coat forms a physically tough barrier against environmental conditions, such as drought, extreme heat, radiation and chemicals which would normally kill the microbe. Additionally the DNA is packaged using special proteins that allow it to remain inactive without degrading over long periods of time. The spores of *Bacillus anthracis*, often referred to as anthrax spores, are particularly resistant. They can remain in the soil for many years and can be transported on clothing and shoes. Because of their long life, anthrax spores can be used in biological weapons. You can read more about the dangers of anthrax spores in Box 2.1.

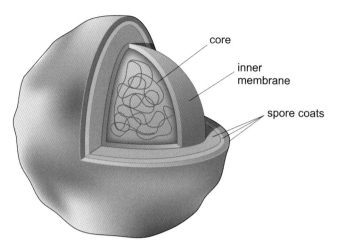
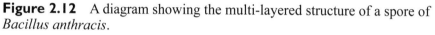

Figure 2.12 A diagram showing the multi-layered structure of a spore of *Bacillus anthracis*.

Box 2.1 The dangers of anthrax spores

Until the 20th century, each year anthrax killed thousands of people who inhaled or ingested anthrax spores, although today the anthrax bacterium is very rare. In 1881 Louis Pasteur developed the first vaccine against the disease and today it can be treated with antibiotics.

In 1942 anthrax was considered as a possible means of biological warfare in Europe. Eighty sheep were taken to Gruinard Island off the west coast of Scotland where they were exposed to bombs filled with anthrax spores. The sheep rapidly died. Fortunately, anthrax was never used as a biological weapon and these weapons are now prohibited by international agreement. However, so resistant are the anthrax spores to environmental extremes that Gruinard Island remained off limits for over 40 years. It was only at the beginning of 1986 that efforts began to decontaminate the island. It required over 250 tonnes of formaldehyde – a chemical that kills most microbes, and their spores – sprayed over the 2 square kilometres of the island to kill the spores in the soil. Only in 1990 was Gruinard Island declared safe after it was shown that a flock of sheep could live there without contracting anthrax.

In 2001, five people were killed and 17 people became ill by contracting anthrax spread by spores added to letters sent through the US postal system. The spores used in this terrorist attack were later shown to have originated from a US military establishment, suggesting that it was a home-grown terrorist attack. The possible use of anthrax spores by terrorists remains an important concern for microbiologists.

Microbial spores, mainly of (harmless) bacteria and fungi, are very common in the air around us and settle out on surfaces both indoors and out. You will investigate the number of fungal spores in the air in your home in Activity 3.1 by providing them with appropriate conditions (source of nutrients, water and warmth). These conditions enable the spore to germinate.

■ Under what conditions might an anthrax spore be activated?

☐ If the spore was ingested by a person or animal in their food, or inhaled (breathed in), then it would be in a warm, moist environment, and that would activate the spore, allowing the microbe to grow and reproduce, and cause another case of anthrax.

DM Slide 1.2 *Bacillus cereus* has spores which can be dispersed in the wind and remain inactive on food for prolonged periods before being ingested, when they can cause food poisoning. So these spores have been studied because of the concern for food safety.

Spores found in sealed vessels from the Egyptian pyramids have germinated, showing that they can survive for several thousand years at least. However, there are hopes that it might be possible to re-activate spores that have been buried for millions of years. Perhaps the best known work of this kind has been attempts to isolate microbial spores from the inside of amber, the resin produced in the sap of certain trees that solidifies, trapping organisms within it. Claims have been made that DNA from another species of *Bacillus* has been extracted from the gut of a bee trapped in 25 million-year-old samples of amber and even from 250 million-year-old salt deposits.

■ Why might these claims be considered controversial? *Hint*: think back to Activity 2.2.

☐ Activity 2.2 showed how many careful procedures need to be undertaken to ensure that no other microbes from the surroundings can contaminate the material being studied. In the case of fossilised material, it would need to have been collected and stored in sterile conditions and then studied in a laboratory where all suitable precautions were taken. If that was not the case, then the DNA could well have come from modern *Bacillus*. It might be possible to compare the base sequences in the supposedly ancient *Bacillus* DNA with those of modern *Bacillus* DNA. If there were distinct differences, it could indicate that the DNA came from an ancient species millions of years old. The relationship to modern species could be deduced using a type of phylogenetic tree (Figure 2.3).

2.6   Why do microbes live where they do?

The study of why particular microbes live where they do, is a vast area of research. Their distribution on Earth can be considered on every scale, from micrometres right up to the size of continents, thousands of kilometres across.

2.6.1   Small-scale distribution: biofilms and microbial mats

You may have noticed that when muddy puddles dry out, sometimes there is a green film on the surface of the mud. There are also often slimy layers on the bottom of ponds and streams, as shown in Figure 2.13. Layers of microbes

1 cm

Figure 2.13   A photograph of a microbial mat in a pond in the Canadian High Arctic, taken from above the water surface. The pale green areas are cyanobacteria and the bubbles are gas being produced by them. The brown areas are either old dead cells or cyanobacteria that have other pigments or compounds that give them a brown colour.

also occur around hot springs in places such as Yellowstone National Park (Figure 1.13). The thinner layers are called biofilms and the thicker ones are microbial mats. Both tend to be associated with surfaces such as rock or soil to which the microbes can attach and form a stable community. They usually contain more than one species of microbe and often there is a clear internal structure with different microbes being found at different levels, with the waste products of some microbes providing food for others. By changing the environmental conditions inside the biofilm, each layer can help the growth of other members of the biofilm. Most microbes live in communities like this rather than in isolation.

The biofilms are held together, and often held to the surface, by slime produced by the microbes. The slime contains polysaccharide, made by linking lots of sugar molecules together. The biofilm then grows, partly by the cell division (binary fission) of those microbes already in the film, and partly by the attraction of other microbes – often of different species – to it. Microbes in biofilms tend to have different properties from free-living individuals of the same species because of the protection provided by the biofilm.

Question 2.9

As you read the following section, write in the details onto Figure 2.14, to provide a diagrammatic representation of the structure of a microbial mat.

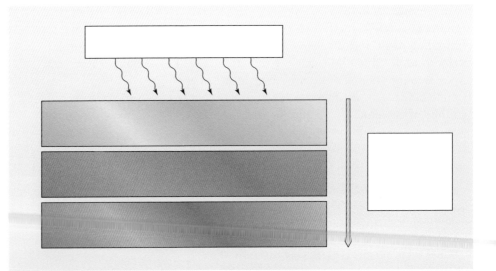

Figure 2.14 A diagrammatic cross-section through a microbial mat, to be completed in Question 2.9.

The microbes within the mat, say on the bottom of a pond, are ordered in vertical layers according to the availability of their essential requirements, particularly energy. On the surface there might be photosynthetic microbes, such as the cyanobacteria (Figure 2.3), which use light as a source of energy. These will be found on the top layer of the mat if there is sufficient light penetrating through the pond water for photosynthesis. Below them are some aerobic non-photosynthetic bacteria which use the excess oxygen produced by the cyanobacteria in daylight.

■ Why in daylight do cyanobacteria produce more oxygen than they use? You will need to consider the processes of photosynthesis and aerobic respiration (Equations 1.4 and 1.1).

☐ During the day, the cyanobacteria will be producing oxygen, and organic compounds by the process of photosynthesis (Equation 1.4). They will be breaking down some, but not all, of these organic compounds by the process of aerobic respiration to produce the energy they need to live (Equation 1.1). This will use up some of the oxygen produced in photosynthesis, but not all of it. So, overall during the day, there will be excess oxygen given off by the mat which will be available for the aerobic bacteria.

Moving down into the mat, oxygen levels fall as oxygen is used up by those microbes that respire aerobically. Frequently there are zones where the oxygen levels are very low, but where light is still available and within these zones photosynthetic microbes that can live at low oxygen levels can be found. The use of raw materials and energy sources by microbes at one depth will influence their availability for the microbes that grow below or above. Only certain species will thrive at particular depths in the mat and thus a series of distinct layers of microbes form. Compare your diagram of these layers with the answer to Question 2.9 at the end of the book.

Biofilms can form on other surfaces too. Biofilms on the hulls of ships at sea make it easier for barnacles and other marine species to attach, causing significant drag and requiring expensive cleaning processes and the use of antifouling paint. In the cooling towers of air conditioning systems, *Legionella* bacteria can form biofilms, leading to outbreaks of Legionnaire's disease in those exposed to the contaminated air. Many biofilms are highly beneficial. Examples include biofilms of microbes in sewage treatment works (Section 4.3), or the biofilms of bacteria inside your gut that help you to digest food (Section 5.2).

2.6.2   Quorum sensing

The well-defined distributions of microbes in microbial mats are achieved partly by the movement of microbes. However, a remarkable ability of microbes to communicate with one another has also been found. Known as quorum sensing, this allows microbes to sense whether other microbes are close to them, and to regulate their chemical processes accordingly.

Quorum sensing was first observed in a member of the Proteobacteria *Vibrio fischeri*. Although *V. fischeri* can live on its own in seawater, it can also colonise the light-producing organs of some fish and squid, where it is responsible for producing the light. The light-producing organ of the Hawaiian bobtail squid helps the squid to camouflage itself by matching the light produced by the squid to the colour of sunlight during the day or of moonlight at night. When the *V. fischeri* microbes are in normal seawater, where they rarely come into contact with another member of the same species, they do not produce any light. However, once they reach a high concentration, such as inside the squid's light-producing organ, they sense the presence of others and the light-producing chemical reactions are triggered. Why would microbes do this?

Quorum sensing provides microbes with a means to sense how much competition there might be for resources and to regulate their activity accordingly. In some ways it is a type of cooperation, but it also benefits each individual microbe to sense whether it is alone or not; for example, if there is intense competition for resources it might be better to use less and become more inactive. In the case of light-producing bacteria, the reasons are more of a mystery, but one explanation is that in return for producing light and helping to catch prey the bacteria get nutrients from the fish, but there is no point in producing light when they are not associated with the fish.

2.6.3   Biofilms inside the human body

Quorum sensing is also important to provide communication between the microbes in biofilms. Such biofilms inside the human body are found in the gut. Unwanted biofilms can also form elsewhere, including on the surface of artificial implants in the body, such as heart valves, and artificial hip and knee joints (see Figure 5.8). The first microbes to arrive initially attach weakly to the surface, but then can anchor themselves more firmly using pili.

■ What are pili and what other function do they have? You may need to look back to Section 2.4.2 and Figure 1.8.

□ Pili are small projections from the surface of a microbe, just a few micrometres long, which allow a twitching type of movement.

Unwanted biofilms in the human body can sometimes cause serious problems, particularly if they contain harmful microbes. Biofilms can require up to a thousand times more antibiotic to kill the microbes in them than would normally be needed for the free-living microbes and this makes them very difficult to destroy if they form deep within the body.

Perhaps the best known biofilm in the body is dental plaque, the material that forms in the mouth, adhering to teeth (Figure 2.15). There is little oxygen available to those microbes nearest to the tooth surface and they can carry out fermentation, converting sugars to acids (Equation 1.3), which attack the tooth and cause decay. Regular and effective brushing removes the biofilm and thus protects the teeth.

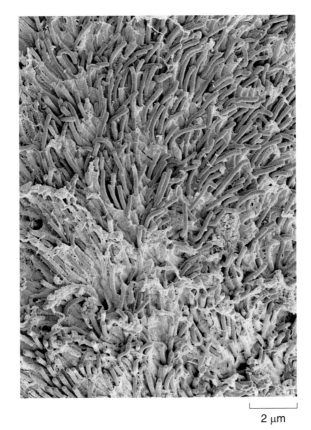

2 μm

Figure 2.15 False-colour electron micrograph of dental plaque. Bacteria (pink) are shown embedded in a slime layer (blue). The biofilm is growing on the surface of a tooth.

2.6.4 Large-scale distribution

The distribution of microbes at the very large scale, up to the scale of continents, has been one of the most controversial areas of discussion in microbiology. It is well known that the distribution of animals and plants is related to their geography and that islands in particular tend to harbour unique organisms that become trapped and over time evolve into genetically different species from those on the mainland. The famous finches of the Galapagos Islands observed by Charles Darwin are one example. The ancestors of these finches were separated from their fellows on the South American mainland and eventually the island finches evolved their own unique characteristics and so became a different species. Can the same be said for microbes?

One view is that microbes are everywhere, distributed all over the globe, and the environment merely allows the growth of different microbes depending on the conditions at any given locality. So, for example, cold-loving microbes are floating around in the atmosphere everywhere but would die in a hot spring, while heat-loving microbes, floating around in the atmosphere, would thrive in such conditions.

The alternative view, which is now gaining considerable support, is that not all microbes are everywhere and the formation of new species in particular environments can contribute to unique communities found in particular places, much like animals and plants. A good example is *Sulfolobus*, a heat-loving microbe belonging to the thermoprotei group of the Archaea (Figure 2.3). Investigations on samples of this microbe taken from volcanic hot springs around the world show that the populations are not genetically identical. There are some subtle variations in the DNA code of the microbes from these samples that are not due to environmental effects. Instead, it seems that distinct populations of the microbe have become established in different hot springs, with the geographical distance between the hot spring sites allowing genetically different groups of microbes to become established.

The distribution of microbes in different environments is a complex and current area of research for microbiologists that will be discussed in more detail in Chapters 6 and 7. In Chapter 3, you will look at the development of the science of microbiology.

Activity 2.3   Movement of microbes – Part 2

The estimated time for this activity is 25 minutes.

In this activity you will watch another short video sequence about microbial motility. The detailed notes for the activity, including some questions, are in the Activities section of the course website.

Question 2.10

If two sets of microbes collected from similar environments in different parts of the world were identical in appearance, explain whether they could be classified as the same species.

Question 2.11

Suggest two ways in which anaerobic microbes could be cultured in the laboratory.

Question 2.12

Fill in the missing words in the following paragraph about movement in microbes.

There are two types of projection used for moving that can be found on the surface of different microbes, long ones called _____ and short ones called _____ . When a microbe with _____ finds itself in an unsuitable environment, the direction of _____ of the _____ changes and the microbe _____ Spiral-shaped bacteria called _____ have _____ located between the _____ membrane and the cell _____. Microbes with short projections move in a manner called _____ .

Question 2.13

Identify which of the following statements are true, and which are false and explain the errors in the false statements.

(a) Microbial mats and biofilms usually consist of more than one type of microbe.

(b) Microbes at any distance from one another can communicate with one another by quantum sensing.

(c) Microbes in biofilms often have different characteristics from free-living microbes of the same species.

(d) Some microbes on teeth produce the acids that cause tooth decay.

Question 2.14

In Figure 2.13, there are several large bubbles visible. What gas is likely to be present in those bubbles?

Summary of Chapter 2

- Although microbes have a habit of exchanging DNA, they can be classified into species much like animals and plants. There are well established scientific conventions for naming species. Species are part of a hierarchy of classification.

- Microbes have quite specific growth requirements which can be used to culture them in the laboratory.

- Microbes are ubiquitous. Two reasons for their ability to colonise many diverse environments are their ability to move and their ability to go into dormant resting states that allow them to survive until better conditions occur.

- In any environment the growth of microbes will depend upon the energy and nutrients available. Often this leads to well-defined biofilms and mats where microbes may be stratified into layers.

- Microbes can communicate with one another and this ability may be important in the distribution of microbes at the very small scale.

Chapter 3
The development of microbiology

During the first two chapters you have learnt about some of the basic characteristics of microbes, how they grow and reproduce and some of the environments in which they live. Before you go on to study in more detail their role in the environment, human health and other contexts, it is valuable to step back a bit to look at the history of microbiology and some of the major advances that were made in the discovery and study of microbes that led to the knowledge explained in the first two chapters. This chapter will provide you with an important historical perspective and will allow you to understand how the role of microbes that you will examine in the following chapters was uncovered.

3.1 Microbes in the air

Although their detailed study only became possible with the advent of microscopes, microbes have been put to use by human society for millennia. The ancient Egyptians used them around 4500 years ago to ferment beer and to make bread, even though they could not see them (Figure 3.1). Both of these processes use a yeast, a kind of fungus, whose spores, along with those of other microbes, are floating in the air all around us now, as they were then. But fungal spores in the air are not always useful; they can also contribute to food spoilage. You will have noticed that if food, such as bread or fruit, is left out for a few days too long in the kitchen, it begins to go mouldy. Activity 3.1 is a scientific investigation of this process. Once the activity has been set up, it takes only a few moments each day to make the observations. Ideally, you should start this activity now, but you will need to make observations over a period of at least a week, so you may need to delay setting up the activity until appropriate time is available.

Figure 3.1 Brewing in Egypt around 2400 BC. The top panel shows the preparation and grinding of the grain. The middle panel shows the malting, kneading and baking of the mash. The bottom panel shows the straining and fermentation of the mash, with the beer being stored in jars which were capped and sealed with clay.

Activity 3.1   Investigating fungal spores in the air – Part 1

The estimated time for this activity is 2–3 hours spread over one or two weeks.

The aims of this investigation are:

1   To carry out a practical study that complements the work you did in Chapter 2 on culturing microbes (Section 2.3), microbial spores (Section 2.5) and microbial distribution (Section 2.6).

2   To gain some practical idea of how difficult it was for early pioneering microbiologists to refute the idea of spontaneous generation. This, as you will see later (Section 3.4) was the belief, widely held until the latter half of the 19th century, that life could arise spontaneously from non-living or decomposing matter.

3   To compare the number of microbial spores that grow when the medium has been exposed to the air for different lengths of time.

You will be exposing a growth medium (tomato soup) to the air to see how many microbial colonies, will grow on it. Most of these colonies will probably be fungal so this is what will be referred to throughout the activity, but some of the colonies you see may be bacterial.

This part of the activity should take you about 30 minutes and then you will need to make observations for a few moments each day for a week or more.

You will need the following equipment:

* small can of cheap tomato soup
* two identical rectangular plastic containers, without lids – ideally old ice-cream containers or something similar *that you are prepared to throw away* at the end of the investigation
* means of labelling the plastic containers
* cling film
* ruler or measuring tape.

When carrying out practical activities, you should always take care to observe simple safety precautions. Very often these precautions will seem quite obvious and just a matter of using common sense. However, that does not mean that you should ignore the safety instructions. The Open University has a duty to give advice on health and safety to students carrying out any activities that are described in our courses. Similarly, you have a duty to follow the instructions and to carry out the practical activity having regard for your own safety and that of other people around you. Whenever you do practical activities you should think about the hazards involved, and how any risks can be minimised.

Take note of the following safety precautions:

* Keep children and animals away while you are working.
* Clear your working area of clutter. Put all food away. Ensure there is nothing to trip on underfoot.
* Always wash your hands thoroughly before and after a practical activity.
* Any household items used should be thoroughly cleaned before returning them to domestic use.

Read through the whole of this procedure before you start the activity

Wash the two plastic containers thoroughly and allow them to dry upside down or dry with kitchen paper towels. Do not dry with a cloth since that might introduce unwanted microbial spores. When dry, open the can of soup and as quickly as you can, pour about half of the contents into each container (it doesn't need to be exact). Immediately cover the first container with the cling film. Label the container with a number 1 and make it clear on the label what it is and who is responsible for it; ensure that the label says 'Not to be eaten'.

If any microbial colonies grow on this soup, the spores must have been in the air that was trapped between the top of the soup and the cling film. So that you can calculate the volume of this air, you should measure the width and length of the container in centimetres (cm). These will be approximate measurements as the corners of the container are likely to be rounded. If you use a translucent container, you will be able to measure the distance from the surface of the soup to the cling film from the outside. If you cannot see the level of the soup through the side of the container, wait until the end of the experiment and then take the measurement after peeling back the cling film a little before re-attaching it. You should not do this during the course of the investigation, as this would allow more fungal spores to enter. Keep a note of your measurements.

Leave the other container with its soup open to the air for about 2 hours. You can leave it inside a room where you live, or outside in the open air, whichever you prefer. Cover with cling film and label it in the same way as the first, but number this as Container 2.

Record the date and time when you set up each container, and then carefully place the containers in a warm location, such as an airing cupboard, near a radiator or wherever in your house is the warmest. *Make sure that the containers are placed where they will not be disturbed and that they are kept out of reach of young children and pets at all times.*

Without lifting the cling film, inspect the surface of the soup every day or two. On each occasion count and record the number of separate areas of microbial growth you can see in each container.

Once it is clear that the number of areas of microbial growth is no longer increasing between inspections in either of the containers, or the colonies begin to merge with one another, the practical part of this activity is complete. This will probably take a couple of weeks. For each container, record: the final number of colonies; on the basis of their visual appearance (including their colour and texture), how many different types of colony there are; how many of each type; and the characteristics you used to identify the different types. Note how long your experiment took to complete. You will find a table for these results, together with instructions on what to do next, in Part 2 of this activity in Section 3.10 near the end of this chapter.

3.2   Unseen organisms

As already mentioned, unseen microbes were being used by the ancient Egyptians in the production of food and drink. In addition, a lot of effort went into preserving the bodies of important people (by mummification), suggesting an awareness that something was triggering decomposition after death. Sanitation practices in early civilisations indicate they may have realised the connections between sewage and disease. Archaeological excavations in the Orkney Islands have found lavatories dating from 2800 BC. In 600 BC, ancient Romans built elaborate aqueducts and, to oversee the safety of the public water supply, a 'Water Commissioner' was employed and contamination of the water system was punishable by death. This early understanding of the spread of diseases led to fear and quarantining of the sick, which meant that those quarantined received little, if any, attention or care.

Ideas of possible invisible organisms were put forward by several people, despite there being no means of seeing them. In the first century BC, Marcus Varro, a Roman scholar, warned people to avoid swamps and marshland for fear of serious disease:

> 'Precautions must also be taken in the neighbourhood of swamps […] because there are bred certain minute creatures which cannot be seen, which float in the air and enter the body through the mouth and nose and there cause serious diseases.'

> Varro, Marcus Terentius, *On Agriculture* Transl. W. D. Hooper and H. B. Ash
> Cambridge, MA: Harvard University Press, 1999, pp. 217–9

In 1546, the Italian physician Girolamo Fracastoro suggested that invisible organisms may cause disease. He was the first to propose that each epidemic disease is caused by different types of tiny particles that could transmit infection by being carried on soiled clothing, linen, etc. or through the air. Fracastoro's theory was widely praised at the time, but was then forgotten for almost 300 years.

3.3 Early microscopes

The oldest known lens, made from rock crystal (quartz), was found in what is now Iraq and dates back to about 1000 BC. There is evidence for glass lenses in ancient Egyptian hieroglyphs, though many were used as burning-glasses, to focus sunlight to start a fire, rather than for magnification. By around 1000 AD, the optical properties of lenses were recorded by Ibn al-Haytham, born near Basra (Iraq) in his *Book of Optics*. However, not until the development in the 17th century of the compound microscope, which uses more than one lens to focus the image of the object, was there any chance of seeing the vast majority of microbes.

The first compound microscope was developed by the English scientist Robert Hooke in 1664 (Figure 3.2), who used it to observe, among other items, fleas (Figure 3.3), bird feathers and plants. (In his honour, one of the OU's science buildings on the Milton Keynes campus is named the Robert Hooke building.) He first used the word 'cell' in relation to living things and, by describing the spores of moulds (fungi), he became the first person to document the appearance of a microbe. He published his work in the book *Micrographia or Some physiological descriptions of minute bodies made by magnifying glasses*

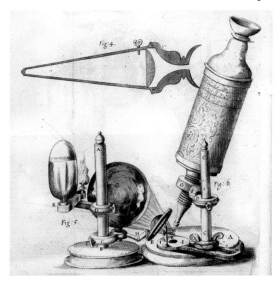

Figure 3.2   A drawing of Robert Hooke's compound microscope.

with observations and inquiries thereupon. However, the magnification he could achieve was not more than about ×20.

Some ten years later, the Dutch tradesman and amateur scientist Antonie van Leeuwenhoek, apparently inspired by seeing a copy of Robert Hooke's book, started making microscopes himself. He became skilled at grinding glass lenses, which he used to produce several hundred microscopes. However, these were not compound microscopes of the type developed by Hooke, but were actually based on single lenses, just very powerful magnifying glasses (Figure 3.4). Nevertheless, they produced clearer images than the compound microscopes of the time and van Leeuwenhoek was able to magnify his samples by more than ×200. He is commonly regarded as the 'Father of Microbiology', and made the first observations of bacteria (Figure 3.5).

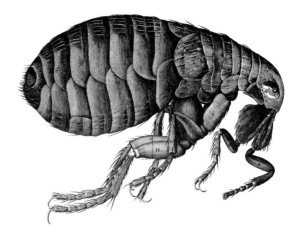

Figure 3.3 A drawing by Robert Hooke of the flea he examined using his microscope.

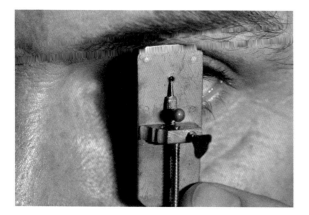

Figure 3.4 One of about ten surviving single-lensed microscopes designed by van Leeuwenhoek. The glass lens is mounted in a hole in the metal plate, which is about 10 cm long. The specimen would be fixed on a sharp point sticking out in front of the lens, with its position, and thus its focus, being adjusted by turning the two screws. The specimen was then observed by holding the whole microscope close to the eye and looking through the lens.

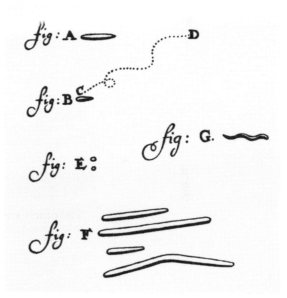

Figure 3.5 Drawings of microbes in dental plaque made by van Leeuwenhoek in 1683.

Question 3.1

Study Figure 3.5 carefully and then answer the following questions.

(a) The caption to Figure 3.5 refers to dental plaque. What is dental plaque? (You may need to refer back to Section 2.6.3.)

(b) Which three types of microbe are visible in van Leeuwenhoek's drawings?

(c) How would you interpret the dotted line drawn by van Leeuwenhoek between C and D?

Rather surprisingly, the work of Hooke and van Leeuwenhoek was not followed up for almost 200 years and the empire of the microbes lay hidden once again until the rise of the Industrial Revolution. It was then that governments and people began to dedicate the financial and physical resources to peer once again into this tiny world. As microscopes advanced in the 19th century, the examination of micro-organisms began again in earnest. A German botanist, Ferdinand Julius Cohn, used a microscope to examine both bacteria and eukaryotic microbes, although at this time the difference was not recognised, and in 1872 he published a landmark paper that included a description of the bacterium *Bacillus* and a microbial classification scheme. Cohn's work with microscopes popularised their use in microbiology and his work became an inspiration for many other scientists to examine microbes.

3.4 Spontaneous generation

For many centuries, there was a general belief in a concept known as spontaneous generation, which says that life can arise spontaneously from non-living or decomposing matter. However, debates went on between philosophers and scientists, and experiments were devised to attempt to resolve the situation. By the late 17th century there was some agreement that spontaneous generation was not true for larger organisms. For example, maggots only appeared in meat if flies had laid their eggs on it, rather than the maggots appearing by spontaneous generation. However, there were many who still believed that very small microbes could be produced by spontaneous generation.

An important experiment was devised in 1745, by John Needham, an English clergyman and proponent of spontaneous generation. He proposed to test whether or not microbes appeared spontaneously in broth (clear liquid in which meat and/ or vegetables had been simmered). It was known that high temperatures were lethal to living organisms so the experiment involved boiling broth, pouring it into a flask, sealing the flask and then waiting to see whether microbes appeared.

■ How would it be possible to detect the presence of microbes in the broth?

☐ Broth becomes cloudy, or turbid, when large numbers of microbes have been grown (see answer to Question 2.3).

The result of the experiment was that the broth became cloudy and Needham claimed a victory for spontaneous generation.

■ Based on what you learnt about culturing microbes in the laboratory (Activity 2.2), what might have been the weak point in Needham's experiment?

☐ When Needham boiled the broth it would have killed those microbes already present in it, but during the process of pouring the broth into the flask, it could easily have been contaminated by microbes in the air, which would then reproduce and make the broth cloudy. Also the flask itself might not have been properly sterilised.

In 1766, the Italian priest Lazzaro Spallanzani tried to refute Needham's work. He repeated Needham's experiment but, suspecting that air was providing the source of contamination, he boiled the broth in a glass flask which he then quickly sealed before it had any chance to cool.

■ How would this process ensure that there was no air in the flask?

☐ The steam from the boiling broth would push out the air which was originally present in the flask, together with any microbes that might have been in it. By instantly sealing the flask, no air would be sucked back in as the flask cooled.

No micro-organisms grew and Spallanzani took this as evidence that Needham was wrong. However, supporters of spontaneous generation asserted that air was required for spontaneous generation to work. It was not until 1859, almost 100 years later, that the debate was finally put to rest by the French chemist Louis Pasteur.

Pasteur passed air through a filter made of cotton. The cotton filter trapped microbial spores from the air, and when the filter was then washed, numerous microbes were found in the solution. Pasteur realised that if these microbes were present in the air, they would be likely to land on and contaminate any material exposed to air. So he then devised a further experiment, as his entry to a contest, sponsored by the French Academy of Sciences, for the best experiment either proving or disproving spontaneous generation.

Pasteur's experiment, like those of Needham and Spallanzani, used broth as the medium in which the microbes could grow. He placed the broth in a flask (Figure 3.6a), and then heated the neck of the flask in a flame, so that it became pliable and could be bent into the shape of an 'S' (Figure 3.6b). He then sterilised the broth by boiling it (Figure 3.6c), which forced the air out of the neck of the flask. When the broth was then allowed to cool, water vapour in the neck condensed and collected at the bottom of the bend (Figure 3.6d). Any microbes in the air settled out into the liquid in the bend, and did not pass over into the broth. When left for several days the broth remained sterile; no microbes grew (Figure 3.6e). To complete the experiment, Pasteur then tilted the flask, so that the liquid in the bend was mixed into the broth (Figure 3.6f), and within a short time the broth became cloudy, demonstrating microbial growth. (Figure 3.6g). With this carefully designed experiment, Pasteur won the French Academy of Sciences contest and finally refuted the theory of spontaneous generation, as well as convincingly demonstrating that microbes are in the air all round us.

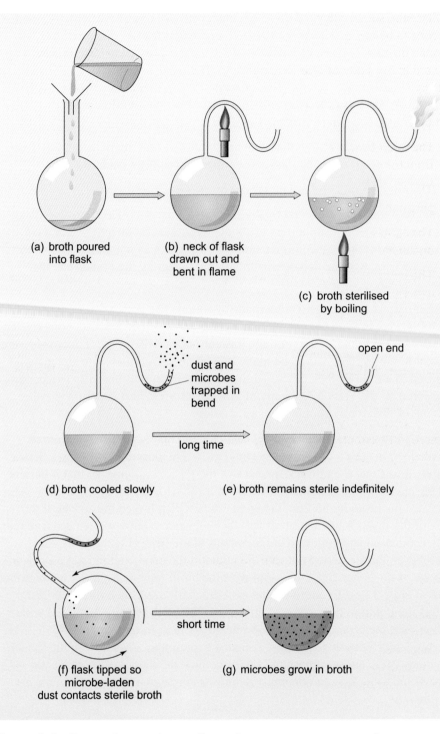

Figure 3.6 Pasteur's experiment disproving spontaneous generation.

3.5 Microbes and disease

As early as 100 BC, the Romans expressed the idea that living things were the cause of disease, but this was not proved until the 19th century, around the same time that Pasteur was working. In 1835, the Italian Agostino Bassi, a relative of

Spallanzani, showed that a disease of silkworms was caused by a fungus, the first microbe to be recognised as the cause of an animal disease. However, it was a German physician, Robert Koch (1843–1910) who provided a monumental step forward in the study of infectious diseases. His work on anthrax in 1876 provided a critical link between microbes and disease. As a result of this, Koch suggested four criteria, known as Koch's postulates, all of which must be satisfied before a particular microbe can be accepted as the cause of a disease:

1   The microbe must be shown to be present in all cases of organisms suffering from the disease, but should not be found in healthy organisms.

2   The microbe must be isolated from the diseased organism and grown in pure culture.

3   The cultured microbe should cause the same disease seen in the original organism when inoculated into a healthy laboratory organism.

4   The microbe must be re-isolated in pure culture from the inoculated, diseased experimental organism.

Figure 3.7 presents Koch's postulates in a diagrammatic form. In fact, Koch later abandoned the second part of his first postulate, since there were occasions when healthy people were found to carry disease-causing microbes (for example those which cause cholera, and typhoid fever), without themselves being ill. He also carefully used the word 'should' rather than 'must' in the third postulate, since he found that not everyone who was exposed to tuberculosis (TB) or cholera microbes necessarily developed the disease. Some people remained healthy because, for example, their immune system was able to destroy the microbe, possibly for genetic reasons, or because they had previously been exposed to a less virulent form of the disease. You will learn more about the immune system in Chapter 5.

Question 3.2

Silkworms are the caterpillars of the domesticated silkmoth. When the caterpillar pupates, prior to emerging as the moth, it encloses itself in a cocoon made of a single thread of silk up to 900 m long, which can then be unwound and used to make silk fabric. In the disease of silkworms studied by Agostino Bassi, the caterpillars became covered by a fine white powder and died. The disease first appeared in Italy around 1805, then spread to France and by 1850, the economically important silk industry had collapsed, with almost all the silk farms in both countries abandoned. Bassi suspected that the white powder consisted of spores of a fungus which infected the insects. How could each of Koch's postulates be applied to confirm that the disease was caused by fungal spores?

In addition to his postulates, Koch also developed many microbiological techniques, some of which are still used today. He developed methods for staining bacteria, for photographing them and for preparing permanent visual records on slides. Whilst formulating his postulates, Koch became aware of the difficulties of isolating disease-causing microbes in a pure culture and he developed several methods of doing so. He found that by exposing a solid surface

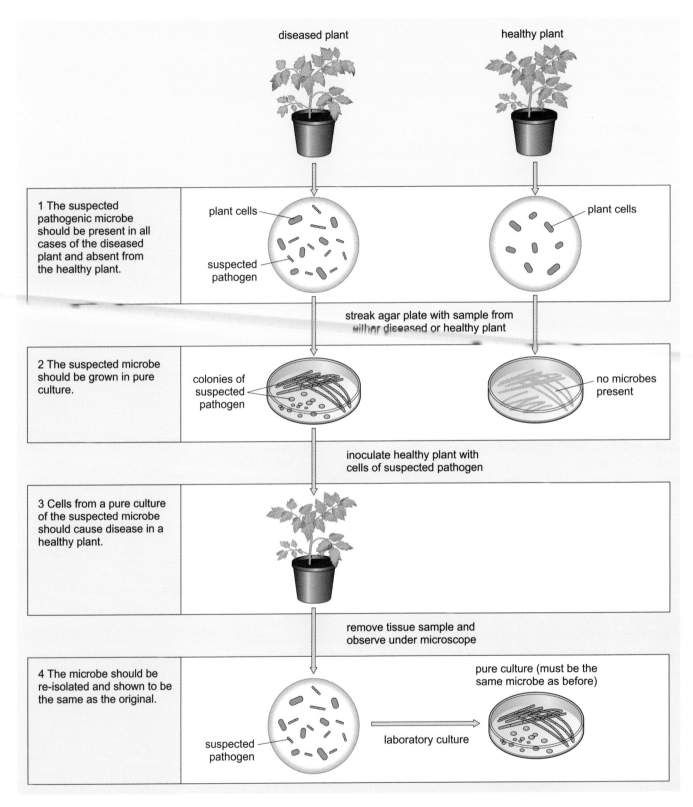

Figure 3.7 A diagrammatic overview of Koch's postulates as applied to microbial disease in a plant.

such as a potato slice to the air various microbial colonies would grow. Different sorts of colonies could be identified by their characteristic shape and colour, and he realised that each colony would have grown from a single microbe that had fallen onto the surface and multiplied. So each colony was a pure culture of that microbe.

■ Based on what you have read in earlier chapters, what would be the main problem with using potato slices for growing microbes such as fungi and bacteria?

☐ Potato slices provide only a limited amount of nutrients, mainly starch, so those microbes which can use these nutrients as their source of energy and raw materials, would grow, whilst others would not.

Koch realised this too and went on to develop solutions containing specific nutrients, to encourage certain microbes to grow, and to solidify those solutions using agar, to make plates similar to those still used today in microbiological labs (as described in Activity 2.2). Koch isolated the bacteria responsible for anthrax and cholera, and he received the 1905 Nobel Prize in Physiology or Medicine for his work on the cause of tuberculosis.

3.6   Infection by viruses

Towards the end of the 19th century, studies led by Martinus Beijerinck, working in Delft, were underway to try to identify the cause of tobacco mosaic disease, which produced mottling and discolouration of the leaves of tobacco plants (Figure 3.8). This disease behaved in a similar way to bacterial infections and met Koch's postulates to some extent, but the microbe causing it could not be cultured in the laboratory. However, more significantly, when sap from infected plants was passed through a porcelain filter with pores small enough to filter out all bacteria, the liquid that passed through the filter could still cause the disease in another plant.

(a)   (b)

Figure 3.8   (a) Normal tobacco leaves and (b) leaves showing the effects of tobacco mosaic disease.

■ Looking back to Box 1.1, can you identify a way in which the tobacco mosaic disease could still be caused by bacteria?

☐ The ulcers and swellings seen in a patient with bubonic plague are not due to the *Yersinia pestis* microbe itself, but to toxins produced by it. Toxins are molecules which could easily pass through the porcelain filter. So, the results for the tobacco mosaic disease could be explained if that was also caused by bacterial toxins.

However, following further experiments, scientists eventually concluded that a new type of microbe was responsible that must be much smaller than bacteria. These microbes could multiply inside living cells and the term virus (Latin for 'poison' or 'toxin') was applied to them.

Looking back to Figure 2.3, the phylogenetic tree of life, you will see that the viruses are not included. Unlike the prokaryotes and eukaryotes, which live independent lives, viruses can only reproduce inside living cells. A virus consists of genetic material, either DNA or RNA, surrounded by a protein coat called a capsid. Figure 3.9 shows the diversity of virus shapes. When it comes into contact with a host cell, the virus inserts its genetic material into the cell and effectively hijacks the cell's processes, causing it to produce multiple copies of the virus. Some viruses may remain dormant inside host cells for long periods, causing no obvious effects. However, when a dormant virus is stimulated, it breaks open and its genetic material is activated; new full-sized viruses are then assembled and emerge from the host cell, sometimes killing that cell and going on to infect others. Because viruses show no signs of life when outside cells, there has been considerable debate about whether viruses can be described as being 'alive' and even about the definition of the word 'life'. You will learn more about viruses in Chapter 5.

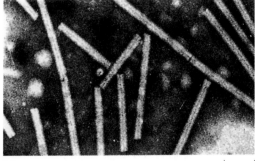

(a)   120 nm

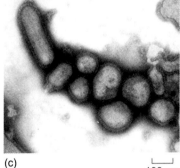

(c)   100 nm

Figure 3.9 Electron micrographs of four examples of viruses showing their wide diversity in shapes: (a) tobacco mosaic virus; (b) an unnamed virus that can infect the bacterium *E. coli*; (c) influenza virus; (d) smallpox virus.

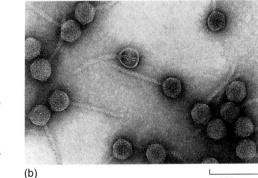

(b)   150 nm

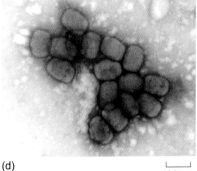

(d)   100 nm

Question 3.3

What characteristics might be used to decide whether something is living? Do (a) bacteria and (b) viruses demonstrate these characteristics?

3.7   Fighting back

All living organisms, including bacteria, have biochemical systems to protect them against other bacteria or viruses. In animals this is called an immune system. Bacteria do not possess an immune system as such, but they can protect themselves against infection by viruses using a relatively simple system in which the genetic material of the invading virus is chopped into pieces by enzymes. Enzymes are a special type of protein produced, as are all proteins, in cells according to the code carried in the DNA. Enzymes speed up chemical reactions which would otherwise go too slowly to be useful; they are a type of catalyst. Catalysts can help to break down other molecules, as here, or they can help to build up other molecules, as you will see in Section 3.9. In humans, the immune system consists of more than just enzymes. Basically the immune system depends on the production of antibodies (another kind of protein) against the infecting microbes, and then their destruction by white blood cells. If the type of microbe has been encountered before, then the human immune system can respond more quickly and powerfully than on the first occasion, and the disease may only occur in a mild form, if at all. This is called immunological memory. You will learn more about the immune system in Chapter 5.

3.7.1   Vaccination

The ancient Chinese were among the earliest people to recognise immunological memory, possibly as early as the 10th century. They used material from the scabs on the skin of recovering smallpox victims to infect other people to protect them from the disease. The smallpox virus is shown in Figure 3.9d. Here is a translation of the detailed advice from the 'New book on smallpox inoculation' written in 1741:

> 'Method of storing the material. Wrap the scabs carefully in paper and put them into a small container bottle. Cork it tightly so that the activity is not dissipated. The container must not be exposed to sunlight or warmed beside a fire. It is best to carry it for some time on the person so that the scabs dry naturally and slowly. The container should be marked clearly with the date on which the contents were taken from the patient.
>
> In winter, the material has *yang* potency within it, so it remains active even after being kept from thirty to forty days. But in summer the *yang* potency will be lost in approximately twenty days. The best material is that which had not been left too long, for when the *yang* potency is abundant it will give a 'take' with nine persons out of ten people – and finally it becomes completely inactive, and will not work at all. In situations where new scabs are rare and the requirement great, it is

possible to mix new scabs with the more aged ones, but in this case more of the powder should be blown into the nostril when the inoculation is done.'

Temple, R. (1986). *The Genius of China: 3,000 Years of Science, Discovery, and Invention*, New York: Simon and Schuster, pp. 136–7

In Britain, Europe and America, the preferred method of inoculation was to rub the material from the scab into a scratch between the thumb and forefinger. But both methods often had serious side-effects, causing a lesion at the site of inoculation and sometimes a rash all over the body. Occasionally, a full case of smallpox occurred and the fatality rate from this immunisation method was 1–2%.

In 1796, an English physician Edward Jenner was attempting to find a safer method of protection against smallpox. He had observed that milkmaids who had contracted cowpox, a milder form of smallpox caught from infected cows, were subsequently immune to smallpox. Jenner hypothesised that the causes of the two diseases were related and so contracting cowpox would protect against the more dangerous smallpox. Jenner decided to test his hypothesis in a classic experiment, which would be considered unethical by today's standards. An eight-year-old boy, James Phipps, was inoculated with 'virulent matter' from cowpox lesions on the fingers of a milkmaid (Figure 3.10). Although James Phipps developed a mild fever and some cowpox lesions, he was protected from smallpox when, several weeks later, he was infected by Jenner with the disease. This effective treatment was later to be called vaccination, a term coined by Louis Pasteur to commemorate Jenner's experiment ('vacca' is Latin for cow).

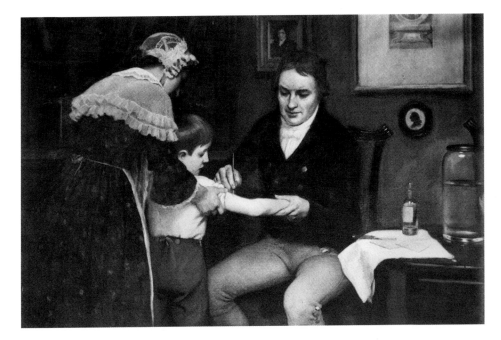

Figure 3.10 A depiction of Edward Jenner infecting James Phipps with cowpox in an effort to give protection against smallpox.

Subsequent to his work on spontaneous generation (Section 3.4), Pasteur made significant advances in the new science of immunology, building on the work of Jenner. Around 1876, he was working on a disease of chickens known as chicken cholera. (Chicken cholera is not caused by the same microbe that causes cholera in humans. The microbe that causes cholera in chickens belongs to the genus *Pasteurella*.) He cultured the bacteria responsible and was surprised to find that, after several weeks in culture, the microbes no longer caused the disease when injected into chickens. He took those chickens and a new group of chickens and injected them both with a fresh culture of the microbe.

■ Based on the work of Edward Jenner, what results would Louis Pasteur have been hoping to get from this experiment?

☐ He hoped that the chickens which had previously been injected with the microbes from the 'old' culture would be immune to chicken cholera and would survive, while the other chickens would succumb to the disease.

This was exactly what happened. Having discovered that it was possible for chicken cholera microbes to become less potent (lose their virulence), by being cultured for several weeks, Pasteur went on to investigate whether there were other ways in which potency could be reduced. He discovered that damaging bacteria by heating them, or exposing them to other environmental extremes could reduce their virulence. Virulence was also reduced if the microbes were used to infect one animal, then removed from that animal and used to infect another of the same species, and so on, through many cycles. The virulence changed gradually until eventually a much less virulent form of the microbe was obtained. This process, known as attenuation, is rather hit-and-miss since it is difficult to predict whether the bacteria will be sufficiently damaged to prevent them causing disease while still acting as an effective vaccine. By using these techniques vaccines have been made for bubonic plague, anthrax, rabies and many other diseases.

3.7.2   The development of antibiotics

As more illnesses were linked to microbes, and more of the microbes were cultured, it became clear that certain compounds were capable of inhibiting microbial growth. The difficulty was in finding drugs that would kill the microbes, but not be toxic to those patients suffering from the disease caused by them. An organic arsenic-containing compound called atoxyl, first synthesised in the 1850s, was effective against *Trypanosoma brucei*, the eukaryotic microbe that causes sleeping sickness. Unfortunately the dosage needed was so high that its side-effects, including blindness, far outweighed the benefits. However, in the early 1900s, the German microbiologist, Paul Ehrlich led a team which identified the chemical formula of atoxyl and then started to synthesise similar compounds which would kill microbes, but have fewer side-effects on patients. Ehrlich was particularly concerned to find a drug effective against the bacterium, *Treponema pallidum* (Figure 3.11), which causes syphilis.

■ Based on the shape of the bacterium, what type of microbe is *Treponema* (Figure 3.11).

☐ It is a spirochaete.

Not until the 606th compound that the team tried, were they successful, with a drug they subsequently named Salvarsan. This still contained arsenic and did have side-effects, but was the first effective anti-syphilitic drug.

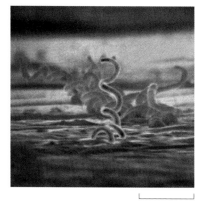

0.5 μm

Figure 3.11   An electron micrograph of *Treponema pallidum*.

Figure 3.12 Alexander Fleming (1881–1955) was a Scottish physician and microbiologist who opened up the field of antibiotic research.

Alexander Fleming (Figure 3.12), a physician by training, spent most of his time studying bacteria. The success in Ehrlich's lab with Salvarsan motivated Fleming to search for other antimicrobial agents. His greatest contribution would come with his discovery of penicillin, the first antibiotic. (An antibiotic is a chemical produced by microbes that kills other microbes.) He later wrote:

'When I woke up just after dawn on September 28, 1928, I certainly didn't plan to revolutionise all medicine by discovering the world's first antibiotic, or bacteria killer. But I guess that was exactly what I did.'

By 1928, Fleming was professor of bacteriology in St Mary's Hospital, Paddington, London and was working with *Staphylococcus aureus* (which you first met in Chapter 1). He was recognised as a brilliant research scientist, but not the tidiest of people in the lab. He often forgot about cultures he was working on and his lab was usually in chaos. Before taking a summer break, Fleming had streaked some plates with *S. aureus*, and left them for examination on his return.

Question 3.4

Looking back to Activity 2.2 if necessary, describe in no more than 100 words what is meant by the statement that 'he had streaked some plates with *S. aureus*'.

When Fleming returned, he found that many of his plates had been contaminated with a fungus, whose spores must have been in the air in the lab, and he put the plates into disinfectant. However, subsequently he retrieved some of those which had not been submerged, to show to a visitor, and noticed that there was a clear area around the fungal colonies in which the *S. aureus* had either not grown or been killed. Figure 3.13 shows an example of antibiotic production by soil bacteria.

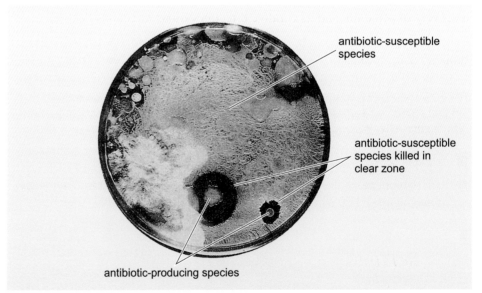

antibiotic-susceptible species

antibiotic-susceptible species killed in clear zone

antibiotic-producing species

Figure 3.13 Antibiotic action of soil bacteria growing on an agar plate. The small round colonies surrounded by clear (dark) zones are *Streptomyces* species. The large irregular colonies are *Bacillus* species, whose growth is inhibited by antibiotic secretions from *Streptomyces*.

Fleming realised that the fungus must be producing an antibiotic compound. He then set about culturing the fungus and he prepared a solution from it, which could kill bacteria. He called the compound penicillin, after the fungus from which it came, which belonged to the genus *Penicillium*.

■ Can you think of a reason why it would be beneficial for microbes to develop a way of killing other microbes that are living nearby?

☐ If the microbes are living close to one another, they are likely to be competing for the same energy source and/or raw materials from their surroundings. So by producing a compound which kills nearby microbes, a species would ensure maximum availability of those resources for itself.

Having found that penicillin was effective against many of the Gram-positive bacteria that he was working on (such as those which caused scarlet fever, pneumonia, meningitis and diphtheria), Fleming published his discovery in 1929 in the *British Journal of Experimental Pathology*, but little attention was paid to it at the time. He continued his work, but found *Penicillium* was hard to culture, the extraction of the drug was difficult and it was not particularly effective when given to people, often because it was used as a surface antiseptic, rather than being injected.

However, during World War II there was an urgent need for antibiotics to treat infections that develop from the injuries received by servicemen. To address this, a study of antibiotic drugs was undertaken in 1939 by Howard Florey and Ernst Chain, working in Oxford. They came across Fleming's work from about 10 years before and, with the advances in various techniques since the original publication, they were now able to purify penicillin. It became available in large quantities and saved countless lives during the war. Fleming, Florey and Chain were awarded the Nobel Prize in Physiology or Medicine in 1945 'for the discovery of penicillin and its curative effect in various infectious diseases'.

Subsequently Fleming cautioned about the use of penicillin unless there was a properly diagnosed reason for its use. He wrote in 1946 that 'the administration of too small doses … leads to the production of resistant strains of bacteria'. This warning has, of course, proved very true, as *Staphylococcus aureus* is one of several bacteria which have, over the years, developed antibiotic resistance and which currently cause significant problems in hospitals.

■ What is the usual abbreviation for this 'hospital superbug'?

☐ It is called MRSA – standing for methicillin-resistant *Staphylococcus aureus* (Section 1.7).

3.8 The development of environmental microbiology

Alongside the early work in microbiology focused on disease-causing microbes, but with a much lower profile at the time, were the beginnings of studies on the role of bacteria in the natural environment. Martinus Beijerinck, mentioned briefly in Section 3.6 in connection with his work on the tobacco mosaic virus, founded the Delft School of Microbiology, and worked mainly on agricultural microbes. Until this time, most microbes had been grown on the same culture medium under similar conditions, but Beijerinck developed the use of special enrichment media with certain compounds added, or removed, to encourage the growth of particular species of microbe, while inhibiting the growth of others. Using this enrichment culture technique, Beijerinck was able to isolate the first pure cultures of many soil and aquatic microbes, including nitrogen-fixing bacteria (important in agriculture and the global cycling of nitrogen) and sulfate-reducing and sulfur-oxidising bacteria, which you will meet in Chapter 7.

Sergei Winogradsky, a Russian microbiologist, was also working in the late 19th century, on similar bacteria to those of Beijerinck. He studied how different species of microbe became established in different regions when they were subjected to a range of environmental conditions. This can be demonstrated in the apparatus he devised which has become known as a Winogradsky column (see *Laboratory methods 3.1*).

Laboratory methods 3.1   The Winogradsky column

A Winogradsky column (Figure 3.14) consists of a tall plastic or glass tube or jar, ideally 30 cm or more long and more than 5 cm in diameter. If a tube is used, it needs to be sealed at the bottom. The following ingredients are mixed together (the exact amounts are not important):

- Mud – ideally mud from the bottom of a pond, but soil will do. The volume of mud or soil needs to be about half the volume of the container.
- Egg shells – a well crushed egg shell provides a source of calcium carbonate.
- Egg yolk or gypsum – an egg yolk or a teaspoonful of gypsum (calcium sulfate, plaster of Paris) provides a source of sulfur.
- Newspaper – some torn up newspaper acts as a source of carbon.

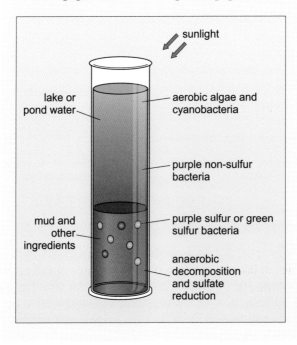

Figure 3.14 A Winogradsky column.

These ingredients are then put into the tube and water (ideally from a pond or other stagnant source) is added to fill up about half of the remaining volume and the top of the column is sealed to prevent evaporation. The column then needs to be left in a warm place, exposed to sunlight, for at least a few weeks and probably several months to develop fully.

Over the weeks varying concentrations of nutrient and oxygen develop in different parts of the column, and different species of microbe (bacteria, cyanobacteria and algae) establish themselves in different zones. The different zones of microbes can often be identified by different colours, due to the pigments in the microbes.

■   What are the possible sources of the microbes which grow in the Winogradsky column?

☐   Most of the microbes will be present, either as active microbes, or as spores, in the mud or soil. Additional ones will be introduced in the pond water. Some may be present in the other ingredients added to the column, and others will be present as spores in the air while the column is being prepared and so will be incorporated into it.

■   In the tube there will be different levels of oxygen. Where would you expect to find the most oxygen and where would conditions be likely to be anaerobic?

☐   The water at the top of the column is likely to be aerobic (since it is nearest to the oxygen in the air above the column). Microbes near the base of the column will very soon use up any oxygen which might be there at the start, and so conditions there are likely to be anaerobic.

■   Is there any possibility of additional oxygen being generated?

☐   Where there is light, photosynthetic microbes may grow and they will generate oxygen. The chlorophyll in the photosynthetic microbes will give the column a green colour where they are present.

Although it is not part of this course, you may like to set up a Winogradsky column for yourself and look for the division of the microbes which grow in it into zones. Detailed instructions are on the course website.

Winogradsky also proposed the concept of chemolithotrophy, the ability of some microbes to live using only simple molecules, for example containing iron or nitrogen. This was a radical idea, and was not widely accepted at the time. You will meet the chemolithotrophs in Chapters 6 and 7.

The work of Winogradsky and Beijerinck in agricultural microbiology paved the way for further microbial studies in lakes, rivers and oceans (aquatic and marine microbiology) in the first half of the 20th century. This led to the establishment of the discipline of microbial ecology and with the development of new techniques in molecular biology, the discipline continues to grow.

3.9 The molecular age

You will recall from Chapter 2 that the identification of different species of microbe, and the study of relationships between them is based on the analysis of their DNA and RNA. To analyse the DNA, to find out the sequence of bases along the strand, requires multiple of copies of the DNA to be made. Once DNA can be multiplied ('amplified') like this, it also opens up the possibility of detecting microbes which are present in only very small numbers in the environment by looking for their DNA.

■ Look back to Figure 1.11 and describe in two sentences how DNA is copied within the cell.

☐ The two strands of the DNA helix unwind and the base pairs (forming the rungs of the ladder) break apart. New bases attach to the single strands, to build new strands alongside the original ones.

In the cell, two important enzymes are used in this process (look back to Section 3.7 if you need a reminder about enzymes). The first, called helicase, unwinds the strand (Figure 1.11b), and the second, called DNA polymerase, detects which bases are needed for the new strand, and joins them together to form a new side to the ladder, complementary to the original one (Figure 1.11c). Scientists needed to be able to perform this process outside cells, to produce more copies of the DNA for their investigations.

It soon became clear that the unwinding process, performed in the cell by helicase, could be achieved by heating the DNA molecule to about 95 °C, but then when the strands were cooled enough for the second enzyme, DNA polymerase, to work, they reassembled into the original double helices. If the temperature was kept high, then the DNA polymerase was only active for a very short time before being destroyed by the heat. A version of the DNA polymerase enzyme which would be active at a high temperature was needed.

■ Can you think of an environment that might contain microbes with such an enzyme?

☐ In Section 1.7, Figure 1.13, you were introduced to microbes that live in colonies in the hot springs in Yellowstone National Park. These microbes, like all others, need to be able to copy their DNA when they divide and so, since they live at high temperatures, presumably their DNA polymerase works at these temperatures.

This was found to be the case. The microbe used, which can live and reproduce at 85 °C, is called *Thermus aquaticus* or *T. aquaticus*. The DNA polymerase extracted from it is, not surprisingly, known as *Taq* polymerase.

So now it was possible to make multiple copies of a DNA molecule outside the cell, in a process called the polymerase chain reaction, or PCR. The technique was developed by the American biochemist Kary Mullis in 1983 and it led him to a share in the 1993 Nobel Prize for Chemistry, with the British-born biochemist Michael Smith.

Now this work could be combined with that of Walter Gilbert and Fred Sanger who, in 1977, had each developed a method to determine the exact sequence of bases in DNA. The first microbial genome, that of *Haemophilus influenzae* (which can cause chest infections and bacterial meningitis), was elucidated in 1995, by a team including Craig Venter, who later went on to lead a team that sequenced the human genome in 2000. Since then, the genomes of many more microbes have been sequenced. The development of these techniques has led to the science of genomics, the comparative analysis of the genes from different organisms, which in turn has advanced knowledge in microbial medicine, microbial ecology, industrial microbiology and other areas. Many of the microbes that you meet in this course have been identified by these methods.

3.10   Microbes in the air – revisited

This is the final part of Activity 3.1 where you will consider your results from the investigation you began at the start of this chapter.

Activity 3.1   Investigating fungal spores in the air – Part 2

The estimated time for this part of the activity is about 30 minutes.

You should now have a value for the final number of fungal colonies on the surface of each of your containers of soup, and measurements of the width and length of Container 1 and the distance from the surface of the soup to the cling film. Before you do anything else, you should dispose of the contaminated soup. For safety reasons, it is recommended that the contents of each container should be poured separately down the toilet, followed by at least one immediate flush in each case. The cling film must go straight in the bin. The containers should be washed thoroughly and then they should follow the cling film into the bin. The items put in the bin should be wrapped up so that any smell doesn't arouse the curiosity of animals on collection day. Finally, the sink in which the containers have been cleaned should be given a thorough disinfecting.

Analysis of results

Use Table 3.1 to record the results for each of your containers. Under Container 2 in the first column, record the time for which you exposed this container, and where it was exposed. In the heading of the second column, record the number of days taken for your experiment.

Table 3.1 Blank table for recording the results of the investigation of fungal spores in the air.

	Total number of colonies after .... days	Number of different types of colony	Observations on colony types
Container 1			
Container 2			

You should now make a few notes in answer to each of the following questions.

(a) You might expect that there would be no colonies on the soup in Container 1, since that was closed immediately with the cling film. If there were colonies, where did the spores come from?

(b) How many more colonies were there on the soup in Container 2 compared with Container 1? Why were there more?

(c) How many different types of colony did you see in each container? How easy was it to separate the different types?

Compare your answers with the Comments on Activity 3.1 at the end of the book.

The experiment shows you just how common spores are in the air and how difficult it would have been for early microbiologists trying to prevent their experiments from becoming contaminated. Without specialist laboratory facilities, keeping cultures and broths free of these spores would have been very difficult, making it impossible for early microbiologists to disprove the idea of spontaneous generation, using this sort of experiment.

Calculation for Container 1

Each area of growth probably represents one fungus, which will have arisen from one fungal spore, which settled out from the air trapped between the cling film and the surface of the soup. So you should be able to work out the density of fungal spores in that sample of air. The density of spores is the number in a particular volume of air.

First you need to find the volume of air in Container 1. To do that, multiply together your three measurements (length and width of the container, and the distance between the surface of the soup and the cling film). You are multiplying three lengths together, so your final units will be cubic centimetres, usually written as cm^3. You can then write your result as 'so many fungal spores' per 'so many cubic centimetres'; for example – 6 fungal spores per 680 cm^3.

However, if you want to compare your results with others who have done a similar activity, then it is more useful to know how many fungal spores there are in 1 m^3 (one cubic metre). There are one million cm^3 in 1 m^3.

Here is a sample calculation, using the figures above:

In this example, there are 6 fungal spores per 680 cm^3.

Since there are 1000 000 cm^3 in 1 m^3, it follows that 680 cm^3 = 680/1000 000 m^3 = 0.000 68 m^3.

If 0.000 68 m^3 of air contains 6 fungal spores, then 1 m^3 will contain 6/0.000 68 fungal spores = 8824 spores.

Since the measurements of the container were not done with any great precision, then it is reasonable to give the results to the nearest 100 spores, which would be 8800 in this case.

In this example, you could conclude that at the time when the cling film was applied, there were 8800 fungal spores per cubic metre of air in the room where the activity was set up.

Now you should calculate your results and fill in below your final answer as the number of spores per cubic metre of air in your room.

Number of fungal spores = _____ spores per cubic metre of air.

You might like to compare your results with those of other students also studying this course, using the online course forum.

Considerations for Container 2

■ Why is it not possible to do the same calculation for Container 2?

☐ There was no cling film on Container 2 for two hours so the spores which will have settled and grown on the soup in this container have come from a much larger environment. It is clearly impossible to calculate the volume in this case.

Question 3.5

Why is the number of fungal spores you calculated almost certainly an underestimate of the number trapped in the air above the soup at the start of the experiment?

Activity 3.2   Using the digital microscope to examine fungi

The estimated time for this activity is 15 minutes.

In this activity, you will use the digital microscope to study the structures of fungi and fungal spores from soils and the atmosphere.

You will find the detailed instructions for this activity in the Activities section of the course website.

You should now complete Question 3.6 below, to summarise the sequence of historical events which have led to our current understanding of microbiology.

Question 3.6

Table 3.2 lists the milestones in microbiology in chronological order. Complete the table with the names of the lead scientists involved in each one, and the century in which each milestone was reached.

Table 3.2 Milestones in microbiology.

Milestone in microbiology	Lead scientist	Century
Development of the first compound microscope		
Improvements in the microscope to allow magnification up to ×200		
Cowpox used for vaccination against smallpox		
Final refutation of the theory of spontaneous generation		
First description of *Bacillus* and classification of microbes		
First link between microbes and diseases (based on work on anthrax)		
Discovery of viruses		
Discovery of first antibiotics		
Sequencing of first microbial genome		

This completes your study of the historical aspects of microbiology. Chapter 4 will look in more detail at how microbes are put to use in society today.

Question 3.7

Identify the terms which correspond to each of the definitions (a)–(e):

(a) A protein that speeds up chemical reactions which would otherwise go too slowly to be useful.

(b) A substance produced by one microbe to kill another.

(c) A medium of a particular composition and with specific conditions of incubation which favour the growth of particular types or species of bacteria.

(d) A substance which can join bases together to make a new strand of DNA.

(e) The process of finding out the exact order of the bases in the genetic material of a species.

Question 3.8

In 1873, the bacillus *Mycobacterium leprae* was the first bacterium to be identified as causing disease in humans, when it was identified in the skin of people suffering from leprosy. It is not found in healthy people and it has never been grown successfully in culture. Using Koch's postulates, could it be accepted as the cause of the disease?

Question 3.9

(a) If a student found 13 fungal colonies growing on the surface of tomato soup in a closed container which was 20 cm in length, 10 cm wide and 10 cm deep, with a 4 cm depth of soup, how many fungal spores were there, per cubic metre, in the air above her soup? Give your answer to the nearest hundred.

(b) If the same student had prepared her soup in a kitchen measuring 4 m long, 3 m wide and 2.5 m high, approximately how many fungal spores might there be in her whole kitchen?

Summary of Chapter 3

• Ancient civilisations were using microbes for brewing beer and making bread before it was known that microbes existed.

• The development of the microscope in the 17th century by Robert Hooke and Antonie van Leeuwenhoek allowed the first look at microbes.

• The theory of spontaneous generation was believed by many people until Louis Pasteur in 1859 proved that life did not spontaneously occur, rather life produced life.

- The 19th century brought about the conclusive demonstration that microbes could cause disease.

- Robert Koch proposed 'Koch's postulates', a set of criteria that needed to be satisfied for a microbe to be accepted as a causative agent of an infectious disease.

- Martinus Beijerinck and Sergei Winogradsky developed the field of environmental microbiology, with their work on soil and aquatic microbes.

- The 20th century brought about the molecular age with the invention of PCR to amplify and sequence DNA to identify and distinguish different microbial species.

Chapter 4
Useful microbes in home and industry

Having learnt about some of the features of microbes and the history of microbiology, the next four chapters will consider how important microbes are in our homes, in industry, for our health and in the environment. In this chapter you will look at microbes in our homes, in some familiar industries such as cheesemaking and in the treatment of sewage.

4.1 Microbes and food

Many types of food and drink depend upon microbes in their production.

Question 4.1

From your general knowledge, which *three* of the following types of food and drink, illustrated in Figure 4.1, do you think do *not* depend on microbes for their production?

Bread, cheese, chocolate, coffee, eggs, ice cream, Marmite, mushrooms, olives, salami, sauerkraut, soy sauce, tea, vinegar, wine and yogurt.

Figure 4.1 A selection of food and drink, some of which may depend on microbes for their production.

Some foods are actually microbes themselves. For example, mushrooms are the spore-producing parts of a fungus, often called the fruiting body, with the main part of the fungus consisting of microscopic threads on, or often under, the surface on which they are growing (Figure 2.4b and Activity 3.2). If you left your tomato soup for long enough in Activity 3.1, you may have seen some tiny fruiting bodies growing up from the surface of some of your fungal colonies.

4.1.1 Preserving food

Like the soup in Activity 3.1, most fresh food if stored for a time begins to decay and become inedible, often as a result of the actions of microbes. So, from earliest times, people have looked for ways of preserving foods.

■ How might people have preserved (i) grapes and (ii) meat and fish, before the advent of fridges and freezers?

☐ (i) Fruit like grapes can be preserved by drying in the sun, to give raisins, sultanas or currants, depending on the size and type of grapes. (ii) Meat and fish were often salted.

The effect of both these types of preservation is to make the food a poorer medium on which microbes can grow, while keeping the food fit for human consumption.

■ What effect do the processes of drying and salting have on the water in the food?

☐ Both processes remove water from the food. In the case of grapes, the water evaporates to the air. In the case of salted meat or fish, the water is drawn out of the food by the salt.

By removing much of the water from the food, and therefore increasing the concentration of sugar, as in raisins, etc., or increasing the concentration of salt, as with salted meat or fish, then any microbes which subsequently land on it would have insufficient water to grow and reproduce and so would die.

■ Can you think of another way of preserving fruit, such as strawberries and raspberries, which works in the same way?

☐ Soft fruits can be made into jam, which contains a lot of sugar. The sugar works similarly to salt and tends to absorb water, denying it to microbes and so preventing them from growing.

Another way to make food unattractive to microbes is for it to be made very acidic, since most microbes cannot grow in very acidic conditions. This is the origin of pickling in vinegar (chemically called acetic acid). It was also discovered that microbes could be harnessed to improve the flavour of preserved food and now many foods we eat are produced using microbes.

4.1.2   Fermentation

Fermentation is the process in which complex organic compounds like carbohydrates, often sugars, are converted by microbes to alcohol (or sometimes to acid), under anaerobic conditions. The alcohol or acid often imparts an attractive flavour to the food or drink.

■ Look back to Section 1.8.1 for the word equation which describes fermentation.

☐ The equation for fermentation is:

organic compounds $\longrightarrow$
carbon dioxide + alcohol (or acid) +
 energy for life (less than in aerobic respiration)   (Equation 1.3)

This can also be expressed using the formulae of the various compounds, as explained in Box 4.1, which you should study now.

Box 4.1 Introduction to some organic compounds

You will recall from Box 1.3, that carbon dioxide has the formula CO_2, which indicates that each molecule of carbon dioxide consists of one carbon atom and two oxygen atoms combined together. Some more complex formulae were given too, just below the box, for the simplest amino acid NH_2CH_2COOH, which is called glycine, and the sugar $C_5H_{10}O_5$, which is called ribose.

■ Which elements are present in each of these compounds?

☐ The amino acid contains nitrogen N, hydrogen H, carbon C and oxygen O. Carbon, hydrogen and oxygen are also present in ribose, but there is no nitrogen.

In organic compounds like these, the atoms actually occur in groups, as shown in the amino acid formula, which is shown split into three groups, an NH_2 group, a CH_2 group and a COOH group. You will notice that all of them contain hydrogen.

■ Add up the atoms of the different elements in the formula of the amino acid glycine to present the formula in the same way as is done for ribose, keeping the order of them as in ribose (C, then H, then O) and putting the N at the end.

☐ Glycine would be written as $C_2H_5O_2N$.

It is usually better to separate the atoms into groups, since it gives more information about the way that the molecule is built up. However, in the case of sugars, this is not easy because some of the atoms are joined together in a circle, and so the atoms are usually added up. The sugar which many organisms, including a lot of the microbes, use to produce energy is glucose. The formula for a molecule of glucose is $C_6H_{12}O_6$.

■ What are the differences between the molecular formulae of glucose and ribose?

☐ Glucose has 6 carbon atoms while ribose has 5 carbon atoms. There are also two more hydrogen atoms and one more oxygen atom in glucose.

The formula for alcohol or, more correctly, ethanol is CH_2CH_3OH. Sometimes the carbon and hydrogen atoms in the first two groups are added together and the formula is written as C_2H_5OH. You will notice that in both these representations, the OH group is kept separate. This is because it is the OH group which is the distinguishing feature of an alcohol.

The compound acetic acid, found in vinegar, has the formula CH_3COOH.

■ Compare the formula for acetic acid with the formula for the amino acid given earlier. Which group is the distinguishing feature of these acids, known as organic acids?

☐ The common feature of both of the acids is the COOH group, and this has not been present in any of the other compounds so far presented. So the COOH group must be the distinguishing feature of acids in organic chemistry.

Knowing the formulae of the individual compounds, they can be used in Equation 1.3 to provide a chemical equation, rather than a word equation. Using glucose instead of the more general 'organic compounds', and noting that energy is a physical quantity rather than a chemical, the word equation becomes:

glucose $\longrightarrow$ carbon dioxide + alcohol + energy (for life)   (Equation 4.1)

■   Write the chemical equation for this process, using the formulae given already.

☐ $C_6H_{12}O_6 \longrightarrow CO_2 + CH_2CH_3OH + energy$ (Equation 4.2)

■   Count the number of atoms of each element on the right-hand side of Equation 4.2.

☐   Adding up the C, H and O atoms in the two compounds carbon dioxide and ethanol, there are 3 C atoms, 6 H atoms and 3 O atoms.

All of the atoms in the glucose molecule must be accounted for, and must appear on the right-hand side of the equation. The process of doing this is called balancing the equation. Equation 4.2 is balanced by showing that one molecule of glucose produces two molecules of carbon dioxide and two molecules of alcohol, like this:

$C_6H_{12}O_6 \longrightarrow 2CO_2 + 2CH_2CH_3OH + energy$ (Equation 4.3)

■   Now add up the C, H and O atoms on the right-hand side of Equation 4.3.

☐   Two molecules of CO_2 contain a total of 2 C and 4 O atoms. Two molecules of CH_2CH_3OH contain a total of 4 C, 12 H and 2 O atoms. So the total number of atoms on the right-hand side of the equation is 6 C, 12 H and 6 O, exactly the same as are on the left-hand side in a single molecule of glucose.

The process of balancing chemical equations is quite a difficult skill, especially when the compounds contain large numbers of atoms as here, and you will not need to demonstrate that skill yourself in this course, though you might like to see if you can do it when you meet other equations.

Question 4.2

Rewrite the following equation, using the molecular formulae rather than words. The formula for oxygen is O_2 and, as before, you should use glucose in place of 'organic compounds':

organic compounds + oxygen $\longrightarrow$
carbon dioxide + water + energy for life

What process is described by this equation?

Activity 4.1 Energy-producing processes of microbes – Part 1

You will meet several more equations of this type as you work through the rest of this chapter. To keep track of them all, as you meet each one, you should add it to Table 4.1, starting with the equation for aerobic respiration from Question 4.2. The equations for alcohol fermentation have already been filled in for you.

Table 4.1 Equations for the energy-producing processes of microbes.

Process	Word equation and balanced molecular equation	Equation number
aerobic respiration		
alcohol fermentation	glucose $\longrightarrow$ carbon dioxide + alcohol + energy	4.1
	$C_6H_{12}O_6 \longrightarrow 2CO_2 + 2CH_2CH_3OH + energy$	4.3
production of vinegar by *Acetobacter*		
production of lactic acid by *Leuconostoc*		
production of lactic acid in cheesemaking		
breakdown of lactic acid by *Propionibacter*		
photosynthesis		

The amount of energy generated by the breakdown of organic compounds like glucose is a complex process but ultimately the amount of energy released depends on how many of the chemical bonds between the carbon atoms are broken. The more that are broken, the more energy is released.

■ Compare the processes of aerobic respiration and alcohol fermentation by counting the number of carbon dioxide molecules produced by the breakdown of one glucose molecule, in Equation 4.4 (from the answer to Question 4.2) and Equation 4.3 (in Table 4.1). Which process releases the larger amount of energy?

☐ When a molecule of glucose is broken down by aerobic respiration (Equation 4.4), 6 molecules of carbon dioxide are generated. Each of these has only one carbon atom and so all 6 carbon atoms in the original glucose molecule have been separated from one another by breaking the bonds between them. The breakdown of a molecule of glucose by fermentation (Equation 4.3) produces only 2 carbon dioxide molecules, each containing a single carbon atom, while the remaining carbon atoms stay attached to one another in pairs in two alcohol molecules. So more bonds between carbon atoms have been broken in aerobic respiration, which therefore releases more energy than is produced by fermentation.

Since fermentation provides less energy for those microbes which depend on it, fermenting microbes tend to grow more slowly than those that respire aerobically. They produce carbon dioxide and alcohol as the waste products. Sometimes, in the production of food and drink, it is the carbon dioxide that is the required product, sometimes it is the alcohol, and sometimes both. The carbon dioxide that is added to fizzy drinks is produced industrially beforehand and is not a product of fermentation.

In the baking of bread a type of yeast – a single-celled fungus called *Saccharomyces cerevisiae* (Figure 4.2), sometimes called baker's yeast – is used.

■ Is the yeast cell in Figure 4.2 reproducing by the usual microbial process of binary fission?

☐ In binary fission, one microbial cell divides into two equal parts. The yeast cells do not appear to be dividing in this way. One of them has grown a small 'bud' out of the side of the cell. That cell, and the one to its left, appear to be about to develop another bud. This process is, not unexpectedly, called budding. The buds eventually break off to become independent daughter cells. (You should also have seen this process in Activity 3.2.)

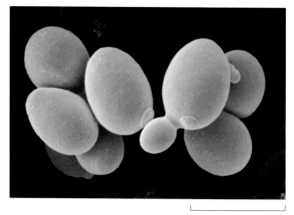

5 µm

Figure 4.2 False-colour electron micrograph of cells of yeast, *Saccharomyces cerevisiae*. The yeast cell in the centre-right is reproducing.

The process of producing new cells in eukaryotes is called mitosis and has some similarities to binary fission, in that in both cases the DNA must be copied, so that a complete copy of the genome is present in both of the daughter cells. In prokaryotes, there is just a single circular loop of DNA which has to be copied. In eukaryotes, there are a number of chromosomes (46 in human cells), each of which has to be copied and then a copy of each one has to be put in each daughter cell. Additionally, eukaryotic chromosomes are inside the nucleus, so the nuclear membrane has to be broken down before the cell divides and then new nuclear membranes have to be created in each of the daughter cells (Section 2.2).

Yeast uses the sugar in the bread dough for energy. You may have recognised the link with sugar from the scientific name of the genus *Saccharomyces*; 'sakkharon' is Greek for sugar and the name of the artificial sweetener saccharin comes from the same word. When the yeast is first put into the dough, it respires aerobically, producing carbon dioxide and water, but when the oxygen in the dough is used up, it turns to fermentation and produces small amounts of alcohol, which breaks down into other compounds during baking and gives bread its distinctive taste. However, most importantly, fermentation produces more carbon dioxide and this causes the dough to expand (rise) as the gas collects as bubbles in the mixture. When the dough is baked, the yeast is killed, the dough becomes solid and the bubbles remain to give the familiar spongy texture of bread.

DM Slides 3.5 and 3.6

Winemaking also uses yeast, but this time, alcohol is the end-product required. Wild yeasts live on the skin of grapes; they are a component of the whitish 'bloom' that you sometimes see on the surface of black grapes. It is probably these wild yeasts which were responsible for the first fermentation of stored grapes and thus the production of the first alcoholic drink. The presence of both the alcohol and the carbon dioxide from the action of yeast produces sparkling wines like champagnes. The alcohol produced by the yeast eventually becomes toxic to the yeast itself and the cells die, leaving behind a product whose alcohol content also makes it an unsuitable medium for the survival of most other microbes.

However, if air is allowed into contact with the alcoholic liquid, then it can be colonised by bacteria, such as *Acetobacter*, which respire aerobically, using ethanol as their energy source and producing acetic acid and water. The resulting liquid is termed vinegar, from the Old French 'vin aigre' meaning sour wine. Acetobacteria are tolerant of acid and can live at pH values below 5, though the pH at which they grow best normally lies between 5.4 and 6.3. Box 4.2 explains more about pH.

Box 4.2 Acids and the pH scale

In pure water, most of the molecules are in the normal form H_2O, with two hydrogen atoms attached to one oxygen atom. However, a very small percentage of the water molecules (about 0.000 01%) split into two parts called ions. These ions carry minute electrical charges, and are written as H^+ (a hydrogen ion, which has a positive charge) and OH^- (a hydroxide ion, which has a negative charge). In pure water, there are equal numbers of these. For mathematical reasons, pure water is given a value of 7 on the pH scale. The water is neither acid nor alkaline and is said to be neutral. If there are more hydrogen ions (H^+) than hydroxide ions (OH^-) in a solution, then it has a pH value below 7 and is said to be acid. If there are fewer hydrogen ions (H^+) than hydroxide ions (OH^-), then its pH value is above 7 and the solution is alkaline.

■ What is the formula of acetic acid and which group of atoms identifies it as being an acid? (You may need to look back to Box 4.1.)

☐ Acetic acid is CH_3COOH and it is the COOH group that identifies it as an acid.

Acetic acid splits into ions in a similar way to water. So some of the molecules of acetic acid become CH_3COO^- releasing H^+. It is the presence of these hydrogen ions which makes the pH value of vinegar about 5.

The pH of a solution can be measured very simply by using litmus paper, which is paper impregnated with a dye that changes from a neutral purplish colour, to a very definite pink in an acid solution, and blue in an alkaline solution. The colour in red cabbage behaves in the same way. To get the distinct red colour, you need to add vinegar (a solution of acetic acid) to red cabbage. If you add sodium bicarbonate (an alkali), the cabbage turns a blue colour.

pH paper is similar to litmus paper, but is impregnated with 'universal indicator', a mixture (usually of five different compounds) that provides a range of colours to indicate more precisely the pH value of a solution. In a laboratory, a pH meter with a glass probe which is dipped in the solution, can be used to measure pH very accurately.

Question 4.3

Write the word equation and then the chemical equation for the breakdown of alcohol by *Acetobacter* using oxygen and producing vinegar.

Under certain circumstances, acids can also be produced by fermentation when oxygen is not present.

■ Look back to Section 2.6.3 to identify an example of this process.

☐ Microbes in the biofilm dental plaque, can produce acids which attack the surface of teeth, causing decay.

The acid produced in dental plaque is lactic acid. If you have ever had cramp after vigorous exercise, that is also a result of the effect of lactic acid, which builds up in muscles when the cells do not receive enough oxygen for aerobic respiration. (You might like to reflect on the fact that exercise might be more popular if human cells fermented and produced alcohol instead!)

The production of lactic acid by fermentation can be harnessed in food preservation. Bacteria of the genus *Leuconostoc* can ferment the sugars in cabbage, as long as oxygen is excluded, to produce pickled cabbage or sauerkraut. The acid produced in this process gives the sauerkraut its characteristic sour taste. Usually there is no need to add a special culture of the *Leuconostoc* bacteria, since they are already present on raw cabbage. Traditional pickled cucumbers are prepared in a similar way. In a sealed container, the pickled food will keep for several months, since the acid produced by the *Leuconostoc* bacteria eventually kills them and any other microbes which might be present on the food.

Question 4.4

The chemical formula of lactic acid is $CH_3CHOHCOOH$. Assuming *Leuconostoc* uses glucose as its energy source, write the word equation and then the chemical equation for the process of pickling cabbage to produce sauerkraut.

Question 4.5

When microbes are used to produce food, it is important that the microbes only continue to grow and reproduce for a certain length of time, otherwise the food is likely to be spoilt. Identify three ways in which microbes are killed in food when they have done their job, with an example for each.

4.1.3   Microbes and dairy products

Probably the most common use of microbes in food production is in the production of a wide range of dairy products (Figure 4.3). Again the process involved is fermentation, but not to the extent of making the food taste particularly acidic or alcoholic.

Figure 4.3 A variety of dairy products, from cheese to yogurt are produced by microbial fermentation.

Cheese was probably first produced by accident in ancient times, maybe around 3000 BC, when milk was stored in a container made from the stomach of an animal. The enzyme rennet, together with acid, both produced by the stomach lining, can convert the milk to curds, the semi-solid part, and whey, a watery liquid. Pressing and adding salt to the curds produces a type of cheese. Nowadays, there are hundreds of different types of cheese. In essence, they are all produced in a similar way using microbes, as shown in Figure 4.4.

Question 4.6

Answer the following questions, based on careful study of Figure 4.4 and information from earlier in the course.

(a) In the process of pasteurisation (named after Louis Pasteur), the milk is typically heated to about 70 °C for about 30 minutes. Why is the raw milk pasteurised?

(b) Microbes, either *Streptococcus* or *Lactobacillus*, are added in the process called inoculation. Using your expertise in the naming and shapes of microbes, identify which genus is shown in Figure 4.4b.

(c) These microbes act on the sugar that occurs naturally in the milk, lactose which has the formula $C_{12}H_{22}O_{11}$. Write down the word equation, and then the equation using the molecular formulae, for the breakdown of lactose to lactic acid (which is similar to the production of lactic acid by *Leuconostoc*). You need to include water on the left-hand side of the equation.

Although the main cheese production process only uses microbes at the start, some cheeses use other microbes towards the end of the process. For example, the bacterium *Propionibacter* is used in the production of the Swiss cheese

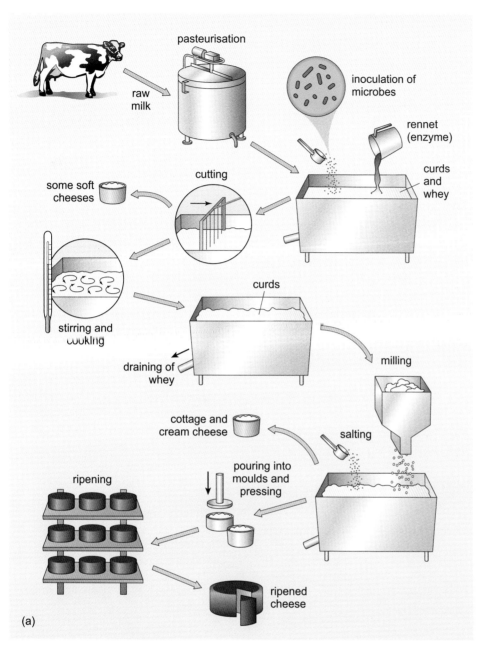

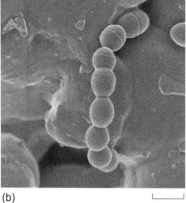

(b)

1 µm

Figure 4.4   (a) The cheesemaking process. (b) Electron micrograph of microbes used for inoculation in the production of cheese.

Emmental. The bacterium uses as its energy source the lactic acid produced by the microbes added earlier. The *Propionibacter* break down the lactic acid to release carbon dioxide, which is trapped in the newly forming cheese and slowly forms the holes for which the cheese is justly famous.

■ How does the process of making Emmental cheese compare to making bread?

☐ The processes use different microbes (bread uses yeast), but they both rely on the production of gas to make the final product – in the case of cheese to make holes, in the case of bread to make bubbles in the dough that cause the bread to rise.

Question 4.7

Write down the chemical equation for the aerobic breakdown of lactic acid to carbon dioxide and water by *Propionibacter*.

In blue cheeses, the coloured veins are also microbial and are caused by a fungus, *Penicillium roqueforti*. According to legend, a shepherd in the Roquefort region of France, lunching on bread and ewes' milk cheese, saw a beautiful girl in the distance. Abandoning his lunch in a cave, he followed the girl and when he returned, some time later one imagines, he found the cheese (and probably the bread too!) covered in a blue mould. Nevertheless, he decided to eat the cheese and found it delicious. Roquefort cheeses are still 'ripened' in the same Combalou caves. Ewe's milk is treated with rennet and spores of *Penicillium roqueforti* are added. After the curds have been drained, salted and shaped (in moulds), each cheese is pierced about 40 times to give holes along which the blue veins of the mould can develop over the next two to three weeks as the cheese ripens. The cheeses are then wrapped and stored at a lower temperature to prevent further growth, where they mature for another few months before the cheese is ready for sale. Other cheeses, such as Brie and Camembert, are ripened by the effects of moulds (*Penicillium candida* or *P. camemberti*) on the outside, forming a flexible white crust and contributing to the soft texture inside (Figure 4.5).

Figure 4.5   Brie, Roquefort and Camembert cheeses (clockwise from the top).

Other dairy products such as yogurt are produced using different microbes, with different times and conditions under which the fermentation is allowed to proceed. Yogurt usually contains a mix of living bacterial species, and a small amount of such live (or 'bio') yoghurt can be used to inoculate a new batch of milk, to act as a 'starter culture' in order to produce the next batch of yoghurt.

Probiotics are types of fermented milk product that contain micro-organisms thought to be beneficial to the naturally occurring microbes in the human gut.

Their effects have been controversial, although probiotics are now widely available. For example, probiotics are taken to protect against pathogens, the idea being that the beneficial introduced bacteria will outcompete the pathogens in the gut. You will read more about probiotics and the gut microbes in Chapter 5.

4.1.4　Other food products

■　Look back to Question 4.1 and list those products whose production involves microbial processes but which have not yet been discussed.

☐　They are chocolate, coffee, Marmite, olives, salami and soy sauce.

Microbes are used in similar ways in the production of both chocolate and coffee. Chocolate is made from the beans of the cacao plant. The beans grow in large pods, about the size of rugby balls, each containing about 50 beans embedded in white pulp. After removal of the outside of the pod, the pulp and the beans are allowed to ferment, using the microbes naturally present in the environment, to break down the pulp and release the beans. Coffee beans grow in berries, and, although the flesh of the berry is removed by machine, that still leaves a slimy layer of mucilage around the beans (which would aid their germination if they were left to grow). Again, fermentation is used to break down this layer, and then the residue is washed away to leave the clean beans, ready to be dried and roasted. The microbes appear to be necessary to develop the flavour of the cacao beans for making chocolate, but do not affect the coffee-bean flavour.

Quite apart from preserving the food, fermentation and other microbial processes can sometimes yield completely new types of food. In Burton-upon-Trent in Staffordshire, beer has been brewed for centuries. Each brew produces large quantities of dead yeast microbes, killed by the alcohol that they have produced; these dead microbes require disposal. Eventually it was realised that this waste product could be converted into a useful food, and in 1902 the Marmite Food Extract Company was formed in Burton. Marmite has gained in popularity over the years, and is still made from yeast extract, together with salt and many flavourings. It is not easy to find outside the UK and is frequently cited as the food that is most missed by British expatriates.

Preserving food has always been a problem in warm countries, including those bordering the Mediterranean. For example, olives when freshly picked from the trees are liable to go off unless they can be quickly preserved. Olives contain a carbohydrate called oleuropein, which makes them bitter and inedible. The oleuropein can be broken down chemically or by allowing microbes which live naturally on the olive skin, mainly species of *Lactobacillus*, to break the oleuropein down by the process of fermentation.

■　Explain what the process of salting meat involves. Why is it so good at preventing microbial degradation of meat?

☐　As its name suggests salting involves covering meat in a layer of salt crystals. The process works by creating a very salty environment which denies microbes water to grow as the salt absorbs the water. Unless the whole meat product is soaked in salt it does not completely prevent the microbes from getting into the meat, but it does act as a very effective barrier.

Another way of preserving meat is to change the pH to a value that prevents microbes from growing. Salami and similar meat products are produced by a process called curing. This involves leaving the spiced meat in warm, moist conditions to encourage the growth of those bacteria involved in the fermentation process. Usually starter cultures are mixed with the meat, rather than relying on naturally occurring bacteria. Lactic acid is produced, making the meat an inhospitable environment for other microbes and adding to the flavour of the product.

Many of these food preservation methods have been used for much longer than humans have known about microbes.

■ Name two types of food that require the use of microbes, but that were being produced long before microbes had been discovered.

□ Bread and beer are just two of the well-known, but very ancient foods that use microbes in their production (Figure 3.1). Other examples might include cheese and pickled vegetables.

One very good example of a very old type of food additive that uses microbes is soy sauce. Soy sauce has been used in China for almost 2500 years as a flavouring for food. Traditionally, soy sauce was made by fermenting soya beans with yeast or with a filamentous fungus called *Aspergillus*.

It would be easy to continue this list, like a catalogue, of the different ways in which microbes are involved in food production, but the examples described should give you some idea of the very diverse foods, produced in different countries around the world, that involve microbes. Having looked at how some microbes are used in the production of food, the next section considers the ways that other microbes spoil food.

4.2 Food-spoilage microbes

Despite the beneficial uses of fermentation, unwanted fermentation is one of the ways in which food is spoiled by the effect of microbes. The acids produced give the food a sour taste and the production of carbon dioxide can cause packaging of foods to swell and split. A different type of food spoilage produces the smell of rotten eggs. This smell is caused by the gas hydrogen sulfide (H_2S) which is produced by the breakdown of a molecule called cysteine, which has the formula $NH_2CHCH_2SHCOOH$.

■ Look back to the beginning of Box 4.1 and identify another compound which has the same groups of atoms at the beginning and end as this formula.

□ The amino acid glycine NH_2CH_2COOH has an NH_2 group at one end and a COOH group at the other.

These two groups, NH_2 and COOH, are the groups shared by all amino acids, whose names often end in 'ine'. NH_2 is called an amino group and COOH is characteristic of organic acids (Box 4.1). Amino acids are the building blocks for proteins (Section 1.6) and it is the breakdown of the cysteine-containing proteins in egg yolks and other food substances that gives off the awful smell of rotten eggs. One of the microbes that can cause this breakdown of egg-yolk proteins is *Salmonella* (Figure 4.6). This bacterium causes a mild illness in chickens and can be present in the yolks of eggs laid by infected birds. It can produce the symptoms of food poisoning in people who eat uncooked eggs. You will learn more about these infections in Chapter 5. If eggs are cooked until the yolk is solid, the bacteria are killed.

■ Can you identify the protrusions on the *Salmonella* surface in Figure 4.6? (Look back to Section 2.4 if necessary.)

□ The protrusions are flagella, which are used in many microbes for movement.

Perhaps the most dangerous of the food spoilage microbes is *Clostridium botulinum*, the cause of botulism. The botulin toxins that it produces damage nerves and so cause muscle paralysis. The symptoms begin from 12 to 36 hours after ingesting the toxin and include droopy eyelids, blurred vision, muscle weakness, difficulty swallowing and major breathing difficulties. In minute doses, the same toxin is used in the 'Botox' cosmetic treatment. *C. botulinum* can grow in any food that has not been prepared properly, including canned and packaged food. Its spores can survive temperatures up to 116 °C, well above the

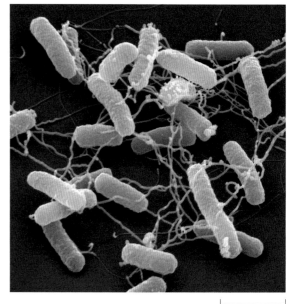

Figure 4.6   False-colour electron micrograph of microbes of the genus *Salmonella*.

boiling treatment (100 °C) that is usually considered sufficient to sterilise foods. However, *C. botulinum* and its spores are intolerant of acid, so foods preserved by lactic acid or vinegar (acetic acid) are safe from this bacterium. This may have been one of the reasons that acids produced by fermentation became so widely used as a preservation method in ancient times.

4.3   Microbes in sewage treatment

All living things, including ourselves and microbes, need food to grow, maintain and repair their cells, and to provide a source of energy for life (Section 1.8). However, we cannot digest all of the food we eat and what remains undigested, ends up in the sewage system. About 10 billion litres of sewage are produced every day in England and Wales and this has to be treated to remove harmful substances and pathogenic microbes before the waste can be safely released into the environment. The main component of sewage is organic matter (undigested food) but there are other substances such as oil, heavy metals, nitrogen and phosphorous compounds (from artificial fertilisers and detergents) which also have to be removed. Here you will consider the important role of microbes in the sewage treatment process.

Sewage is actually a mixture of all types of waste water, including rain water and domestic water from toilets, baths and sinks. When sewage arrives at a treatment works (shown schematically in Figure 4.7), it is first filtered to remove large objects (e.g. condoms, tampons and cigarette ends) which have got into the system. These usually go to a landfill site or incinerator. The remaining material is then allowed to 'settle' so that much of the solid material drops to the bottom of a tank. This solid material is then removed and usually buried in landfill, burnt or, after further treatment, used as fertiliser on agricultural land.

What then remains is the liquid portion, or effluent, which is rich in suspended organic matter and some pathogenic microbes. This liquid portion will ultimately be released into rivers or the sea but it is vital to first reduce the organic matter content and eliminate harmful microbes. To do this the liquid is fed into an aeration tank containing a complex community of microbes. The contents of the tank are mixed mechanically with air or air is bubbled through the tank. The microbes then use the organic material in the sewage as their source of carbohydrate for respiration.

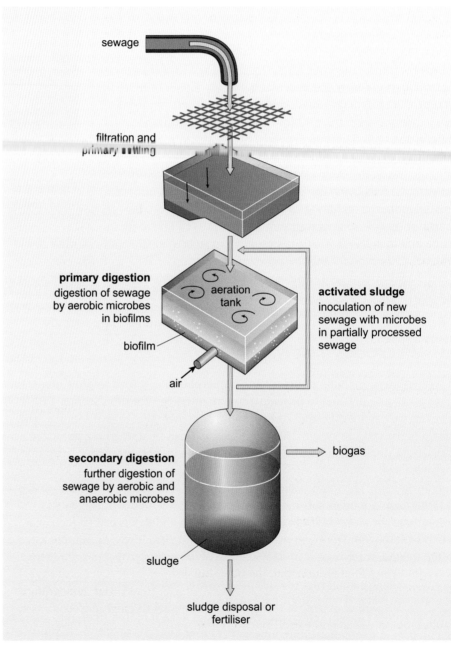

Figure 4.7 A simplified diagram of a sewage treatment works.

- The oxygen in the air allows the microbes to respire aerobically. What are the products of the aerobic respiration of carbohydrates like glucose? (You may need to check back to Table 4.1.)

☐ Aerobic respiration can break down carbohydrates completely, producing just carbon dioxide and water (together with energy needed for the microbes to stay alive).

Aerobic respiration is the most efficient way of breaking down organic matter although some compounds in the effluent are not broken down completely. The tanks often contain porous solid materials, on which biofilms can develop, increasing the numbers of microbes and so the efficiency of the breakdown process. During this process, a fairly solid material known as activated sludge is formed. This contains a mix of microbes and undigested material. Since it contains all of the essential microbes to break down incoming waste, some of it is added to batches of new sewage (Figure 4.7). After this aerobic digestion, and a variety of other purification procedures, the liquid portion of the sewage is usually safe to discharge into rivers or the sea. The remaining activated sludge material is subjected to various other types of biological processes to reduce further the amount of organic matter it contains. Anaerobic bacteria are often used in this subsequent stage, since, although they grow more slowly, they can break down more complex materials that are difficult to degrade using microbes that respire aerobically. The gases produced in this anaerobic process are carbon dioxide and methane, a mixture called biogas, which can be collected and subsequently burned for energy production.

Sewage processing reduces the concentration of potentially harmful bacteria such as *E. coli* and *Salmonella* in the original sewage as many of them die during the processing because the conditions are not appropriate for them. It is also important to reduce the amount of organic compounds in the effluents released into rivers from sewage works. If this is not done, then microbes naturally present in the river use the organic compounds as a source of energy and reproduce in huge numbers. Since they respire aerobically, they use up much of the oxygen dissolved in the water, leaving little for other organisms such as invertebrates or fish, many of which will die. Sewage must therefore be treated to reduce the amount of organic matter, and thus reduce the Biological Oxygen Demand or BOD, defined as the amount of oxygen required by the aerobic microbes to decompose the organic compounds in a sample of water.

The process of sewage treatment can be thought of as a complex form of composting. The compost heap which you may have in your garden is like a miniature sewage treatment works. The centre usually becomes anaerobic as existing oxygen is used up. Closer to the top of the heap aerobic processes take place. Apart from the raw material, the other big difference between a sewage treatment works and a compost heap is that inside a compost heap, temperatures become high – well above 60 °C – which is detrimental to most species of microbes, but in which some can flourish. There will be more about these heat-loving microbes in Chapter 6.

■ Sewage works rely on the diverse capabilities of microbes for the complete process to be effective. Name three types of microbial activity that are used in the process and one that is not.

☐ Aerobic and anaerobic respiration and fermentation play an important role in sewage treatment. Photosynthesis is generally not used in the sewage works because it is a process that builds organic compounds from carbon dioxide, whereas the objective of sewage works is to break down organic compounds.

Many of the microbes used in food and in industry are anaerobic so that they must be cultured in conditions without oxygen. In principle, anaerobic culturing is very similar to the aerobic culturing that you learned about in Chapter 2. However, it does involve some specialist equipment and procedures which are described in *Laboratory methods 4.1*.

Laboratory methods 4.1   Growing anaerobic microbes and large-scale culturing

■ Why do you think anaerobic culturing would be more challenging than aerobic culturing?

☐ Although some anaerobic microbes can tolerate small amounts of oxygen, many are obligate anaerobes, which means they are killed by oxygen. When culturing them, special efforts must be made to ensure that at no time during their manipulation using aseptic techniques are they exposed to oxygen.

Microbiologists have devised a range of methods for culturing anaerobic microbes. One of the most important pieces of equipment is a cabinet flushed with a gas such as nitrogen which allows manipulations to be carried out in an oxygen-free environment. The operator carries out the work through rubber gloves connected to the inside which prevents oxygen from entering the cabinet. When anaerobic microbes are cultured on Petri dishes, the dishes are also stored in airtight containers that are constantly flushed with nitrogen or carbon dioxide to keep them anaerobic. Many anaerobic organisms also need some unusual elements to grow, and these are added to the culture media.

Growing anaerobic microbes on a large scale is essential for the industrial processes of brewing beer, making wine and carrying out other types of fermentation and for producing large quantities of microbes, for example yeast for bakeries. This is often done in giant metal vats called fermentation reactors which can hold many hundreds or thousands of litres of microbial culture (Figure 4.8c). The vats are provided with sensors to measure temperature and nutrient levels that allow computers to control the conditions within the reactors to ensure maximum growth of the microbes. One of the difficulties with such cultures is preventing the microbes from settling to the bottom of the vats.

■ Why is this likely to be a problem?

☐ Those microbes which settled first would be covered by those settling later and therefore would not be able to access the nutrients in the culture medium. They would probably die and decompose, and their breakdown products could then contaminate the culture, as well as resulting in a lower yield of microbes from the whole vat.

To prevent settling, the vats can be stirred mechanically by large paddles (Figure 4.8a) or oxygen-free air (mostly nitrogen) can be bubbled through to circulate the contents of the vat (Figure 4.8b). If aerobic microbes are being cultured, then similar vats are used but air or oxygen is bubbled through.

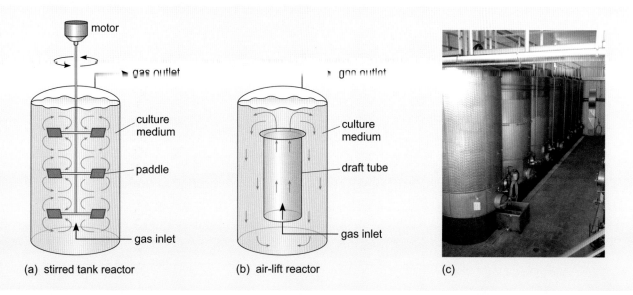

Figure 4.8   Fermentation reactors: schematic diagrams of (a) a stirred tank reactor and (b) an air-lift reactor; (c) in a winery in California.

The growth of populations of microbes in the fermentation reactors (and in all other situations too), follows the basic pattern shown in the growth curve in Figure 4.9. When microbes are first added, they begin growing and dividing slowly as their enzyme systems adjust to the presence of new nutrients. This is referred to as the lag phase. After a period of time the microbes begin to grow and divide very rapidly to take advantage of the favourable growth conditions – the exponential phase. There may then come a point at which the microbes have used up some vital nutrient in the growth medium and they are no longer able to divide – the stationary phase. Eventually the microbes become old and start to die – the death phase. These growth stages are important for industrial processes. To produce the maximum amount of microbes and microbial products, they must be constantly provided with new nutrients to prevent them entering the stationary phase, hence the valves and tubes entering the fermentation reactors in Figure 4.8c. These are then harvested by being extracted from the medium in which the microbes are growing.

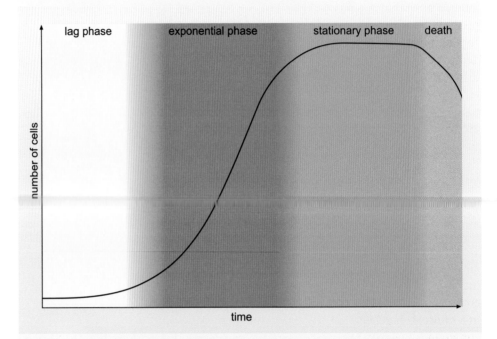

Figure 4.9   Graph of microbial growth showing how the number of cells changes with time in a culture in which the microbes are reproducing by binary fission.

4.4   Drugs from microbes

Humans are susceptible to infection by microbes; you will find out more about this in Chapter 5. Treatment for these infections is often by means of drugs which are themselves produced by microbes. This section looks at some of these.

4.4.1   Antibiotics

As you will recall from Section 3.7.2, antibiotics were first discovered by Alexander Fleming in 1928. They fall broadly into two classes: those that kill microbes, which are termed bacteriocidal; and those that merely inhibit their growth, which are termed bacteriostatic. In the natural environment, antibiotics produced by one species of microbe give it a competitive advantage by affecting the growth of, or by killing, other species living nearby. Antibiotics are produced and industrially harvested from a range of microbes including bacteria that belong to the phylum Actinobacteria and fungi such as *Penicillium*. Production is carried out in vats containing up to 20 000 litres of microbial culture; each vat is periodically tapped for the valuable microbial products.

All antibiotics work by disrupting some critical aspect of the functioning of microbial cells. One of the most important classes of antibiotics is the beta-lactams – so called because of the chemical structure of the molecules – which include penicillin and ampicillin. They disrupt the ability of a microbial cell to produce proteins and thereby interfere with many biochemical processes vital for cell functioning and growth. Antibiotics from another group, which includes gentamicin and erythromycin, also affect protein production, but in a slightly different way. These can be used for patients who are allergic to penicillin. For reasons which are not clear, Gram-positive bacteria belonging to the phylum Actinobacteria are the most prolific producers of antibiotics and many of the ones now in commercial use come from these microbes. One such antibiotic, actinomycin, affects the copying of DNA so disrupts both cell division and protein production. Some actinobacteria (Figure 4.10) have the unusual characteristic of forming filaments, making them look more like fungi (Figure 2.4b and Activity 3 ?) than typical bacteria. There are over 500 known species in the Actinobacteria genus *Streptomyces*, and from these are extracted two-thirds of current antibiotics, such as neomycin and chloramphenicol, as well as the now less commonly used streptomycin, and some antifungal compounds. As more and more microbes show resistance to antibiotics it is becoming urgent to find new classes of compounds that can disrupt the microbial machinery and prevent the spread of disease. You will learn more about antibiotic resistance in Chapter 5.

DM Slide 2.5

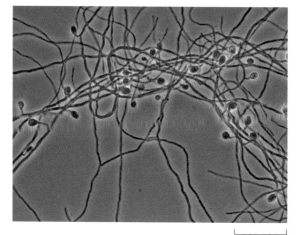

10 μm

Figure 4.10   A light micrograph of filaments of Actinobacteria.

Question 4.8

Identify which of the antibiotics beta-lactams and actinomycin affect which of the steps in the processes shown in Figure 4.11.

4.4.2   Genetic engineering and drug production

The production of drugs from microbes took a new twist in the late 1980s with the advent of genetic engineering. The ability to manipulate DNA in the laboratory allows scientists to add into microbes foreign genes that code for important products. As well as the main circular loop of DNA forming the chromosome (Section 1.5), most microbes also contain other much smaller circular pieces of DNA called plasmids. These are from ten to a thousand times smaller than the chromosomal DNA and, as you will see in Chapter 5, plasmids can be naturally transferred from one microbe to another. Because many of them contain genes that code for resistance to antibiotics, plasmids are one important way in which antibiotic resistance is moved from one microbe to another and they account for the rapid spread of antibiotic resistance in hospitals. But plasmids can also be harnessed for beneficial purposes, to transfer useful genes into microbes. Although technically complex, the principle behind this process, known as genetic engineering, is quite straightforward. A gene (length of DNA) that is the code for a useful protein, such as a drug of some kind, is inserted

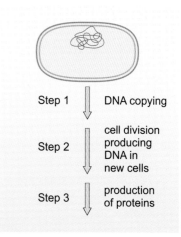

Step 1 — DNA copying

Step 2 — cell division producing DNA in new cells

Step 3 — production of proteins

Figure 4.11   Bacterial cell division and growth; for use in Question 4.8.

(spliced) into a plasmid which is then put into a chosen species of microbe. When the DNA of the plasmid is then used to make proteins, the microbe also starts to produce the alien product alongside the proteins that it would normally produce.

A very important example of the use of microbes to produce a drug vital to many people is in the synthesis of insulin for diabetics. People who suffer from type 1 diabetes are missing insulin which allows the body to store glucose, locking the sugar up for times when blood sugar is low, for example between meals. If insufficient insulin is produced, glucose remains in the blood causing serious health problems.

■ Before genetic engineering, insulin was extracted from the pancreases of animals from abattoirs. From your general knowledge, what disadvantages can you think of with this method of obtaining insulin?

☐ It requires a continuous supply of large numbers of animal carcasses from which to extract the insulin and thus it is likely to be expensive.

There is also the risk that in some people animal insulin, which is slightly different from human insulin, could cause an immune reaction in which the body recognises it as a foreign protein and destroys it. In 1988 the human insulin gene was successfully incorporated into the microbe *E. coli* by genetic engineering (Figure 4.12) and the microbe was then used to synthesise large quantities of the protein. Today, most people with diabetes use microbe-produced human insulin. The cost is far lower than it was previously and the issues with immune responses have been removed.

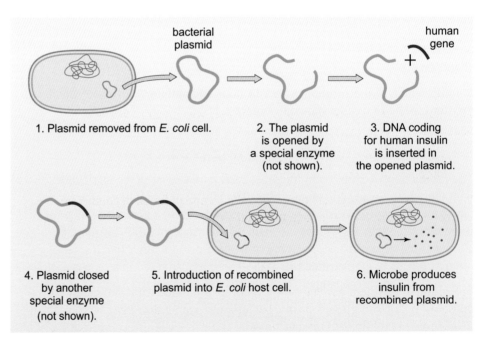

1. Plasmid removed from *E. coli* cell.

2. The plasmid is opened by a special enzyme (not shown).

3. DNA coding for human insulin is inserted in the opened plasmid.

4. Plasmid closed by another special enzyme (not shown).

5. Introduction of recombined plasmid into *E. coli* host cell.

6. Microbe produces insulin from recombined plasmid.

Figure 4.12 The incorporation of the human insulin gene into the bacterium *E. coli* by the process of genetic engineering.

Genetic engineering in microbes is also being used to combat malaria, a debilitating disease which infects over 500 million people a year and kills between 1 and 3 million of them. Malaria is caused by a microscopic parasite called *Plasmodium* (a eukaryotic microbe) which is carried in the saliva of mosquitoes and is transferred into human blood through mosquito bites. Finding drugs to combat malaria has been an on-going battle. One of the most promising anti-malarial agents is artemisinin, which is found naturally in the leaves of the sweet wormwood plant. The Chinese have been using the anti-malarial properties of these leaves for over 2000 years, but the plant is not easy to cultivate and so mass production of the drug has been difficult. Artemisinin is produced in the plant from a precursor molecule called amorphadiene. The genes which code for the production of this molecule have been isolated from the plant and introduced into *E. coli*, in a similar way to the human insulin gene (Figure 4.12). The amorphadiene that is then produced by the microbial culture can be extracted and converted into artemisinin in the laboratory. Work continues to identify the genes which will do this conversion so that they can be introduced into the microbe too, and the complete drug could then be synthesised relatively cheaply in large quantities, for use against malaria.

Insulin and artemisinin are only two of the many drugs now being produced by the genetic engineering of microbes and the list grows each year.

Question 4.9

Identify the type of compound represented by each of these formulae:

(a) CH_3OH

(b) $HOOCCOOH$

(c) NH_2CHCH_3COOH.

Question 4.10

The equation for the process of photosynthesis was given in words in Section 1.8.1, as follows:

carbon dioxide + water + energy from Sun $\longrightarrow$
organic compounds + oxygen   (Equation 1.4)

Write this as a chemical equation, using the formulae for each compound, with glucose as an example of an organic compound.

Question 4.11

In Section 4.1.2, there was a description of how pickled cabbage, sauerkraut, is produced by allowing *Leuconostoc* bacteria to ferment the sugars in the cabbage in anaerobic conditions to give lactic acid. If air was not excluded from the container, what products would the bacteria produce and how would the taste and keeping properties of the food be altered?

Question 4.12

Describe, in your own way, using less than 100 words, how the microbe *E. coli* can be used to combat the microbe *Plasmodium*.

Activity 4.1   Energy-producing processes of microbes – Part 2

You should now have completed all the rows in Table 4.1 of Activity 4.1. Compare your table with the completed version in the answers to the activity.

Summary of Chapter 4

- Microbes have historically played an important role in many beneficial processes, one of the most important being food production.

- Fermentation is the most common process used in food production and microbes that ferment sugars anaerobically can make alcohol and acid. Many of these products help not only in the production of new types of food, but also in their preservation by excluding other microbes.

- These preservation processes are not always effective. Because many types of food are a source of nutrients and energy, some microbes can spoil food and cause food poisoning.

- Microbes have an important role to play in the intentional degradation of waste in sewage plants and in compost heaps.

- Genetic engineering has allowed the manipulation of the DNA of microbes in such a way as to use them to produce novel drugs and other products.

Chapter 5
Microbes and human health

Although so far this course has focused on microbes in the environment around us, one of the most important habitats for microbes, at least when we are concerned about ourselves, is the human body itself. It is estimated that there are between ten and a hundred times as many microbes in and on a human body as there are human cells in the body and some scientists have jokingly, but quite accurately, pointed out that humans are actually more microbe than human. Understanding the microbes on and in us has profound importance for our health.

5.1   Bacteria on the human body

Microbes can be found wherever there are suitable environmental conditions for growth. There are many microbes on the human skin but it is generally too dry for most microbes to grow, which prevents it being covered by a biofilm of microbes. The best places for microbes on the skin are damp areas such as the armpits and areas around the nose and mouth. Sweat also provides food for microbes which can lead to body odour – the product of the breakdown of sweat by microbes. If you want to think of body odour in a pleasant light, just think of it as the smell of microbes having had a good meal.

■ If microbes cannot thrive on human skin, why is it so important that health professionals wash their hands between treating patients?

☐ Although microbes cannot live permanently on the skin, they can be transferred on the skin from one person to another or transferred into wounds, particularly as spores.

In some circumstances microbes do grow on or in the skin, particularly in the formation of acne, a problem for many teenagers whose young skin overproduces oils that provide food for a bacterium called *Propionibacterium acnes*. The acne bacterium is an important example of the way in which microbes are opportunists and will take advantage of any environment that has suitable conditions for growth.

■ Would you expect the surface of the eye to be a suitable place for microbes to live?

☐ The surface is warm and moist and so it would appear to be a good environment for microbes.

The reason why microbes do not generally colonise eyes is that the tears which continually bathe the surface contain an enzyme called lysozyme. This breaks down bacterial cell walls and so destroys any bacteria which might land on the surface of the eye before they can grow and reproduce. The eye condition, conjunctivitis, is caused when a particular bacterium (or less commonly a virus) manages to thrive because the protective lysozyme system is not working as efficiently as it should. Although antibiotics are normally prescribed, the condition generally resolves itself in about a week. Tear fluid is a very effective antibacterial agent.

■ Where in the human body is it common to find a biofilm if normal hygiene precautions are not observed?

□ Biofilms (in the form of plaque) can develop on teeth which are not regularly brushed and can cause damage to the teeth (Section 2.6.3).

Elsewhere in the mouth microbes can cause a variety of problems. Microbes that grow on the tongue are involved in halitosis (bad breath), and many microbes are involved in causing gum disease, resulting in inflammation and damage. However, the place where microbes reside that is most important for our health is the digestive system.

5.2 Bacteria in the human digestive system

■ Thinking about the conditions microbes need to survive, why might living inside a person's digestive system be a good environment for microbes?

□ It is warm, moist and there is plenty of food provided by the person's eating habits.

The human digestive system (often called the gut) provides a plentiful supply of food for microbes and so it is not surprising that it is one of the most populated regions of the body. It is estimated that the number of microbes in the human gut is about 50 trillion, that is 50 followed by 12 zeros. All of these microbes are packed into the gut, giving the gut one of the highest densities of microbes of any environment. Most of the volume of faeces consists of dead and some living microbes, yet another indication of the importance of microbes in digestive processes.

Activity 5.1   Microbes in the gut

The estimated time for this activity is 30–45 minutes.

Imagine that you are working in a microbiology laboratory in a hospital and you have been asked to investigate, using conventional techniques, the microbes present in a sample of the contents of a particular part of the human gut removed during an operation. You will probably find it useful to refer back to Activity 2.2, and possibly watch the video sequence again. Then answer the following questions:

(a) Would aseptic techniques be necessary?

(b) Would the microbiologist need to dilute the sample and, if so, how would that be done?

(c) Would it be better to culture the microbes on a spread plate or a pour plate or both? (Think about how much oxygen you might expect to be present in the human gut.)

(d) How, in principle, could the density of microbes in that part of the gut be calculated?

(e) How could you identify how many different bacterial species were in the gut sample?

Most of the microbes within the gut (sometimes called the gut microflora) not only get advantages from living there, but in return provide a benefit to the person harbouring them. The food we eat is broken down by enzymes (introduced in Section 3.7) produced mainly in the stomach and small intestines (see Figure 5.1). The process of digestion produces small molecules which can then be absorbed through the gut wall into the blood which transports them to provide nutrients to all the cells of the body. This process of digestion is facilitated by microbes. They use some of the food in the gut to provide their own source of energy and, in doing so, they break it down more quickly into smaller molecules. In particular they work on large complicated carbohydrate molecules.

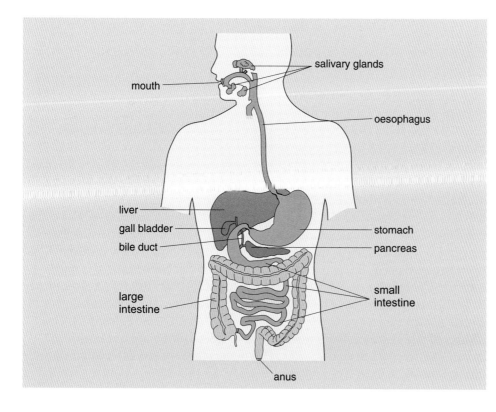

Figure 5.1 A very simplified diagram of the human digestive system.

In addition to helping to break down food, microbes also produce some vitamins – a group of essential nutrient molecules that are required in only tiny amounts by animals. They cannot be produced by the human body so they must either be taken up in food or made by microbes. Vitamin K is one of the molecules essential for the normal clotting of blood, after an injury, for example. It is present in some foods but the amount is supplemented by production from microbes. Death of much of the microbial population of the gut, which can be caused by excessive use of antibiotics for other reasons, can lead to a shortage of vitamin K and so a reduction in the body's ability to clot blood successfully at the site of wounds.

We rely even more on microbes for vitamin B12, which cannot be produced by animals or plants but is produced by members of the genera *Streptococcus*, *Bacillus* and *Pseudomonas*, amongst others. The microbes in our own gut do produce vitamin B12, but the production occurs in the large intestine; this is too far down the digestive system for most of the B12 to be absorbed and so it is lost in the faeces. It is essential therefore for us to obtain vitamin B12 in our food, from animals which have been able to absorb the B12 from their own microbes (due to having a digestive system that is very different from ours). It is present in meat, eggs and dairy products, so vegans may need to take a supplement.

Vitamin B12 has various functions in the body; for example, it is needed for DNA synthesis, and is particularly important in the production of red blood cells. Disruption of the absorption of B12 results in pernicious anaemia. It is also important for the health of the brain and nervous system and a lack of B12 has been linked to mania and psychosis and can cause irreversible brain damage. So this provides an excellent example of how microbes are not merely beneficial to us, but are required for our health, including (in the case of vitamin B12) our mental health. A major challenge for microbiologists is attempting to understand the full diversity of microbes in the gut and their roles.

5.2.1 The diversity of gut bacteria

All life on Earth has some regions of its DNA that vary very little between species (they are said to be 'highly conserved'), because these regions carry the code for proteins which are vital to the functioning of all cells. One such region of DNA is called ribosomal DNA or rDNA. It provides the code for the production of ribosomal RNA (rRNA). There are several types of RNA, all involved in various ways in the production (synthesis) of proteins in cells. Ribosomal RNA is the main component of structures in the cell called ribosomes which are the site of protein synthesis. Without ribosomes, or with faulty ribosomes, a cell cannot function and will die, so it is important that the rDNA remains essentially unchanged. However, it is possible for occasional changes in the bases to occur without affecting the function. It is these changes that can be used to identify how closely different microbes are related. The particular length of rDNA that has been used is most commonly referred to as 16S rDNA. So, for example, if the 16S rDNA pieces from two different microbes have one base difference, then they are likely to be more closely related than two microbes which have four differences (Figure 5.2). The number of differences in bases indicates the length of time since one microbial species split into two distinct species. This is sometimes called the 'evolutionary distance' between them. Four different bases in the 16S rDNA would suggest the split was probably millions of years ago.

Figure 5.2 An illustration of how species of microbes can be classified according to differences in the bases in their 16S rDNA and how the evolutionary distance between them can be determined. The sequences used for DNA analysis are in reality much longer than this. (a) A single strand of DNA from two closely related microbes shows only one difference. (b) Strands from two more distantly related microbes show four differences.

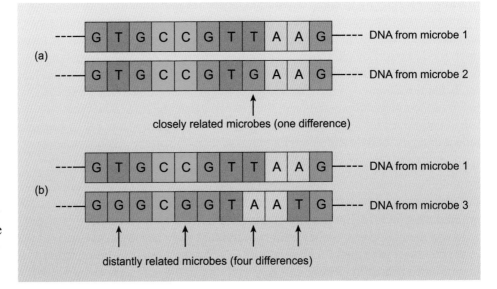

So, by identifying the sequence of bases (a process known as sequencing) in the 16S rDNA from different microbes, it is possible build up a phylogenetic tree as illustrated in Figure 2.3, showing how closely different microbes are related. It is also possible to identify particular species simply from their rDNA sequence.

■ How might this change the task for the microbiologist in Activity 5.1 above?

☐ The microbiologist would no longer have to culture the microbes to find out how many different species were present, since they could be identified by their rDNA sequences. However, although the number of species could be identified, it would be harder to get information about the total numbers of microbes of each species, since this would require methods to work out the total amount of 16S rDNA belonging to different species.

Scientists at Stanford University in the USA extracted the DNA from human faeces and from samples taken within the gut, and sequenced the DNA to get an idea of how many microbial species were in the gut. Almost two-thirds of the bacterial species they found within the gut had not previously been described, suggesting that the human gut contains an incredible diversity of microbes whose roles are not yet understood. Another interesting finding from the study was that different people have a different gut microflora. Each of us appears to have our own unique microbial menagerie living in our gut; this menagerie is probably influenced by the environment in which we were born and brought up, the food we have eaten and the places we have visited.

Activity 5.2   Reading media reports on microbiology

The estimated time for this activity is 15 minutes.

Read Extract 5.1 and then answer the following questions.

(a) Explain in your own words why the title 'Bacterial mix and match is the key to good digestion' has been given to Extract 5.1.

(b) What two other points were reported as conclusions from the study?

Extract 5.1 Bacterial mix and match is the key to good digestion

New Scientist, 6 December 2008, Vol. 199, Issue 2685, p 16.

Without the 'good' bacteria in our guts, we could not digest food. You might expect that we would all have the same set of bacteria to provide the chemical machinery that does the job. But this turns out to be only half true.

Knowing that gut bacteria are key to digestion and metabolism, Jeffrey Gordon of Washington University School of Medicine in St Louis, Missouri, and his colleagues went in search of a core group of bacterial species that aid digestion. They expected to find these species living in the guts of most healthy people.

When the researchers analysed faeces from 154 people this turned out not to be so. The subjects did, however, all possess the same core group of bacterial genes needed for digestion, albeit from different species.

It is this combination of genes, rather than any particular species, that is necessary for a healthy gut, says Gordon. 'We've learned that you can have different collections of species, yet the gene functions represented in these collections are broadly shared.'

The analysis also flagged up differences between the bacterial genes of obese and lean people. Obese individuals had a greater proportion of genes for digesting fat, protein and carbohydrates, which might make them better at extracting and storing energy from food. Gordon hopes that a better knowledge of these genes might suggest new ways of combating obesity.

Interestingly, participants who were related shared similar gut bacteria species as well as genes.

5.2.2   Probiotics and prebiotics

Some diets may not provide all the nutrients needed for the growth of a normal balance of gut microbes. There is some evidence that certain chronic inflammatory diseases (particularly those in the gut, such as inflammatory bowel disease, etc.) may be linked to an abnormal balance of microbial species in the gut. When a course of oral antibiotics is taken for an infection, as well as killing the infecting bacteria (e.g. those causing a throat infection), the antibiotics may also destroy large numbers of the normal microbes in the gut. Probiotics (Section 4.1.3), including milk products containing live microbes, are recommended by some nutritionists as an aid to restoring a more normal microbial balance. The microbes present in probiotics are usually species belonging to the genera *Bifidobacterium* and *Lactobacillus*. However, it is not yet clear whether sufficient numbers of the microbes survive the very acidic conditions in the stomach, to reach the intestines where they might be effective.

Some foods, particularly a group of complex sugars called oligosaccharides, are thought to encourage an appropriate balance of gut microbes by selectively stimulating the growth of beneficial microbes. Unlike probiotics, which contain microbes, these so-called prebiotics are nutritional supplements thought to be beneficial to the existing microbial population. Traditional sources of these prebiotics are Jerusalem artichokes, bananas, garlic, leeks and onions. Alternatively, the oligosaccharides, which are complex sugars, can be added to foods such as breakfast cereals and bread, or can be bought in capsule form. Again, there is as yet insufficient evidence that these compounds are effective.

5.3   The human immune system

From the natural populations of microbes in and on humans, this section looks at those microbes that are less welcome, to try and understand the diversity of ways they can cause health problems. Of course, the number of diseases caused by microbes is large and so in the rest of this chapter you will learn about just a few of them, to understand some of the ways in which microbes can cause disease and some of the challenges they pose to hospitals and human health in general. However, most microbes encountered by the body do not cause disease partly because of a very effective system which keeps them in check – the immune system.

The human immune system is a very complex set of biological processes, involving many different types of cell and the substances produced by them, and only a very simplified version is described here. Essential to the correct functioning of the immune system is its ability to recognise foreign (or non-self) chemical substances in the body. Overreaction of the immune system to foreign substances results in allergies and hay fever, and a faulty immune system, which attacks parts of the body as though they were foreign, can result in diseases such as coeliac disease, lupus, rheumatoid arthritis and many others.

A crucial part of the immune system involves two types of white blood cell. (Blood also contains red blood cells which are principally concerned with moving oxygen around the bloodstream (Figure 5.3).)

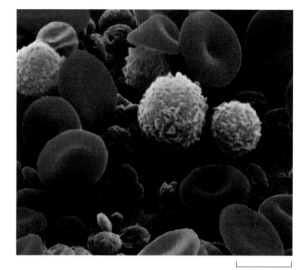

10 μm

Figure 5.3   Red and white blood cells, the latter are often coloured pale yellow.

■ Why might it be particularly valuable for cells of the immune system that are able to attack invading microbes, to be carried around in the bloodstream?

☐ Blood travels to all parts of the body and so the immune system cells can be transported to wherever they are needed. For example, whenever your skin is grazed or cut, blood is visible. Damaged skin is a place where microbes are likely to get into the body and so the immune cells can arrive on the scene very quickly if that occurs.

One type of white blood cell crucial to the immune system is called a phagocyte (literally 'cell eater'). When tissues are damaged, such as when the skin is cut, the damaged cells produce particular chemicals that can be detected by phagocytes. The phagocytes collect in the area, and bind to any invading microbes which they recognise by the proteins on their surface. The microbes are engulfed by the phagocytes (Figure 5.4) and broken up and destroyed by a range of enzymes produced by the phagocytes, one of which is lysozyme (Section 5.1). The phagocytes themselves often die in the process, and the collection of dead microbes and dead phagocytes forms the whitish–yellow substance called pus that is often seen around infected wounds.

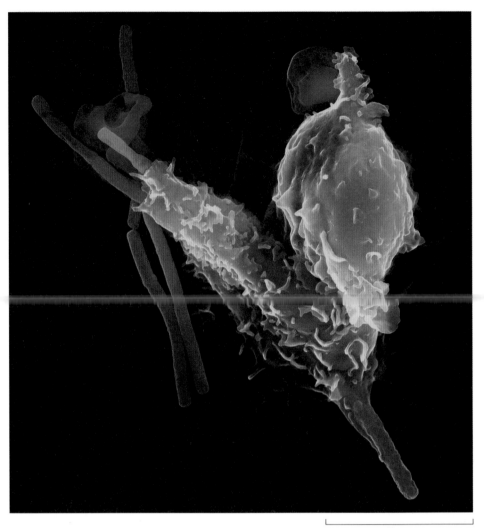

5 μm

Figure 5.4 A phagocyte, artificially coloured yellow, engulfing anthrax bacteria, artificially coloured orange. The egg-shaped area of the phagocyte is the nucleus.

While some phagocytes travel around the body in the bloodstream, others are found at places in the body where microbial attack may be expected on a day-to-day basis, such as the lungs.

■ Why might the lungs be under daily attack from microbes?

☐ Microbes will be breathed into the lungs which provide a moist protective environment for microbes to live.

The phagocytes are effectively on permanent standby to engulf and destroy any foreign particles. However, as the human immune system has evolved to destroy microbes, so the microbes have evolved ways of avoiding the destruction. An excellent example is *Streptococcus pneumoniae*, a Gram-positive bacterium which causes pneumonia as well as many other infections. This bacterium covers itself in a slime layer that hides the proteins on its surface.

■ How does the production of this slime layer allow *Streptococcus pneumoniae* to avoid detection by the immune system?

☐ The cells of the immune system recognise foreign microbes by the proteins on their surface and so if these are hidden the bacteria are not recognised and so can begin to multiply within the lung cells, causing infection.

Another bacterium that successfully hijacks the immune system is *Salmonella*. It is recognised by the phagocyte and engulfed, but then its surface coating resists the digestive enzymes and so it remains alive inside the phagocyte, which transports it around to new areas of the body, where it can break out and cause infection

These phagocytes form a part of the immune system that is identical in all people and is called the innate immune system. However, it is another part, called the adaptive or acquired immune system that allows the human body to respond very rapidly to those microbes that it has encountered before.

■ What is the name for this process, which you met in Section 3.7?

☐ It is called immunological memory.

The adaptive immune system uses the second type of white blood cell called lymphocytes, which have chemical receptors, called antibodies, on their surfaces. Antibodies can bind to any materials which are foreign to the body – so-called antigens. Antibodies are Y-shaped proteins, with the two prongs of the Y made up of small chains of amino acids. By an unusual process of shuffling the genes in the DNA of lymphocytes, a vast number of different antibodies can be made, each unique to one lymphocyte. If a lymphocyte encounters an antigen, such as a non-self protein on the surface of a microbial pathogen, that matches its antibody, then the lymphocyte attaches to the antigen, forming an antibody–antigen complex on the microbe. Two processes then occur. Firstly, the formation of an antibody-tagged microbe triggers the phagocytes to come in and destroy the invading microbe. Secondly, the lymphocyte is stimulated to divide, to produce large numbers of identical cells, with the same antibodies on their surface (Figure 5.5). Many of these lymphocytes release their antibodies into the blood, where they circulate and can link to the antigens on other pathogens of the same type. Phagocytes are attracted, as before, to destroy these antibody–antigen complexes on the microbial pathogen and hopefully prevent a serious infection. When the pathogens have been destroyed, those lymphocytes carrying the antibodies to that pathogen remain in the blood and produce a continuous supply of identical antibodies into the bloodstream, so that the body is prepared for another attack by the same microbe.

However, the antibody system can be circumvented by some bacteria. For example, *Streptococus pneumoniae* discussed above covers itself in slime to hide its own proteins. The microbe that causes syphilis, a spirochaete called *Treponema pallidum* (Figure 3.11), covers itself in proteins from the human body to fool the immune system and then penetrates into the nervous system where there are fewer

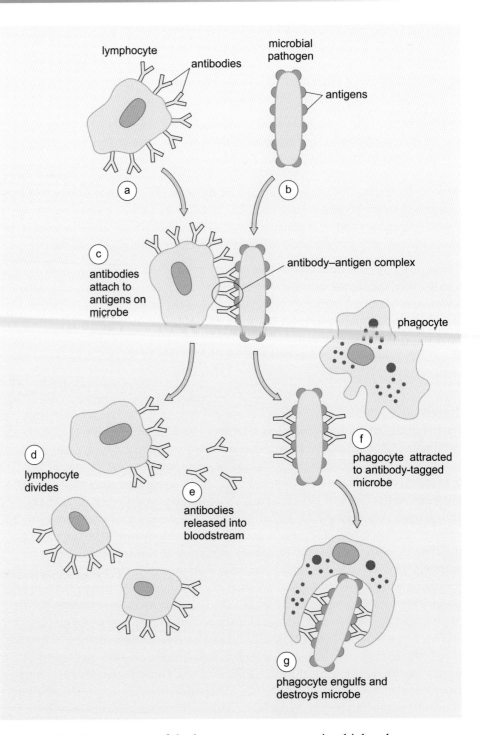

Figure 5.5 The response of the immune system to a microbial pathogen.
A lymphocyte (a) and an invading microbial pathogen (b) are in the bloodstream.
They meet (c) and the lymphocyte's antibodies attach themselves to the antigens
on the pathogen's surface. Separation soon occurs, after which the lymphocyte
divides (d) and antibodies are released into the bloodstream (e) to attach to more
microbes. The antibody-tagged microbes are now prepared for an encounter with
a phagocyte (f), which results in the death of the microbial pathogens (g). (The
antibodies and antigens are hugely enlarged in relation to the cells.)

lymphocytes and so fewer antibodies which would destroy it. Since the adaptive immune system depends crucially on the recognition of foreign substances (antigens) and on the production of antibodies against them, any microbe that can overcome this system is likely to be able successfully to invade the body.

Question 5.1

Two of the following statements about the immune system contain errors. Identity those statements and correct the errors.

A   Phagocytes are white blood cells which recognise non-self molecules on the surface of pathogens and engulf and destroy them; they are part of the innate immune system.

B   Some phagocytes travel around the body in the bloodstream, while others are found in places where pathogens might enter the body, such as the lungs.

C   Lymphocytes are part of the adaptive immune system and carry Y-shaped antigens on their surface.

D   The antibodies released from the surface of lymphocytes are able to recognise and bind to antigens on the surface of pathogens, forming antibody–antigen complexes.

E   When a lymphocyte divides, it produces large numbers of identical cells, each of which will recognise the same antigen.

F   When the antigens on a pathogen have been recognised by antibodies, and antibody–antigen complexes have been formed, then lymphocytes come in to destroy the pathogens.

■   Figure 5.6 shows the different types of immunity which can occur in the human body. Which of the types listed here have been described in this section so far?

☐   Two of them have been described: innate immunity and one type of natural adaptive immunity, namely active immunity related to infection.

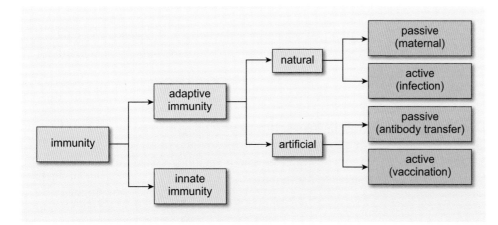

Figure 5.6   Types of immunity in humans.

The second type of natural adaptive immunity is given in Figure 5.6 as 'Passive (maternal)'. This is, as you may have guessed, the immunity received by a baby from its mother. Antibodies can pass from mother to baby via the placenta during pregnancy and in the breast milk after birth. These help to protect the baby against infections during the early weeks of life.

Two types of artificial adaptive immunity are listed. The first is 'Passive (antibody transfer)', which involves injecting antibodies directly into the person, and is sometimes used when someone is at serious risk of infection and their own immune system may not have time to respond. The antibodies have normally been taken from the blood of another animal (horses are sometimes used), but in future it may be possible to manufacture them in the laboratory (these manufactured antibodies are called monoclonal antibodies). Direct antibody transfer is used as the first stage of the treatment of people suspected of being infected by the rabies virus, for people who develop tetanus as the result of an infection by *Clostridium tetani* and for a number of other conditions, including poisoning by snake venom where the damaging agent is chemical not microbial.

■ The *Clostridium tetani* bacterium is described as being Gram-positive and an obligate anaerobe. What is meant by these terms?

☐ Gram-positive describes the way in which the bacterium responds to the Gram staining process (described in Activity 2.2). It would stain purple. Anaerobic bacteria are those which respire without the use of oxygen and obligate anaerobes are those bacteria that are unable to survive if oxygen is present (they are 'obliged' to live without oxygen).

■ If someone receives antibodies as treatment for tetanus, will that protect them from a further infection in the future?

☐ Injecting antibodies will *not* stimulate the lymphocytes in the body to produce any antibodies of its own, so the protection will only remain for as long as the injected antibodies remain in the blood, probably no more than a few weeks. However, a tetanus vaccination would stimulate the adaptive immune system to produce the antibodies to the tetanus bacteria.

In order to stimulate antibody production in the body, it is necessary to inject antigens. This is the process of developing artificial immunity by vaccination – the final type in Figure 5.6.

Question 5.2

Describe in general terms how a vaccine against tetanus could be produced (refer back to Section 3.7.1 if necessary) and how this would provide protection against a future tetanus infection when injected into a person who had not previously been exposed to the causative bacterium.

5.4   Disease-causing bacteria

Surprisingly, many bacteria that cause disease are ones that are naturally present in or on our bodies. Bacteria that co-exist with the human body are known as commensal bacteria. It is a change in the normal situation, caused for example by a wound, which gives them a chance to grow and become a menace rather than remain a harmless natural inhabitant. Commensals also maintain a natural microbial balance in the body and help prevent pathogens from becoming abundant.

One of the most important groups of commensal bacteria is the genus *Streptococcus*, which can cause numerous infections including pneumonia. *Streptococcus pyogenes* is perhaps the most infamous and is sometimes known as the 'flesh-eating' bacterium. In fact, the condition known as necrotising fasciitis, an infection of the deeper layers of the skin, causing large-scale deterioration of flesh, is very rare. More commonly *Streptococcus pyogenes* strains are involved in causing skin infections, meningitis and pharyngitis ('strep throat'); each one of these may be caused by different strains (Section 1.3). About one-tenth of the population carry the *Strep. pyogenes* bacterium around in their throats and noses and usually it does no harm at all. (Note that because the genera *Streptococcus* and *Staphylococcus* can be easily confused if referred to in their abbreviated form, simply by the first letter of their genus, their names are instead often shortened to *Strep.* and *Staph.*) *Strep. pyogenes* is not destroyed by the immune system because it carries proteins on its cell surface that resemble human proteins, thus fooling the system into thinking it is part of the human body and preventing it being destroyed. About one-fifth of the population have *Strep. pneumoniae* in their body and it too can produce a surface layer that allows it to evade the immune system. A commensal species can cause an infection if its growth becomes out of balance with the rest of the natural microbial population in the human body. The population size and activity of each commensal species are normally kept in check by competition from other commensals, but if the balance is disrupted then some commensals or even foreign microbes may get a chance to multiply and become more active.

Many of the anaerobic bacteria naturally found in our gut may also become the cause of disease. The most common culprits are those in the phylum Bacteroides (Figure 2.3), which most of the time are beneficial. They exclude more dangerous pathogens from the gut, essentially by out-competing them for space and food. However, outside the gut and out of control in other areas of the body, these organisms can become a serious problem, causing abscesses, blood infection, infections under the skin and infections of the abdominal cavity.

Bacteria of the genus *Clostridium* are common in soil and can be responsible for a range of diseases in people. Often they are picked up from soil or from poorly cleaned food.

■ Which species of *Clostridium* causes tetanus?

☐ Tetanus is caused by *C. tetani* (see Section 5.3).

The clostridia produce toxins, which affect the nervous system. So, if *C. tetani* gets into a wound and multiplies, the toxins are released, enter the bloodstream and from there travel to the nerves and result in the excessive contraction of some of the muscles in the face, causing lockjaw (the common name for tetanus). Of all the clostridia species in the wild, *C. botulinum* produces the most powerful toxin and it is responsible for botulism, a type of food poisoning that is potentially fatal (Section 4.2). The best known of the clostridia is *C. difficile*, one of the few clostridia naturally present in the human population. About 3% of adults are thought to carry it in their gut. It rarely causes disease unless the natural population of microbes in the gut has been disturbed, such as during the administering of antibiotics, which kill off many of the natural gut microbes. In this case, *C. difficile* can multiply uncontrollably and release its toxins causing toxic shock syndrome (TSS), with a range of symptoms including a rash, high fever, low blood pressure, confusion and ultimately coma and multiple organ failure, resulting in death.

■ Not all bacteria produce spores, but *C. difficile* does. Why might this be a problem in treating it?

☐ The spores produced by the bacterium allow it to be spread around easily in the environment, including amongst staff and patients in hospitals. The spores also give *C. difficile* resistance to many extreme environmental conditions, which allows it to survive for long periods of time in the natural environment outside human bodies and makes it difficult to kill on surfaces and in the air.

Question 5.3

Using the data in the current section, of a group of 100 people how many would, on average, be found to carry one of *Streptococcus pyogenes*, *Streptococcus pneumoniae* or *Clostridium difficile*? Why are individuals carrying these microbes generally not ill?

DM Slide 2.3   Equally infamous is *Escherichia coli*, a Gram-negative bacterium found naturally living in the gut. *E. coli* normally colonises the gut within the first two days after birth. Like so many bacteria, usually it is a harmless commensal, but there are some strains of the bacterium that are harmful. One of the most well known is *E. coli* strain O157 (Figure 2.2) which can cause serious food poisoning by producing toxins. In young children and the elderly or in people whose immune system is not functioning properly, it can be fatal.

5.4.1   Evolution of antibiotic resistance in microbes

Infections caused by bacteria but not treatable by common antibiotics, are one of the greatest healthcare concerns today. One of the most problematic microbes, alongside *C. difficile*, is the so-called hospital 'superbug' MRSA.

■ What do the initials MRSA stand for? You may find it useful to look back to Section 1.7.

☐ MRSA stands for methicillin-resistant *Staphylococcus aureus*.

Methicillin is a type of antibiotic that was previously used to kill this bacterium, though it has now been superseded by more stable antibiotics such as flucloxacillin. In fact, the initials can equally well mean 'multiple-resistant DM Slide 1.5   *Staphylococcus aureus*', a reference to the bacterium's resistance to a range of antibiotics. There are well over 30 different *Staphylococcus* species that grow in characteristic clumps, like tiny bunches of grapes (Figure 5.7). About 10 of these species are natural human commensals but can, under some conditions, develop into serious pathogens.

Staph. aureus is of particular concern because it can cause a wide range of disease conditions from toxic shock syndrome (TSS) to skin infections, particularly infecting people with weakened immune systems or with wounds, making it a problem in hospitals. Although the bacterium can grow without oxygen, it grows and reproduces more quickly if oxygen is present. Such bacteria are called facultative anaerobes. In healthy people *Staph. aureus* naturally lives in the armpits and in the nose, but once it is inside the body it forms biofilms which protect it against the immune system and allow it to proliferate. Biofilms can form anywhere bacteria can find a surface to attach to, even including an apparently smooth surface such as plastic (Figure 5.8).

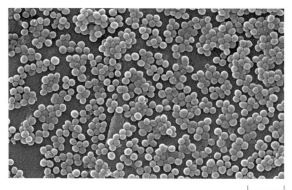

5 μm

Figure 5.7   MRSA (methicillin-resistant *Staphylococcus aureus*). The individual microbes cluster together in colonies that look like miniature bunches of grapes.

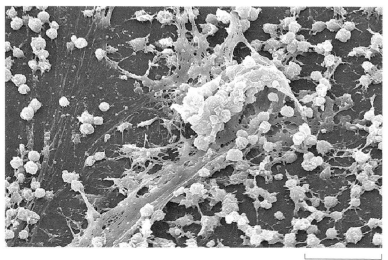

5 μm

Figure 5.8   A biofilm of *Staphylococcus* which has formed on the inner surface of a plastic connector used to join medical tubing. The bacteria can be seen amongst filaments of polysaccharide produced by the bacteria. The background is the surface of the plastic tubing. Similar biofilms can form inside the human body.

Understanding how microbes develop resistance against antibiotics is one of the most important challenges in modern microbiology. It appears that antibiotic resistance genes arose by the process of mutation.

■ What is meant by the term mutation? You may need to look back to the end of Section 1.7.

☐ Mutations are random changes which occur in the DNA of living organisms, due to the DNA replication process not being perfectly efficient every time.

Although mutations occur naturally, they can also be induced by radiation and certain drugs. Most mutations are harmful to the organism possessing them, and so that individual dies. However, occasionally, by chance, a mutation can occur that is beneficial to the organism. In the case of microbes, this could be a mutation in a gene which allows the microbe to survive in the presence of antibiotics, i.e. to be resistant to antibiotics. Because microbes divide by binary fission, the mutant gene can spread very rapidly, as every offspring of the resistant microbe has an exact copy of the DNA and so will also carry the mutant gene. So, if one in 10 000 bacteria in a colony within a wound being treated with an antibiotic such as flucloxacillin, developed a mutation which made it resistant to the antibiotic, the other 9999 bacteria would die, but that one would survive and divide and within a few days, there could be a new colony of 10 000 resistant bacteria in the wound.

The antibiotic resistance genes may function in several ways. For example, they can cause the microbes to produce substances that change the structure of the cell wall to prevent the antibiotic entering or that break down the antibiotic before it can do any harm. Or they may change biochemical pathways (sets of reactions which produce important substances in the microbe), to by-pass the parts of the pathway which are normally sensitive to the antibiotic. The antibiotic resistance genes seem to be amongst those genes that are carried on plasmids.

■ What are plasmids and how do they relate to chromosomal DNA? You may need to refer back to Section 4.4.2.

□ Plasmids are small circular pieces of DNA found in bacteria. They are from 10 to 1000 times smaller than the main circular DNA loop (bacterial chromosome) which forms the genomic DNA.

Crucially, for the progress of antibiotic resistance, plasmids can be transferred from one microbe to another by a process called conjugation. In Section 1.7, you learned how microbes reproduce by binary fission.

■ In one sentence, describe what happens to the chromosomal DNA of a microbe when it undergoes binary fission.

□ The DNA of the microbe is copied and one copy is put into each of the two new microbial cells produced in the binary fission process.

Although plasmids were not mentioned in Chapter 1 when you looked at binary fission, you will not be surprised to know that these small circles of DNA are also replicated and transferred into both of the new cells when one cell divides. There can be from one to more than a thousand copies of the same plasmid in any one microbe. In the process of conjugation, illustrated in Figure 5.9, one microbe can pass a plasmid to another of the same species. Two microbes come together and one of them extends an appendage called a pilus.

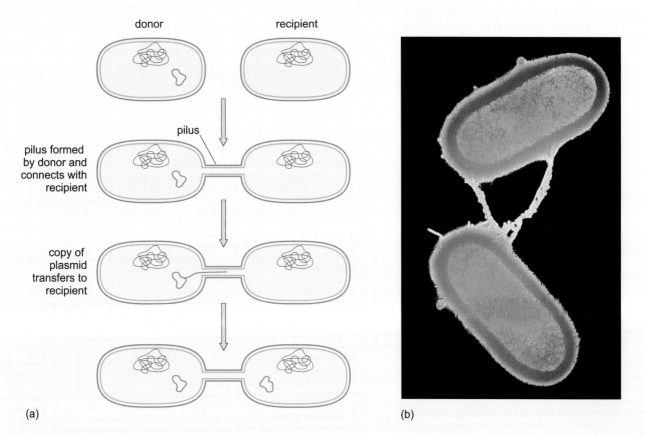

Figure 5.9 The process of conjugation. (a) First, a hollow pilus is established between the two microbes leading to a connection. The open channel is then used to pass a copy of the plasmid which is transferred from one cell (on the left) to the cell on the right. (b) Two bacteria attached together with pili.

■ Pili were mentioned previously, in Section 2.4.2, with a different function. What was that function?

☐ Pili can also be used for movement by species such as *Pseudomonas aeruginosa*. The pili are extended and, by means of short jerks, they allow the microbe to move.

In conjugation the pilus is a hollow fibre a few micrometres long, that can connect the two microbes. One of the plasmids in one of the microbes opens up, is copied and is transferred along the length of the pilus into the attached microbe. Since the antibiotic-resistance genes are on the plasmids, this can result in the transfer of such resistance from one microbe to another. When that microbe divides (by binary fission) the resistance will be passed on to all of its offspring. This appears to be one of the reasons for the rapid spread of resistant microbes in hospitals. Conjugation does, of course, occur between microbes in other environments too and is a way in which genes that enable microbes to survive particular environmental stresses can be passed from one to another.

Question 5.4

It has been suggested that conjugation in microbes is a form of sexual reproduction. Identify one similarity and one difference between the two processes. You may find it useful to re-read the information about the behaviour of DNA in sexual reproduction in Section 1.7.

Yet another reason for the rapid spread of resistance genes and the adaptation to new antibiotics is the remarkable ability that microbes have to take up DNA, across the wall of their cells, from their environment without receiving it from another microbe. This process is known as transformation and is illustrated in Figure 5.10.

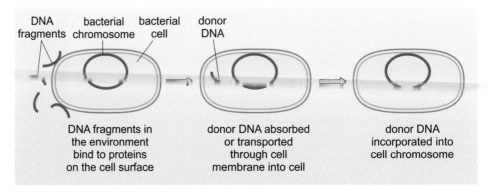

Figure 5.10 A schematic diagram showing a microbe taking up a DNA fragment from the environment by transformation. Note that, for clarity, the chromosome is shown differently from in earlier figures.

■ How could 'naked' DNA (that is, DNA not inside cells) be present in the environment?

☐ The DNA must have been produced by living cells, probably other microbes, originally. After their death, the walls of the cells would break down and the DNA would be released into the environment, to be taken up in the transformation process.

Question 5.5

Give two differences between conjugation and transformation in bacteria.

Transformation allows genes which are completely new to that species to be taken up and incorporated into its DNA, where they may function correctly. Thus a microbe in which resistance to a particular antibiotic had never previously been seen, could take up a fragment of DNA which had been released into the environment on the death of another entirely different microbe. This fragment of DNA could contain a gene which confers resistance to that antibiotic if successfully integrated and, after several cycles of binary fission, a new resistant population could appear.

The spread of resistance to antibiotics can be surprisingly rapid. After the antibiotic penicillin was introduced for general use in 1947, *Staphylococcus aureus* became resistant to it in four years. In 1959, a new antibiotic, methicillin, was used to treat these resistant strains but the first methicillin-resistant strains (MRSA) were detected only two years later in 1961. These strains have recently spread to hospitals throughout the world. More recently, new strains are emerging that are resistant to the more modern antibiotic, vancomycin. VRSA (Vancomycin-resistant *Staphylococcus aureus*) appeared in 2002. The introduction of a new synthetic antibiotic linezolid in 2000, resulted in resistant strains appearing in 2003.

- ■ Linezolid is a synthetic antibiotic, that is, it is produced by chemical synthesis initially in a laboratory, then on a commercial scale. How are antibiotics like penicillin produced? You may find it useful to look back to Sections 3.7.2 and 4.4.1.

- ☐ Antibiotics like penicillin are all produced by microbes such as the Actinobacteria (Figure 4.10). Penicillin itself is extracted from the fungus *Penicillium*.

Antibiotic resistance can be thought of as an arms race between microbes and humans. Each time a new antimicrobial agent is developed, a microbe eventually undergoes a genetic alteration that allows it to acquire resistance which may spread through the microbial population. A major activity in microbiology is to find new antimicrobial agents to keep up with the ever-changing resistance of microbes. The spread of resistance has been made easier by two particular aspects of medical practice. The widespread use of antibiotics for minor infections increases the chance that a resistant strain of microbe might arise because more species of microbes come into contact with antibiotics. Resistance to antibiotics is also caused by patients taking incomplete antibiotic courses. This exposes microbes to concentrations of antibiotics which are not lethal, but are at sufficient concentrations preferentially to give an advantage to bacteria in the population that do have resistance. There is the risk that microbes with partial resistance may be more likely to survive and more quickly develop complete resistance. These resistant bacteria then multiply and dominate the population. By finishing a course of antibiotics one is more likely to kill the target microbes and so prevent them from developing resistance.

Behind the scenes in a hospital and in many medical clinics are microbiology laboratories which perform an immensely important task, as described in *Laboratory methods 5.1*.

Laboratory methods 5.1   Hospital microbiology

Unlike microbiology research laboratories which tend to focus on one particular scientific area, such as the study of a particular soil microbe, hospital microbiology laboratories are called upon to provide assistance to many health professionals. One of their most important tasks is to track the spread of organisms that might be involved in diseases such as MRSA, to keep records of who has the infection and to keep samples from people who have been infected so that the microbes can be studied later if necessary, particularly if it is a specific strain that might be traced back to the place where it originally infected people. An example is bacteria causing food poisoning, where monitoring the spread of a local outbreak may be very important. Information gathered at a hospital microbiology laboratory could be used in national monitoring.

Many pathogens can be cultured using specific media (broth or agars) that contain nutrients on which only certain microbes will grow. For example, 'chocolate agar' is made by heating blood to 56 °C and allowing it to cool in agar. Certain bacteria from the respiratory tract will grow on this agar. 'Blood agar' which is made from unheated blood, is used to grow many *Staphylococcus* species involved in causing infections.

■ What problems are there in culturing these types of pathogens?

☐ There is an obvious hazard in culturing pathogens as they could infect the hospital workers themselves, although the use of aseptic techniques means that these events are very rare. However, another problem is that it takes time for colonies of microbes to grow on agar plates, so it may take time before the type of an infection can be confirmed. In serious cases much quicker methods of identifying microbes are needed.

For these reasons many automated methods have been developed for detecting pathogens. These include machines which can extract lipids (a type of fat) from the membranes in bacteria and identify particular pathogens based on the chemical content of these lipids. (You will learn more about lipids in Chapter 6.) Some automated methods are based on the genetic identification of microbes using the polymerase chain reaction (PCR) (Section 3.9). Specific genetic sequences can be recognised as belonging to particular pathogens, allowing for the automated screening of samples for very specific microbes. These approaches are not only safer, but they allow many tens or even hundreds of samples to be screened in a single day, improving the monitoring of the spread of disease and allowing patients and the doctors treating them to receive information on their conditions much more quickly. Most hospital microbiology laboratories are now equipped with machines that can do this kind of analysis.

Activity 5.3 Interpreting media reports on microbiology

The estimated time for this activity is one hour.

This activity is designed to give you more practice in interpreting media reports about microbiology and identifying the errors which sometimes appear in them, and also in doing a longer piece of writing yourself.

You should read Extract 5.2 and then answer the questions below. Some text has been omitted from the extract (…) for the purpose of the activity.

(a) In the extract the *C. difficile* organism is referred to as a 'bug'. Why is this scientifically inaccurate?

(b) Based on what you have read in the course, what would you expect the blank in the fourth paragraph to be?

(c) (i) Based on your reading of the extract, explain what you understand by a 'false positive' and 'false negative' test.

   (ii) What might be the consequences for the patient if the test gave a 'false negative' result?

   (iii) Explain why a false positive in the case of *C. difficile* may endanger a patient.

(d) What do you think the term 'carrier' in the introduction means?

(e) Three patients in your local hospital have been positively identified as having MRSA. Write a short (about 150 words) news piece for the science page of your local paper explaining what MRSA is, how it became resistant to antibiotics and what can be done to treat it.

Extract 5.2 *C. diff* testing 'is often wrong'

BBC News website, 1 November 2008.

Many carriers of the potentially lethal *Clostridium difficile* bug are missed by unreliable tests, researchers say.

Analysis of 18 studies by St George's, University of London, found one test had wrongly given the all-clear to a quarter of those infected. The variation in performance between the six tests studied could mean misleading infection rate comparisons between different hospitals. The study was published in the *Lancet Infectious Diseases* journal.

Bacteria balance

While deaths related to the 'superbug' MRSA have shown falls in recent years, those related to *C. difficile* are rising fast. The bug is found naturally in the gut of approximately 3% of adults, and presents no threat as long as the normal balance of gut bacteria is maintained. However, in weak or frail patients, particularly those on antibiotics, which can disrupt this balance, the bacterium can cause diarrhoea and severe inflammation of the bowel, which can be fatal.

Quick and accurate diagnosis is key, so that patients can be isolated and other measures taken to try to control the spread of the bug to other vulnerable people. Currently, a single test is used on a stool sample from the patient, looking for higher levels of _____ produced by the active bacteria. However, the London analysis suggests this may not be enough to find the right patients.

While most tests produce a small proportion of 'false positives' and 'false negatives', the percentage of cases missed ranged from 5% to just over 24.3%, and the percentage of 'false positives' ranged from 3% to 45%.

Double test

Dr Timothy Planche, a clinician at St George's Healthcare NHS Trust, who led the study, said: 'A false negative result could mean that infected patients don't get the right treatment and could pass the infection on to others … As many as one in five test results could be wrong.'

5.5 Disease-causing viruses

Viruses are among the most numerous microbes on our planet and infect all types of organisms.

■ Some human diseases caused by viruses have already been mentioned in Sections 1.1 and 3.7.1. Recall these, and add to the list any other diseases, from your general knowledge, that are caused by viruses.

☐ Those diseases already mentioned are the common cold, influenza and smallpox. Other viral diseases are cold sores, chickenpox, and more serious illnesses such as AIDS (acquired immunodeficiency syndrome), Ebola and SARS (severe acute respiratory syndrome).

Viruses are much smaller and simpler than bacteria. As mentioned in Section 3.6, they are constructed only of a piece of nucleic acid (DNA or RNA) in a protein coat and they cannot divide on their own. Instead they need a host cell (which could be a human cell, the cell of another animal or plant, or even a bacterium) to enable them to replicate. Viruses are usually referred to as particles. Because they are so small, typically only about 30 to 500 nanometres in size, it is very difficult to see viruses using a light microscope. Instead they tend to be studied using an electron microscope (see *Laboratory methods 5.2*).

DM Slide 1.1 ■ The bubonic plague bacterium (*Yersinia pestis*) is about one micrometre (1 μm) long. How many times longer is this than a virus 50 nanometres (50 nm) long? You may find it useful to refer back to Box 1.2 to revise information about the units of measurement.

☐ There are several ways to do this calculation. Probably the simplest is by using the information that there are 1000 nanometres (1000 nm) in one micrometre (1 μm). So *Y. pestis* is 1000 nm long and is therefore 1000/50 = 20 times longer than a virus that is 50 nm long.

Laboratory methods 5.2   Electron microscopy

The electron microscope (EM) uses a beam of electrons instead of a beam of light to make microbes and their structures visible. While the best light microscopes can magnify no more than about 1500 times (*Laboratory methods 1.1*), a typical electron microscope can magnify well over one million times. The first EM was built in 1931 and was a transmission electron microscope (TEM). This requires the sample to be so thin that electrons can pass through it, in a similar way to the light beam shining up through a light microscope slide. The sample has first to be dehydrated (all the water removed) and then impregnated with resin, before it is cut into very thin slices with a diamond or glass knife. A flu virus prepared in this way and then viewed under a TEM is shown in Figure 5.11.

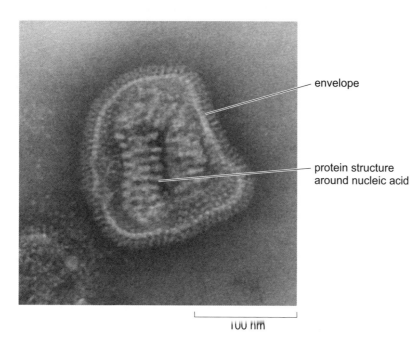

100 nm

Figure 5.11   The internal structure of a flu virus particle as seen under a TEM. The virus envelope is shown on the outside. The protective protein structure around the nucleic acid can be seen in the centre.

Subsequently, scanning electron microscopes (SEM) have been developed. They allow the surface of an object to be studied closely, by scanning across it with a moving beam of electrons. The scanning process causes electrons to be given off by the object, and these can be collected and used to construct a three-dimensional image. The magnification achievable is about one-tenth of that with a TEM.

■ How many times greater is the magnification of an SEM compared with a light microscope?

☐ Since a TEM can magnify 1000 000 (one million) times, and an SEM 10 times less, that indicates a 100 000 magnification for an SEM. Light microscopes can generally magnify up to 1000 times, so the magnification achievable by an SEM is usually about 100 times greater than using a light microscope.

The original SEMs required samples to be dry and in a vacuum, which meant that samples of microbes could not be imaged directly. Instead, they were coated with very thin layers of a substance, often gold, and the shape of the gold coating was observed. However, later models, called environmental SEMs allow samples to be observed wet and at normal pressures so that microbes can be studied directly. SEM images are particularly good at showing three-dimensional aspects of a structure and therefore the shape of microbes can be seen. Electron micrographs are formed as black and white images but usually false-colour is used to enhance the features.

Question 5.6

With that information, look through this chapter (backwards and forwards) and identify those images of microbes which have been taken using a light microscope and those which have been taken using an electron microscope.

When SEM images are taken, they are only in black and white, indicating those areas where more or fewer electrons have been detected. The colours shown in Figure 5.4 (and in Figure 5.3) have been added subsequently to enhance the appearance of the image.

Question 5.7

The basic structure of viruses was discussed in Section 3.6. Use information from that section to complete the following paragraph with the words from this list:

acid, biochemical, capsid, coat, copies DNA, genes, hijack, host, nucleic, protects, replication, RNA, viruses.

Viruses consist of a strand of genetic material, either _____ or _____, surrounded by a protein _____ or _____ which _____ it. All the _____ needed to make new _____ are present in the _____ _____ but the _____ process can only take place when the virus is inside a _____ cell. Viruses _____ the host cell's _____ processes to make new _____ of themselves which then burst out of the host cell.

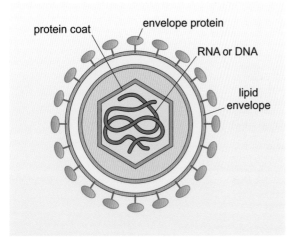

Figure 5.12 A diagram to show the structure of a typical virus particle.

protein coat

envelope protein

RNA or DNA

lipid envelope

Figure 5.12 shows the structure of a virus particle with the protein coat surrounding the nucleic acid. Sometimes the virus has an additional envelope made from proteins and lipids, similar to a bacterial cell wall (Section 1.5), surrounding it. Viruses are classified according to whether the nucleic acid they contain is DNA or RNA, and are further subdivided according to whether the nucleic acid is single or double stranded. It is not known why some viruses, such as the one which causes the common cold, contain only RNA. Some of the RNA viruses can translate their RNA back into DNA using the enzyme reverse transcriptase, and insert this DNA into the genetic material of the host, cleverly taking up permanent residence in the host. Among these so-called retroviruses is HIV, the virus responsible for causing AIDS.

When viruses are outside cells, no biochemical processes go on in them and the viruses are totally inactive. However, when the viruses enter human cells and begin to replicate, and in some cases kill the cells, then the person can begin to suffer from the disease, though a viral infection does not always cause disease. An infection means you have acquired the virus, but if it does not go on to affect your body, then you may not develop a disease. Some viruses can exist harmlessly within an organism. For example, the herpes simplex virus, which causes cold sores, can be dormant within the human body for years, without any effect. There are some viruses such as the hepatitis-B virus that cause a life-long infection. A person harbouring a virus that is not currently causing disease is called a carrier (Activity 5.3).

5.5.1   Common cold and influenza

One of the most common types of virus is the Picornaviruses, which are small RNA viruses. Amongst them are the viruses that cause polio and hepatitis-A and also a group called the Rhinoviruses that cause about 60% of common colds. Rhinoviruses are spread by being coughed or sneezed into the air by an infected person. Usually within one to five days of being infected, a person may develop a cold as the viruses lock on to cells in the nose, throat and airways, enter the cells and begin to divide. These viruses lose their virulence quickly if they dry out, and so must be transferred in droplets of water, which is why sneezes are particularly effective. The runny nose and sneezing produced by a cold are not caused by the virus particles themselves, but by an inflammatory response of the immune system to the infection.

■   What other response to the viruses would you expect the immune system to show?

☐   The innate immune system will recognise the molecules on the outside of the virus as being non-self and phagocytes will engulf and digest the virus particles. In fact, this is what causes the inflammation mentioned above. If the virus has not been encountered before, then the lymphocyte that carries antibodies matching the antigens on the virus will proliferate and release the antibodies into the bloodstream. These antibodies will attach to the viruses and more phagocytes will arrive to destroy them. If the virus has been encountered before, then antibodies will already be present in the blood and the viruses may well be destroyed before symptoms have time to develop.

You may be wondering, then, once you have had a cold, why you later get another one. There are two reasons for this. One is that there are over 100 different known cold-causing Rhinoviruses and so each cold that you get may be caused by a different one. The second is that viruses can undergo genetic changes via a number of different mechanisms. These changes can result in different proteins being present on the outside of the virus, and so antibodies made against the virus when it was met on the first occasion, may be ineffective against the same virus when it is encountered again.

Another group of RNA viruses that produce similar symptoms are the Orthomyxoviridae. This group of viruses contains members that cause influenza (flu). Many people use the term flu to refer to a bad cold, but the infections are actually caused by two distinct groups of viruses, although they are spread and infect the human body in much the same way. There are many different types of flu virus, but most of them can be placed in one of three groups, called (without much originality!) A, B and C. Group A are the most virulent and dangerous and include the infamous avian or bird flu. Groups B and C contain only one species each and they can both infect humans. They are less common than the viruses in group A. Most viruses have evolved to infect only one particular type of host cell, which explains why most of them cannot easily move from one species to another. However, this is not always the case. Since many animals share similarities in their cells, there are some viruses that can transfer from one organism to another – in other words they can cross the species barrier. Avian flu is one such virus.

Avian flu can occur in many different bird species. It can be spread between birds of the same or different species by close contact and can travel to new areas when birds migrate. It does not transfer easily from birds to other animals such as humans. This appears to be because the virus cannot readily attach to the cells in the human nose and throat because the receptor molecules on the cells, onto which it must lock, do not match. However, there are cells deep in the lungs which have the appropriate receptor molecules and so it is possible for humans to contract the disease if they inhale the virus right down into the lungs. This only usually happens if people are in very close, prolonged contact with domestic poultry. So it is important that avian flu does not reach domestic poultry and, to achieve that, there have been suggestions that all poultry should be kept indoors, to reduce the risk of contact with wild birds that might be carrying the virus.

■ If a person is infected with avian flu, are they likely to pass it on to other people? Think about how other cold and flu viruses are spread.

□ Viruses that cause colds and flu are passed on through coughs and sneezes when particles in the nose and throat are expelled into the air in droplets of water. The avian flu virus affects the cells deep in the lungs and does not cause the usual cold symptoms, so there is much less chance of the viruses being expelled into the air in droplets. Furthermore, even if they were, the viruses need to be inhaled deep into the lungs of the next person before they can cause an infection.

Among those people who have contracted avian flu, from contact with infected poultry, the mortality rate is high. Figures published by the World Health Organisation (WHO) showed that by January 2009, about 400 human cases had been reported and 63% of those infected had died.

Scientifically the avian flu virus is named H5N1 after the types of protein found on its surface. H stands for haemagglutinin, a protein that is involved in binding the virus to the receptor molecules on the surface of the host cell and N stands for neuraminidase, a protein that helps break down the host cell to release new viruses in the infected organism. The numbers refer to particular sub-types of these proteins recognised by virologists. Figure 5.13 shows how these proteins are arranged on the surface of the virus. If the virus should undergo genetic changes in the future, of the sort seen in the common cold virus, these could change the types of protein on its surface so that it could infect people more easily and be passed from person to person. Then there is the chance that it could infect and potentially kill millions of people round the world in a global pandemic. An outbreak of a related virus, the H1N1 subtype (the word 'subtype'

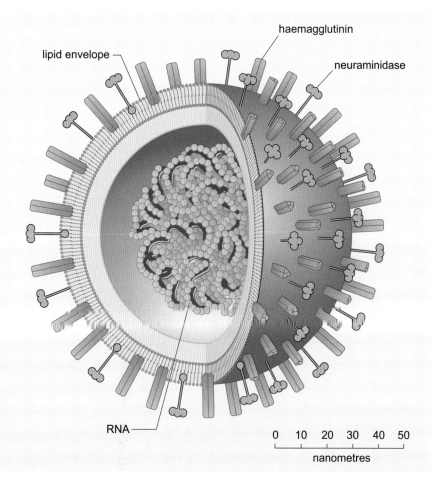

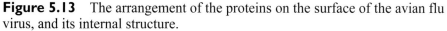

Figure 5.13   The arrangement of the proteins on the surface of the avian flu virus, and its internal structure.

is often used about viruses and means the same as strain), which caused the so-called 'Spanish' flu, is estimated to have killed between 20 and 100 million people in 1918–19. There are varying views amongst scientists about how likely an avian flu pandemic is to occur, but strenuous efforts are being made to restrict the spread of the virus. In Asia it has already killed tens of millions of birds and many more have been culled in an attempt to control its spread. Vaccines for domestic poultry have been developed and these appear to be reducing the number of outbreaks. By mid-2008, three vaccines specifically against the H5N1 avian flu virus had been licensed for use in humans, though all were produced in eggs (see Section 5.5.2) and it would take many months for sufficient quantities to be produced to help combat a pandemic.

Swine flu, a virus that was first recognised in humans in Mexico and the United States in early April 2009, is a type of H1N1 virus thought to be produced from a genetic mix of nucleic acid, including from bird and pig viruses. The virus quickly became of concern when it was shown to spread by human-to-human transmission. When the swine flu virus appeared most of the world's attention was on preventing avian flu, which shows how viruses are unpredictable and how important it is to remain vigilant for any new outbreaks. Within one month there were a considerable number of formally confirmed cases worldwide and some deaths caused by the virus (as determined by laboratory analysis). However many more cases of illness and death were suspected to have been caused by the virus at that time, showing how a virus can spread quickly and outpace the ability of medical services to track properly its spread through a population. The rapid spread around the world was due to Mexico being a popular international holiday destination. As this book goes to press (June 2009), the WHO has declared a pandemic of swine flu.

One approach to dealing with a pandemic is to produce a vaccine against the specific strain of flu virus involved. The World Health Organisation and national governments have laboratories that can react to new flu outbreaks, but at the current time vaccines can take months to produce, meaning that attempts still have to be made to mitigate the spread of viruses once they emerge by public health precautions such as closing schools and reducing public gatherings.

The threat from flu viruses underlines in stark reality that human civilisation is still at the mercy of potentially lethal microbes.

5.5.2 Culturing viruses to produce vaccines

■ Recalling from Section 3.7.1 how vaccines to bacteria have been made, what problem might arise in producing vaccines to viruses, such as those for various strains of flu?

☐ Many vaccines to bacteria are made by culturing the relevant bacteria in the laboratory and then damaging them to reduce their virulence. Since viruses need host cells in which to grow, culturing them in the laboratory cannot be done in the same way as for bacteria.

To produce large quantities of virus, as needed for vaccine production, the viruses are grown inside fertilised hens' eggs. In the 1930s, it was noticed that human viruses grown in such eggs for several cycles tended to lose their virulence in humans, as they became more adapted to growing inside the cells of a bird.

■ If flu viruses were used in this process, why would they then be suitable for use as a vaccine for people?

☐ If the proteins on the outside of the viruses remained sufficiently similar to the original ones, then they would still act as antigens when injected into people, but they would not cause people to suffer from flu itself. In response to antigens antibodies would be produced in the blood which would be ready to bind with any future human flu viruses with which the person came into contact, and then destroy them before the disease could take hold.

Most flu vaccines are still made this way. However, it is a lengthy process, taking several weeks, possibly months, and needing a lot of fertilised eggs, and so manufacture and distribution of the vaccine for a particular outbreak of flu cannot be done quickly when the outbreak occurs, even when the particular flu virus involved has been identified.

So work continues in an attempt to scale up an alternative method, which is to use cell culture. This involves working with single cells, originally obtained from humans, and then treating them so that they separate from one another and undergo cycles of cell division. They can then be grown in containers of an appropriate size and infected with the virus, which produces many copies of itself inside the cells. It would probably be quicker to scale up the production by cell culture in an emergency situation, such as the early stages of a pandemic, than to use the standard method requiring fertilised eggs. But the disadvantage is that the cost of preparing the pharmaceutical plant with fermentation reactors to grow the cells is prohibitive if it is going to sit idle for months or possibly years. The plant required to produce the egg-based vaccine is much less complex and cheaper. Although the yield may be slightly lower, the cell culture method has other advantages. The vaccine made in eggs may cause an allergic reaction in some recipients, due to the presence of small amounts of egg proteins. Also, some viral strains, well adapted to human cells, do not grow well in chicken cells. Overall it seems likely that vaccine production in cell culture will ultimately supersede the process using eggs. Vaccines can also be made from parts of viruses, just the protein coat, for example, and new methods which involve the manufacture of these parts are also being investigated.

Currently a new flu vaccine is produced each year. Three strains are chosen by the WHO Global Influenza Surveillance Network, as being the ones most likely to cause illness in the coming season and a so-called trivalent vaccine is prepared. In the UK, this is offered to those at risk of serious complications if they were to catch flu, including the elderly and to health care workers. The vaccination seems to be about 75% effective in preventing hospitalisation of patients with flu complications. The most effective vaccine is, of course, that against the strain of virus which the patient contracts. However, even when there is not a particularly good match, the vaccine does give some protection, and it is hoped that it may also provide some protection against avian flu, if that were to spread amongst the population.

Work is ongoing to develop a universal flu vaccine which would not need to be tailored each year to the viruses in circulation at the time, but would be effective against a broad range of viruses.

5.5.3   Human immunodeficiency virus (HIV)

HIV, the human immunodeficiency virus, is another microbe which is having huge effects across the world. Since this virus, which is the cause of AIDS (acquired immunodeficiency syndrome), was first recognised in 1981, it has killed over 25 million people, giving it the status of a pandemic.

When cold or flu viruses enter human cells, the RNA from the virus is released and the cell treats the viral RNA as its own and starts to read the code, generating many more virus particles. The virus particles are released from the cell and can then go on to infect other cells.

HIV works in a rather different way, as shown in Figure 5.14. Like cold viruses it has its genetic code as RNA but, after binding to the cell (a), it enters and the single-stranded RNA molecule is used to make a molecule of double-stranded DNA (b). This is then incorporated into the DNA of the genome of the host cell (c) and so is replicated when the cell divides. New viral RNA can be produced in the cell (d), packaged into viral particles (e) and then released by budding out of the infected cell (f). Some viral DNA remains in the cell DNA without being released; these viruses are said to be latent (g) and may be released

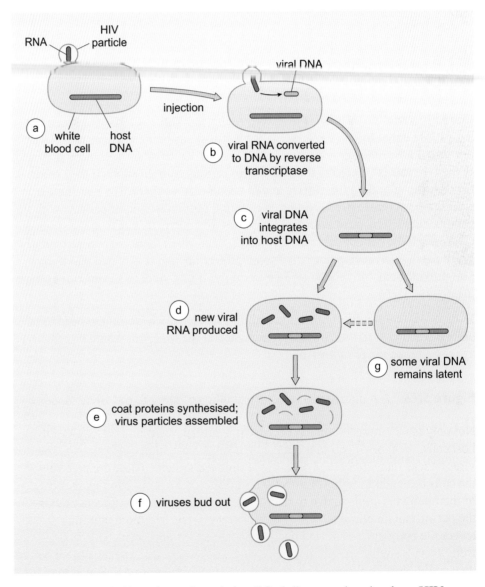

Figure 5.14   Highly schematic and simplified diagram showing how HIV incorporates itself into a host human white blood cell and replicates.

later by going through processes (d), (e) and (f). This process of back-copying RNA into DNA is the reason why HIV, and other viruses that behave similarly, are called retroviruses. Figure 5.15 shows an HIV particle budding off from a host cell.

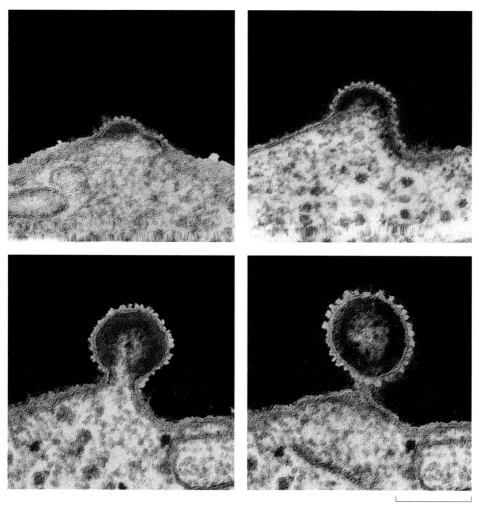

0.1 µm

Figure 5.15   A replicated HIV particle budding off an infected white blood cell.

Not only is HIV hard to combat because it is incorporated into the DNA of the host cells, the type of cell that it targets makes it particularly devastating. The virus attacks the white blood cells of the immune system. These are precisely the cells designed to fight off infection, so if they are not functioning properly or their numbers are low, due to many being killed by the HIV infection, then the person cannot eliminate the virus from their body. But more importantly, it leaves the body open to other infections, often called opportunistic infections, from microbes which would normally be destroyed by the immune system before they could result in illness. This is the derivation of the term AIDS, acquired immunodeficiency syndrome. In reducing the effectiveness of the immune system, the virus can also cause a series of conditions, including nervous system problems and cancers, making it a complicated medical challenge. Furthermore, there are multiple strains of HIV, and infection by one type does not provide immunity from other types meaning that multiple HIV infections have been recorded in some individuals.

About 90% of people who contract the virus eventually go on to develop full blown AIDS and it often kills within a year unless anti-viral drugs are taken. The virus can be spread by a number of routes including blood from needles used to inject drugs, from blood transfusion and from unprotected sex. Transmission by blood has resulted in the infection by HIV of large numbers of haemophiliacs who received blood transfusions and blood products to combat their condition, though nowadays extensive tests are carried out to ensure the blood is not infected. The virus can also be transmitted from mother to child during the last weeks of pregnancy, during birth and breastfeeding. The virus is found in low concentrations in saliva and tears of infected individuals, but there have been no recorded cases of transmission through these fluids.

5.5.4 Combating viral diseases

Like bacterial diseases, viral diseases can be treated with drugs. In some ways, these resemble the antibiotics used against bacteria, since they are designed specifically to kill viruses and not to damage other cells, such as human cells.

■ Based on what you now know about how viruses replicate, why is producing an anti-viral drug a challenge?

☐ Viruses replicate inside the host's cells, so developing a drug that can get at a virus, whilst having no effect on the host cell is extremely difficult.

Only a few anti-viral drugs have so far been developed, and they are used mainly for HIV, herpes virus and influenza A and B. These are effectively 'designer drugs', often called 'rational drugs', developed to target specific parts of a particular virus, such as the proteins on its surface, or to disrupt a particular part of its life cycle. You will probably have heard of oseltamivir (Tamiflu®) and zanamivir (Relenza®), which affect the neuraminidase on the surface of the virus and are used to provide protection against a range of flu viruses. Another well-known drug is the anti-retroviral drug, zidovudine (also known as AZT and sold under various trade names such as Retrovir®) which is used to treat AIDS, often as part of a complex set of treatments, including other drugs designed to prevent the mutation of HIV into a zidovudine-resistant form. This mirrors the concerns about antibiotic resistance in bacteria. Zidovudine works by inhibiting the action of reverse transcriptase, the enzyme which HIV uses to make a DNA copy from its RNA.

■ Why is this copying process essential?

☐ When HIV enters a cell, its genetic material is in the form of RNA. In order for the next stage of infection to occur, the RNA has to be copied into DNA, which is then incorporated into the host cell's genome. If this step is inhibited by a drug like zidovudine, then infection cannot proceed.

As well as being used in patients known to be HIV-positive (in other words carrying the HIV virus), zidovudine can also be used for medical staff and others to reduce the risk of infection after they have been put at risk of contracting the virus perhaps due to a needle-stick injury. It is also recommended to HIV-positive pregnant women to help to lower the risk of the infection being passed on to their babies. Without treatment, about 25% of babies born to infected mothers are themselves infected. This reduces to 8% when drug treatment is given during pregnancy and then to the baby for 6 weeks after birth. The overall infection of babies can be reduced further, to about 1%, by using a combination of anti-retroviral drugs, delivery by caesarean section and avoiding breastfeeding.

The other way to combat viruses is by using a vaccine, as described in Section 5.5.2. The once common disease, smallpox, is the first, and so far the only, disease to have been completely eradicated from the world's population by the use of vaccines. Smallpox first emerged in the human population about 12 000 years ago, and during the 20th century was probably responsible for 300–500 million deaths worldwide. Even as recently as 50 years ago, estimates indicate there were 50 million cases each year. Following a global vaccination programme, by 1977 there were no more cases and the WHO certified that the disease had been eradicated in December 1979. Luckily, unlike the flu virus, the smallpox virus does not mutate so readily and so one vaccine could be used on all cases. However, stocks of the virus are still held in the US and Russia for research purposes, probably because of the concern that some unknown stock of virus would be discovered and used as a biological weapon by terrorists (see the discussion about anthrax spores in Box 2.1).

As knowledge of viruses improves, medical science may well be on the verge of exciting developments that could profoundly improve society's ability to deal with these tiny, but pervasive microbes.

5.6   Disease-causing fungi

Like bacteria, fungi like to grow in places where there is moisture and there are a host of fungi that can cause disease if they overcome the natural microbial balance in the body. Diseases caused by fungi are known as mycoses. One of their favourite habitats is the human respiratory tract.

■ Identify one feature of the human respiratory tract that makes it favourable for fungal growth. What characteristic of fungi gives them a good advantage in colonising human body surfaces?

☐ The human respiratory tract is a moist environment, which will tend to encourage fungi to grow. One major reason why fungi can take advantage of surfaces in the human body to grow on is that they have a filamentous structure (see Figure 2.4b) which allows them to colonise surfaces quite quickly.

A serious infection of the respiratory tract is aspergillosis, caused by fungi of the genus *Aspergillus* which grow along the surfaces of the lungs and can cause severe immune response and respiratory difficulties.

■ Based on what you know about bacterial infections, what type of people are at high risk of contracting aspergillosis?

☐ The types of people at risk are those with a compromised immune system, the elderly and people with other medical conditions, especially respiratory problems, or in a weak physical state.

Another fungal disease that you may have heard of is athlete's foot, so-called because the feet tend to be moist and warm and provide a good habitat for fungi. Athlete's foot can develop on anyone. It is caused by skin colonisation by the fungus *Trichophyton*, resulting in flaky skin and itching. It can be treated by a range of antifungal chemicals.

Activity 5.4   Using the digital microscope to examine medically important microbes

The estimated time for this activity is 30 minutes.

In this activity, you will use the digital microscope to study the shapes and growth patterns of some disease-causing microbes.

You will find the detailed instructions for this activity in the Activities section of the course website.

That concludes this survey of some of the microbes which live in or on the human body and have implications for health. The next chapter will look at those microbes which live in much more demanding environments, the extremophiles.

Question 5.8

Three hypothetical microbes P, Q and R have the following sequence of bases in part of their DNA. Which two are likely to be more closely related? To which of these two is the third microbe more closely related? *Hint*: Look for the number of differences in the letters for the three microbes.

Microbe P: ATT CAG AGG TCA TGA CGG AAA TGC TAG TCA ACC CGT CAT

Microbe Q: ATG CTG AGG TCT TCA GGG AAA TGC TAC TCA TAC CCG TAT

Microbe R: ATT CAC AGG TCA TCA CGG AAT TGC TAG TCA ACC CGT CAG

Question 5.9

Identify and correct the errors in the following paragraph about the immune system.

The phagocytes form part of a system that is identical in all people and is called the adaptive immune system. However, it is the innate immune system that allows the human body to respond very rapidly to microbes that it has encountered before. The immune system uses a type of white blood cell called lypophytes, which have chemical receptors on their surfaces that can bind to any materials which are foreign to the body. The basis of the unique recognition of different microbes is the antibody system. Antibodies are U-shaped proteins, with the two prongs made up of small chains of enzymes that can be arranged in an enormous number of different ways to recognise the antigens on the surfaces of different foreign microbes.

Question 5.10

Why is it not appropriate for antibiotics to be given to patients who are suffering from flu?

Question 5.11

Read the following information about a disease of livestock called bluetongue, taken from the UK DEFRA (Department for Environment Food and Rural Affairs) website in January 2009, and then answer, in two or three sentences for each, the questions which follow:

> **'Bluetongue – Don't hesitate, vaccinate**
>
> Vaccination is the only effective way for individuals to protect the welfare of their animals and their own livelihood. The nature of this disease is such that keepers cannot rely on their neighbours' vaccination: midges can be carried by winds and by human activity. The only sure way is to vaccinate your own animals.
>
> We strongly encourage all livestock farmers to remain vigilant and report any clinical signs of disease. Even those who have already vaccinated against BTV8 need to remain vigilant: BTV is on the move in Europe, and we need to be on our guard against it.
>
> The disease, caused by a virus spread by midges, affects ruminants but not pigs, horses or humans. Check the declarations and maps to see if your premises are in a Zone. All movement licence conditions for bluetongue must be complied with. Surveillance and epidemiological investigations are continuing.'

(a) How would a vaccine to the BTV8 strain of the bluetongue virus be produced using eggs?

(b) Explain how vaccination will protect animals from the bluetongue disease.

(c) Suggest why the virus causes an infection in some animals (ruminants such as cattle and sheep) but not in others (pigs, horses or humans).

(d) How does the disease spread and why is it necessary for all farmers to vaccinate their animals?

Summary of Chapter 5

- There are more microbes in humans than there are human cells. Most of these microbes (called commensals) live a harmonious existence with human cells, but disease and infection can be caused when this balance is disrupted or when the body or immune system is weakened. This category includes *C. difficile*.

- The human digestive system contains a huge number and diversity of microbes. Many of these play a vital role in helping to digest food, and some produce vitamins that we cannot get from our food, such as vitamin K.

- Microbes can transfer genetic information from one to another and this is one of the means by which antibiotic resistance is spread amongst the microbial population. The process is the origin of MRSA.

- Many diseases are caused by viruses, which require host cells to replicate. Some viruses can change their genetic code rapidly leading to new types emerging very quickly. An example is the virus responsible for the common cold.

- Viruses are very difficult to target using drugs because they invade the interior of host cells, but knowledge of the genetics and life cycle of viruses is leading to 'rational' drug design to combat them.

Chapter 6
The extremophiles

6.1   Life at the limits

The chapters so far have dealt mostly with microbes in the places you probably expected to find microbes – in the body, in hospitals, in food, etc. But microbes also turn up in the most unlikely places, in places where environmental conditions are so extreme that no other organisms can survive. These are the extremophilic (extreme-loving) microbes or extremophiles.

■   What characteristics of an extreme environment would make it very difficult for most organisms to live there?

☐   The most obvious one is the temperature. Most organisms cannot survive in extremely hot or extremely cold environments. Additionally, you may have thought of lack of oxygen, very high or very low pressures, high salinity (saltiness) and lack of nutrients or of water.

Specialised microbes can cope with all these extremes and actually do better there, often failing to thrive in what would be considered normal conditions for supporting life. Microbes that survive without oxygen, the anaerobic microbes, were introduced in Section 1.8 and have been mentioned throughout the course, so they will not be considered further here.

■   What strategy have you already met that would allow microbes to survive extreme desiccation, (i.e. drying out from lack of water)?

☐   Some microbes form spores (Section 2.5). They go into an inactive or dormant state that allows them to survive extreme conditions.

By studying microbes that can live in extreme environments, insight can be gained about how life might have started on Earth and the likelihood of finding life on other planets. Microbes that survive some of the harshest environments on Earth are ideal candidates to withstand the extreme conditions associated with outer space and other planets, as you will see in Chapter 8. Extremophiles also have more practical uses for us. The enzymes of those microbes that are adapted to live at high temperatures will, of course, function at those temperatures. Such enzymes have been extracted from microbes for use in, for example, biological detergents, so that clothes washing can take place at temperatures that would destroy other enzymes. These thermophiles – microbes that grow best at unusually high temperatures – are discussed in the next section.

6.2   Microbes and extreme temperatures

The temperature at which a species of microbe grows and reproduces most rapidly is called the optimum temperature for that species. At temperatures above and below the optimum, but relatively close to it, the microbe will survive, but its growth rate will be reduced.

■ What do you think is the optimum temperature for those microbes which live inside the human body?

☐ Their optimum temperature is likely to be around the normal human body temperature of 37 °C.

Question 6.1

Figure 6.1 shows how the growth rate (indicated up the left-hand side of the graph) of five different microbes changes with the temperature (indicated along the bottom of the graph) at which they are grown. Use the graph to answer the following questions.

(a) Which microbe probably lives inside the human body?

(b) Which microbe could survive in boiling water?

(c) Which microbe grows successfully over the largest temperature range?

(d) How many degrees above its optimum temperature can Microbe B survive, and how many below?

(e) What is the temperature range for the growth of Microbe A?

(f) Even at its optimum temperature, Microbe A has a much lower growth rate than any of the other microbes. Why might this be?

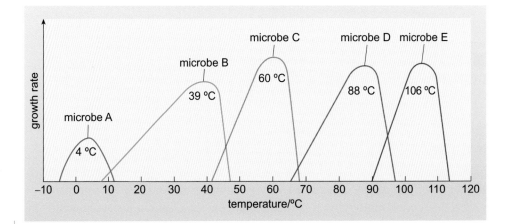

Figure 6.1 Graph showing how the growth rate varies with temperature for five microbes A–E, and their optimum temperatures.

Having looked at Figure 6.1 you may be wondering exactly how temperature affects microbes. You should now study Box 6.1 which explains how the components of the microbial cells are affected by temperature.

Box 6.1   Cell components and temperature

In Section 1.5, there was a brief description of the components of a generalised bacterial cell and other aspects of cell structure have been mentioned subsequently.

Question 6.2

Identify any errors in the following statements.

A   On the outside of bacterial cells is a plasma membrane, which is selectively permeable, controlling which substances can enter and leave the cells.

B   Inside the cell is a fluid called cytosol, containing carbohydrates, proteins and other substances dissolved in water.

C   The chromosome is made of a circular loop of RNA which is attached to the plasma membrane.

D   There can be circles of DNA in the cytosol called plasmids.

E   A section of DNA that codes for a protein is called a gene.

F   Enzymes are special proteins which act as catalysts, to speed up reactions in the cell.

There are other components in the cytosol, such as ribosomes (Section 5.2.1), which are involved in translating the code from DNA and making proteins. However, the most critical components which are affected by heat are the DNA, the enzymes and the plasma membrane.

When the temperature of any molecule is raised, the atoms in it start to 'jiggle' more and they may move to such an extent that the weak bonds which are holding parts of the molecule together, can break so that the molecule becomes distorted from its normal shape.

■   What shape is the DNA molecule? Look back to Section 1.6 if necessary.

☐   DNA is in the form of a double helix, similar to a minute twisted ladder, with bases forming the rungs of the ladder (Figures 1.9 and 1.10).

You will recall that the two sides of the DNA ladder can be separated, a process which happens when the DNA is being copied. The first stage in the copying process involves breaking the weak bonds that hold the bases together (the bonds coloured red in Figure 1.11), in a carefully controlled way. However, if the DNA is heated above the temperature at which it is stable, these bonds can break in an uncontrolled way. The two strands of the DNA fall apart and it no longer functions properly, almost certainly leading to the eventual death of the cell.

Enzymes, which are proteins, are affected in a similar way when the temperature rises. Proteins are made of very long chains of amino acids, often with hundreds or even thousands of amino acids in the chain (Section 1.6). To make the functioning enzyme, the chain folds up, to produce what looks like a minute tangled piece of string. But, unlike a piece of string, every molecule of the enzyme folds up in exactly the same way, to produce an identical tangle (Figure 6.2a). The enzyme has to be such a specific shape, because it needs to fit exactly with the substance on which it has its effect, called its substrate, at a particular area of the enzyme called the active site (Figure 6.2b).

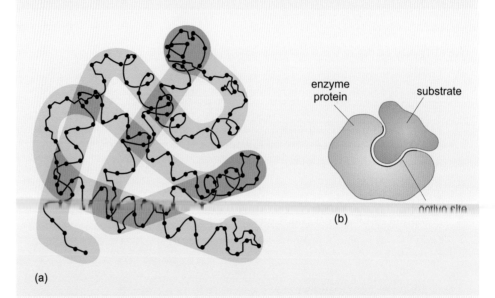

enzyme protein substrate

(b)

active site

(a)

Figure 6.2 (a) An enzyme, showing the very specific folding of the amino acid chain to form a protein. (b) A schematic diagram showing how the substrate fits into the active site on an enzyme.

■ Egg white (albumin) is about 15% protein. How is egg white affected by heat?

☐ Egg white changes from a very runny liquid to a firm solid mass when it is heated to 100 °C, when an egg is boiled.

Since enzymes are proteins, heating them has a similar effect. The amino acids forming the protein chain are held together by strong chemical bonds (called covalent bonds) but the folding of the chain relies on other much weaker types of bond to hold it in the correct shape, including bonds like those that hold the two strands of DNA together to make the double helix (hydrogen bonds). These weak bonds are broken by the heat as the atoms jiggle around and the neat shape of the enzyme is destroyed. In the case of the egg white, the unravelled proteins tangle around one another causing the white to become solid as the egg is cooked. In the case of enzymes, the shape of the enzyme molecule is changed so that the active site will no longer fit with the substrate, and so the enzyme ceases to function. It is said to be denatured. If the many enzymes which are needed for the chemical processes of the cell (the cell's metabolism) cease to function, then the cell will die.

Finally, there is the plasma membrane. Plasma membranes are made mostly of fats, with some protein molecules embedded in them. Each of the fat molecules (chemically called a phospholipid) has a head and two tails and they are arranged in a double layer (bilayer), as shown in Figure 6.3a. Figure 6.3b shows how the protein molecules are embedded in the membrane. Some of these proteins provide channels through which certain substances are allowed to enter or leave the cell, which is why the plasma membrane is described as selectively permeable.

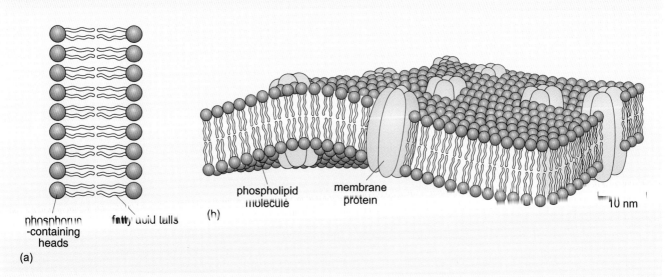

phospholipid molecule

membrane protein

10 nm

phosphorus -containing heads

fatty acid tails

(b)

(a)

Figure 6.3   (a) A schematic section through a plasma membrane, to show the phospholipid bilayer structure. (The structure of the phospholipid molecule will be covered in Box 6.2.) (b) A larger piece of plasma membrane, to show some of the proteins embedded within it.

■ Based on general knowledge of what happens to fats like butter as they are warmed, what would you expect to happen to a plasma membrane when it is heated above its normal temperature?

☐ Fats get softer as they are heated, and eventually melt completely. So this is what you might expect would happen to a plasma membrane, and it does.

As the temperature of the cell is raised, the membrane becomes soft and probably one of the first effects would be that the proteins which are normally held firmly in the membrane structure would become loose and stop functioning properly. Their own structure would change too, as their weak bonds were broken. So the cell would no longer be able to control which substances entered and left; its membrane would no longer be selectively permeable. Substances which were not needed could flood into the cell, and essential molecules from inside the cell could be lost. Very soon this would lead to the death of the cell.

Question 6.3

List the three main components of the cell that can be damaged when the temperature gets too high and summarise, in one sentence for each, the effect of heat on the three components.

Look back to Figure 6.1. You will notice that most of the curves are a similar shape. As the temperature at which each microbe species is living rises above the optimum temperature, there is a steep drop in the growth rate of the microbes. This is largely a result of the denaturing of the microbes' enzymes. Once the enzymes are denatured, the microbes soon die, so the growth rate drops very steeply to zero. Lowering the temperature of the microbes below the optimum value does not denature the enzymes but simply causes all the reactions in the cell to proceed more slowly. Thus the microbes are not killed immediately, but their growth rate is reduced, so the curve falls more gently at temperatures below the optimum value. They do eventually die, probably because their plasma membranes become too stiff for normal functioning of the cells.

■ How does the curve for Microbe A differ from the others?

☐ The curve for microbe A falls in approximately the same way on either side of the optimum temperature.

When microbe A is placed at temperatures a few degrees above its optimum temperature of 4 °C, these are still too low to denature its enzymes. So the more gentle slopes of the growth curve on both sides of the optimum, probably simply reflect the effects on the plasma membranes of the cell, which become too soft and flexible above the optimum temperature and too stiff below.

Question 6.4

Microbes can be grouped according to their preferred temperature ranges. Table 6.1 gives the names of the microbes in Figure 6.1. With the information that 'psychro-' means cold and 'hyper-' means high, complete the table by inserting these descriptions into the correct spaces: hyperthermophiles; psychrophiles; mesophiles; thermophiles.

Table 6.1 Description of microbes according to their optimum temperature.

Temperature range/ °C	Description of microbes with their optimum temperature within that range	Names of microbes in Figure 6.1
below 15		A: *Polaromonas vacuolata*
15–40		B: *Escherichia coli*
40–80		C: *Bacillus stearothermophilus*
above 80		D: *Thermococcus celer*
		E: *Pyrolobus fumarii*

6.2.1   Cold environments

Cold environments can be cold all the year round, such as within glaciers, frozen soils or in deep oceans. Others are only seasonally cold. In seasonally cold environments temperatures can fall as low as −20 °C in the winter and yet can get as high as 40 °C in the summer. Microbes that live in such seasonally cold environments often grow optimally at warmer temperatures, but can still grow slowly at cold temperatures. These microbes are called psychrotolerant, because they only tolerate cold temperatures, but do not actually require cold temperatures to grow optimally.

In May 1818, an expedition, led by Captain John Ross, left England in four ships to map the coastline of North America and search for a way through to the Pacific. On December 4, 1818 the following article appeared in *The Times* in London:

> 'Captain Sir John Ross has brought from Baffin's Bay a quantity of red snow, or rather snow-water, which has been submitted to chymical analysis in this country, in order to the discovery of the nature of its colouring matter. Our credulity is put to an extreme test upon this occasion, but we cannot learn that there is any reason to doubt the fact as stated Sir John Ross did not see any red snow fall, but he saw large tracts overspread with it. The colour of the fields of snow was not uniform; but, on the contrary, there were patches or streaks more or less red, and of various depths of tint. The liquor, or dissolved snow, is of so dark a red as to resemble red port wine. It is stated, that the liquor deposits a sediment; and that the question is not answered, whether that sediment is of an animal or vegetable nature.'

'Red snow from the Arctic regions', *The Times*, 4 December 1818, p. 2.

At the time, it was suggested that the red colour was due to iron from meteorites which had fallen on the snow, and it was not until the end of the century that the correct interpretation was made. The red colour as seen in Figure 6.4a was caused by a psychrophilic microbe, *Chlamydomonas nivalis*, the snow alga

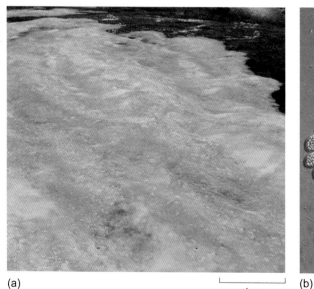

(a)   1 m   (b)   10 μm

Figure 6.4   (a) A snow bank in the Mount Rainier National Park, Washington State, USA, with red colouration caused by the presence of snow algae, *Chlamydomonas nivalis*. (b) Light micrograph of *C. nivalis* cells. Here they are green.

(Figure 6.4b). Algae (Figure 2.3) include microbes that photosynthesise, and so normally contain the green pigment chlorophyll, the same as in green plants. However, chlorophyll can be damaged by the intense visible and ultraviolet (UV) radiation present at high altitudes and at high latitudes and *C. nivalis* has developed an additional pigment, a bright red carotenoid (related to the red pigments in carrots). This protects the cell, including the chlorophyll, from damage by absorbing some of the radiation. Because the pigments in the algae absorb sunlight, the algae warm up slightly and melt the snow around them. Thus they are often found in small depressions in the snow which are called 'sun cups'. During the winter, when the algae are covered with snow, they form spores. When the temperature rises in spring, and slight melting begins, these spores germinate and release tiny green cells (Figure 6.4b) with flagella, which swim towards the surface of the snow. The individual cells then develop the red pigment once they are at the surface of the snow and the annual cycle is repeated.

A comparison of psychrophiles with other microbes shows that their plasma membranes are particularly well adapted to allow them to survive at low temperatures. You should now study Box 6.2 to find out more about membrane structure.

Box 6.2 Fatty acids and membranes

You will recall from Box 6.1 that the phospholipids which make up the main part of plasma membranes, have a head and two tails. The tails (fatty acid tails) are long chains of carbon atoms, with hydrogen atoms attached. Figure 6.5 shows the structure of the fatty acid tails of a phospholipid in more detail.

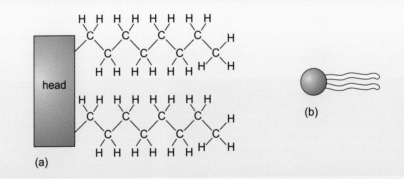

Figure 6.5 Representations of phospholipid molecules, showing the fatty acid tails (a) with all the carbon and hydrogen atoms shown and (b) with yellow tails representing the carbon chains. Note that here there are only 8 carbon atoms shown in each tail in (a), but more typically the chains would consist of between 12 and 24 carbon atoms.

■ Look at each of the carbon atoms in Figure 6.5a. How many other atoms are attached by bonds (shown as straight lines) to each of the carbon atoms?

☐ Each carbon atom is attached to four other atoms. Most of them are attached to two neighbouring carbon atoms, one to the left and one to the right, and then to two hydrogen atoms. The carbon at the left-hand end of the fatty acid chain is attached to the head, then to one carbon and two hydrogen atoms. The carbon at the end of the fatty acid tail is attached to one carbon atom to its left and then to three hydrogen atoms.

Carbon chains like the ones in Figure 6.5, where most of the carbon atoms have two hydrogen atoms attached (bonded) to them are said to be saturated with hydrogen atoms, usually just referred to as saturated. However, some fatty acids have a slightly different structure. Part of one possible chain is shown in Figure 6.6a. One pair of carbon atoms is different from the others. Each carbon atom of this pair still has four bonds (there are still four straight lines associated with each one) but this time two of the bonds are attached to the other carbon of the pair, leaving only one bond to attach to a hydrogen atom. This pair of bonds between two carbon atoms is called a double bond. Chains with double bonds, where some carbon atoms are only attached to one hydrogen atom, are said to be unsaturated. If there is one double bond in the chain, they are monounsaturated and if there are two or more, they are polyunsaturated. Crucially for the structure of the plasma membrane, each time there is a double bond, it puts a slight 'kink' in the carbon chain. (There are, in fact, two orientations of the double bond, which create 'kinks' at slightly different angles.)

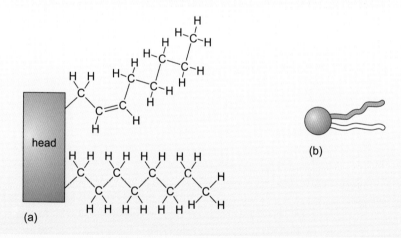

(a)

(b)

Figure 6.6   (a) A phospholipid with a carbon chain containing a double bond. (b) A phospholipid with one saturated tail (yellow) and one polyunsaturated kinked tail (brown).

When the phospholipids are packed together to form a plasma membrane, if all the fatty acid tails are saturated, they pack together very neatly, as in Figure 6.7a, but even if only a few of the phospholipids are unsaturated (with double bonds in their tails), then the packing is much looser, as shown in Figure 6.7b.

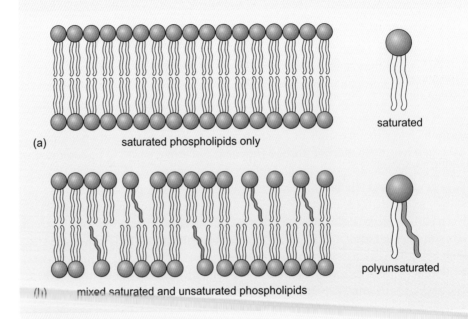

(a)   saturated phospholipids only

saturated

(b)   mixed saturated and unsaturated phospholipids

polyunsaturated

Figure 6.7 Phospholipids packed into plasma membranes (a) saturated phospholipids only and (b) mixed saturated and unsaturated phospholipids.

This packing affects the physical behaviour of the membrane. A membrane composed of saturated phospholipids (Figure 6.7a) will be relatively stiff while a membrane which includes some unsaturated tails will be much softer and more flexible. In fact, this applies not only to phospholipids, but also to fats which are used as foods such as butter, margarines, olive oil, sunflower oil, etc. These have a slightly different structure in that each molecule contains three tails, but the principle is the same.

■ The labels on olive oil and butter state that one contains 64% saturated fat, while the other contains only 14% saturated fat. Which is which, and why?

☐ The butter, which is a hard fat, contains the higher percentage of saturated fats, with straight chains which pack more closely together. A fat containing only 14% saturated fat must contain 86% of unsaturates (monounsaturates and polyunsaturates) which, due to the kinks in the chains, will not pack at all closely together. This fat will therefore be much softer and in this case is actually liquid olive oil.

You might like to compare the labels on other fats and oils to which you have access and check that unsaturated fats generally make the fat softer and more liquid.

There is an optimum stiffness for a plasma membrane. It must not be so hard that substances which should be passing through it are prevented from doing so, and it must not be so soft that it becomes too flexible or permeable to too many substances (Box 6.1).

■ Summarise the two factors that affect the stiffness of a plasma membrane.

☐ The stiffness is affected by the temperature; at higher temperatures a membrane is softer than at low temperatures. It is also affected by the make-up of the fatty acid tails in the phospholipids; at a given temperature unsaturated fatty acid tails make the membrane softer than a membrane containing only saturated fatty acid tails.

Question 6.5

If an analysis of the type of fatty acid tails found in the plasma membrane of a psychrophile was compared with that of a mesophile, how would you expect the two analyses to differ?

Psychrophiles are those which must live at low temperatures and cannot survive if the temperature rises (such as Microbe A in Figure 6.1), while psychrotolerant microbes can live at normal temperatures but are not killed by low temperatures, although they grow much more slowly. The latter are particularly important to food microbiologists, since they can cause spoiling of food which is stored by being refrigerated or frozen.

6.2.2 Hot environments

■ Can you think of a domestic situation in which microbes that live at relatively high temperatures are common?

☐ Inside a garden compost heap are vast numbers of such microbes, which help with the breakdown of organic material (Section 4.3).

Compost heaps generally do not reach temperatures above about 70 °C. If they do get hotter, then many of the microbes die and the temperature falls again. In nature, much higher temperatures are found in conjunction with volcanic areas, either on land or under the sea. On land, hot springs can reach temperatures up to the boiling point of water, 100 °C.

■ Would you expect to find (a) thermophiles and (b) hyperthermophiles in and around hot springs? Check back to Table 6.1 for the meaning of the terms if necessary.

☐ Thermophiles live between 40 °C and 80 °C, while hyperthermophiles live at temperatures above 80 °C. So both types of microbe might be found in and around hot springs.

One of the best known thermophiles is *Thermus aquaticus* (Figure 6.8), which can survive in temperatures of 50 °C to 80 °C. At these temperatures, it is particularly important that the microbe has thermostable enzymes.

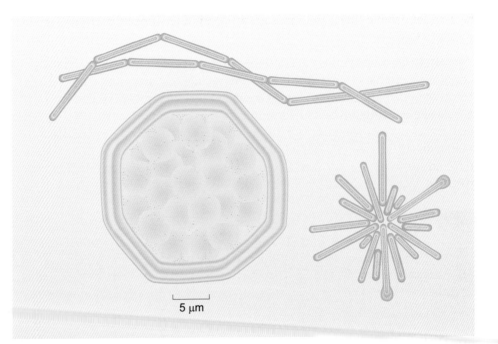

5 μm

Figure 6.8 Sketches of *Thermus aquaticus*, a thermophilic bacterium with varied morphology, which can produce in culture single rods, long filaments, rosettes or large spheres, depending on the conditions.

■ What do you think is meant by the phrase 'thermostable enzymes'?

☐ Since 'therm-' is related to heat, it would be reasonable to suggest that thermostable enzymes are enzymes which are not denatured (destroyed) by heat, but which continue working at temperatures that would destroy normal enzymes (Box 6.1).

Thermostable enzymes appear to contain sequences of amino acids which cause them to fold in such a way that more bonds than normal, or particular configurations of bonds, hold them into the correct shape so that they are less likely to become denatured at high temperatures. Additionally, some thermophilic microbes contain proteins known as chaperonins, which are able to refold enzyme molecules which have been denatured, back into the correct shape to function again. *Thermus aquaticus* has many thermostable enzymes, of which the best known is one which is used to link the components of DNA together to make new DNA strands when the cell divides (Section 1.6). Such an enzyme is called a polymerase, and because this one has been identified in *Thermus aquaticus*, it is called *Taq* polymerase.

■ You met *Taq* polymerase in Section 3.9. What is it used for?

☐ *Taq* polymerase is the enzyme used in the polymerase chain reaction (PCR) which is used to make multiple copies of DNA in a very short time outside cells.

The PCR is extensively used in molecular biology. It is used to study gene function and the relationships between microbes and other living things. It can be used for genetic fingerprinting, such as identifying suspects in crimes, and in paternity tests.

Thermophiles are found on the sea floor as part of one of the most astonishing ecosystems on Earth. In some places where molten rock (magma) is not far below the sea floor, seawater travels down through the rocks of the Earth's crust, is heated up, sometimes to temperatures of almost 400 °C, and then rises up again and gushes out of the sea floor at hydrothermal vents. The superheated water is rich in dissolved minerals that it has picked up in the crust, and on contact with the cold sea water, many of the minerals come out of the solution and form solid particles, making the water look like black smoke (Figure 6.9).

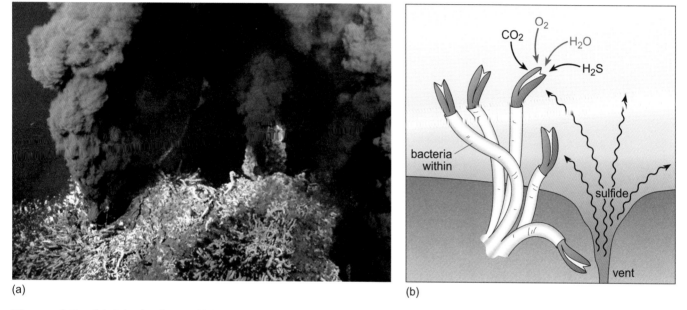

(a)   (b)

Figure 6.9   (a) A hydrothermal black smoker emitting mineral-rich water at temperatures of 350 °C. Around the base of the plume are tube worms, showing the white sheath and red plume of the worm body. (b) The tube worms take up sulfide in the form of H_2S from the vent water and also take up oxygen (O_2) and carbon dioxide (CO_2) from seawater which feed the bacteria.

Normally there would be little life in the dark depths of the oceans, but things are different at black smokers. There are complex communities of thermophiles, both bacteria and archaea. Amongst them are some of the world-record holders for high-temperature living including *Pyrolobus fumarii*, Microbe E in Figure 6.1 and Table 6.1.

■   Reading from Figure 6.1, what is the optimum temperature and what is the temperature range for this microbe?

☐   *Pyrolobus fumarii* has an optimum temperature of 106 °C and can grow between 90 °C and about 113 °C. It is a hyperthermophile.

Associated with these microbial communities are various species of animals, including the remarkable tube worms shown in Figure 6.9. These worms are two metres long and have no anus, gut or mouth. Instead they have a modified gastrointestinal tract consisting primarily of spongy tissue which is loaded with sulfur granules and microbes. The microbes have a symbiotic relationship with the worms, that is, they live together to their mutual benefit. The tube worms contain a protein that binds and transports the gases oxygen and hydrogen sulfide (H_2S). Hydrogen sulfide within the spongy tissues of the worm can be used by the microbes to make the energy they need to live. In return the microbes produce nutrients and sugars for the worm. These microbes are known as chemolithotrophs (literally translated as chemical-rock-feeders but the source of their energy can be any inorganic chemicals, not just rock).

Activity 6.1   How do thermophiles survive?

The estimated time for this activity is 15 minutes.

The following sentence is a very brief summary of how thermophiles manage to grow and reproduce at high temperatures.

'Thermophiles can live at high temperatures because their enzymes can still work and, unlike psychrophiles, their membranes contain mostly saturated fats.'

Explain in more detail what is meant by this sentence, imagining your audience is a student on this course who has not yet studied this chapter. You should aim to write about 200 words.

6.3   Microbes in acidic and other toxic environments

The acidity of a solution is measured on the pH scale. You may find it useful to revise Box 4.2 *Acids and the pH scale*. Most cells, including those of microbes, function best at approximately neutral pH values and even a slight change in pH can be very harmful to the functioning of the cell.

■   What pH value is neutral? Which values would be given by acidic solutions?

☐   pH 7 is neutral. Values of pH less than 7 indicate acidic solutions.

pH is a measure of the concentration of hydrogen ions and it is an excess of these ions which causes serious detrimental effects on cells, mostly by affecting the stability of the weak bonds that hold proteins, including enzymes, in shape. As you know, temperature is another factor which affects such bonds and, as with temperature, microbes have an optimum pH for growth and a pH range which they are able to tolerate. Those microbes which prefer an environment with acidic conditions are called acidophiles. Not surprisingly, microbes that prefer pH values close to 7 are called neutrophiles and those favouring pH values much greater than 7 are called alkalinophiles.

In the human body, the inside of the stomach is very acidic (pH values below 7), due to the production of hydrochloric acid by cells in the stomach wall.

Question 6.6

Based on what you have just read, what might be the effects of acid in the stomach on (a) any microbes that were present in the food that was eaten and (b) on the proteins in the food?

There is however a bacterial species in the phylum Proteobacteria (Figure 2.3), *Helicobacter pylori*, which is an acidophile and can live very successfully in the human stomach. *H. pylori* possesses four to six flagella which allow it to burrow through the mucous layer of the stomach and reach the stomach lining where it takes up residence. It is able to detect the local pH, which is somewhat higher (nearer to neutral) in the stomach lining, and if it senses that it is being carried nearer to the low pH (acidic) contents of the stomach, it uses its flagella to burrow deeper again. To survive the low pH, *H. pylori* produces an enzyme called urease. This breaks down a compound in the stomach called urea $(NH_2)_2CO$, along with water, to produce carbon dioxide (CO_2) and ammonia (NH_3).

Question 6.7

Write the word equation and the chemical equation for the breakdown of urea by urease.

Ammonia is an alkali which goes some way towards neutralising the stomach acid, benefiting the bacterium, but not the person, since it causes chronic inflammation of the stomach lining, a condition called gastritis. This can lead to stomach (gastric) ulcers and possibly even to stomach cancer. Antibiotics, usually a combination of amoxicillin and clarithromycin, together with another drug which temporarily prevents the stomach producing so much acid, are used to kill the bacteria and allow the stomach lining to recover. Although these have been generally effective, antibiotic-resistant strains of *H. pylori* have developed, requiring alternative treatment regimes.

In the environment, natural events such as volcanic eruptions can make areas acidic by producing acidic gases. Acidic conditions are also often caused by pollution. When coal, iron ore, copper ore, etc. are mined from the ground, surface water often enters the mine. While the mine is active, the water is routinely pumped out so it does not stay in contact with the rocks for long. However, once the mining ceases, and the pumping stops, the water accumulates underground. In many types of mine the surrounding rocks contain significant amounts of sulfide minerals which dissolve in water to produce sulfuric acid (H_2SO_4). This lowers the pH of the water significantly and can cause further dissolution of substances in the rocks. Eventually the water, with dissolved minerals, especially metals, as well as the acid, can accumulate in the mine to such an extent that it flows out and is referred to as acid mine drainage. Acid water can similarly be produced by the passage of rain water through spoil heaps around both active and closed mines. This acid water is extremely toxic to almost everything in the environment (Figure 6.10), but not, as you will probably now have come to expect, to all microbes.

Figure 6.10   Effect of acid drainage on the Rio Tinto (red river in English), in south-western Spain. Rio Tinto is very acidic and high in dissolved iron, which is caused by a history of mining in the region. Apart from microbes, no other organisms grow close to the river.

The microbe commonly found in acid mine water is the acidophile *Acidithiobacillus ferrooxidans* which uses iron or other metals as a source of energy and thus can induce further breakdown of the rocks and the release of more acid into the water. However, *A. ferrooxidans* can also be used in the extraction of metals such as copper, gold and uranium, which are present as sulfide ores in rocks. The traditional method for releasing such metals is by adding cyanide to the crushed ore and then chemically treating the liquid so produced to recover the metals. The cyanide is then recycled. However, since cyanide is so toxic, even the smallest spillage can cause major pollution. So more recently a method called bioleaching has been devised using *A. ferrooxidans*. The metal ores are crushed and then stored in heaps and the microbes are added. These grow on the surface of the crushed grains, releasing the metal from the sulfide ore by their activity. The process, using iron sulfide FeS_2 (pyrite) as the example of a metal ore, can be summarised by the following balanced chemical equation:

$$FeS_2 + 3O_2 + 2H_2O \longrightarrow Fe + 2H_2SO_4 + energy \qquad \text{(Equation 6.1)}$$

Question 6.9

Write the names of each of the five chemical substances below their chemical formula in Equation 6.1.

The process shown in Equation 6.1 is rather different from the process of aerobic respiration that is used by the many microbes that produce their energy in the same way as we do, by breaking down sugars, as summarised by Equation 4.4 in Chapter 4.

$$C_6H_{12}O_6 + 6O_2 \longrightarrow 6CO_2 + 6H_2O + energy \qquad \text{(Equation 4.4)}$$

Acidithiobacillus ferrooxidans uses the iron within the pyrite as a source of energy, in the same way that the sugar is used in aerobic respiration. Instead of the products being carbon dioxide and water, they are iron and sulfuric acid. Clearly, in order to survive using this method of energy production, *A. ferrooxidans* must be able to tolerate the acid which it produces. The liquid that runs off from the crushed ore will contain the iron, or other metal, and the acid, and can then be treated to recover the metal. The microbes remain attached to the particles of crushed ore, and some of this ore, with the microbes attached, can be used to seed new heaps of ore. At least 25% of the world's copper needs are now met by bioleaching, so the copper core in the electrical wiring in your home may have been produced by the action of microbes. Copper and many other metals are, however, toxic to many microbial (and other) cells.

■ Copper ions can bind to both DNA and to amino acids. How might this binding affect microbes exposed to high copper concentrations?

☐ Binding of copper to DNA might prevent the cell copying its DNA prior to cell division (Section 1.6). If copper binds to some of the amino acids as well, then this might directly affect the production of the proteins and/or their function. Since enzymes are proteins, the activity of these will be affected too and the cells would probably not function correctly.

As well as copper, many other metals which are toxic to cells, such as cadmium, lead, manganese, mercury, nickel, and zinc (often known as heavy metals) have industrial uses. Their production, use and subsequent disposal, can create high concentrations in the environment and microbes have been found living in such contaminated areas. Such microbes are termed metallophiles. For example, a Gram-negative, non-spore-forming bacillus *Cupriavidus metallidurans* was originally isolated in 1976 from a tank polluted with high concentrations of zinc and several other heavy metals. It has subsequently been found growing naturally in volcanic environments which often have high concentrations of metals.

■ *Cupriavidus metallidurans* can spread its metal resistance to other microbes. Where in the microbe are these metal resistance genes likely to be located?

☐ Genes that can be transferred from one microbe to another, are usually present on the plasmids (Section 5.4.1).

In fact, there are two different relevant plasmids in the *Cupriavidus metallidurans* CH34 strain. One plasmid carries the genes that are required for resistance against high levels of cobalt, zinc and cadmium while the other has genes that confer resistance against high levels of cobalt and nickel. Microbes like this may be used in the future to decontaminate polluted industrial sites, a process termed bioremediation. The microbes' high resistance to metals allow them to accumulate or change the characteristics of metals, making them less available to cause damage to other living organisms, such as plants.

At the other extreme from acidic environments are those that are very alkaline, such as the soda lakes in the African Rift Valley. These are usually lakes in enclosed valleys where water enters from rain and streams draining surrounding carbonate rocks, but leaves only by evaporation. They are very salty (see Section 6.5), as well as having a high pH.

It was noted earlier that volcanoes can be the locations of very acidic environments. High pH (above 7) can also be associated with some other volcanic areas, and some thermal pools near volcanoes can reach pH values of above 10. Processes such as cement and paper manufacturing produce alkaline environments around them. In all these environments, alkalinophiles are found, many belonging to the *Bacillus* genus.

6.4   Microbes in high pressure environments

As well as microbes that can cope with extremes of temperature and pH, there are some microbes that have to cope with extremes of pressure. Microbes living in the surface waters of the world's oceans experience pressures only slightly higher than those of the atmosphere above, but microbes have been found at a depth of about 10 000 m in the Mariana Trench in the Pacific Ocean. Pressure at depth in the oceans is often measured relative to the atmospheric pressure at the surface which is defined as 1 atmosphere (1 atm) and increases by about 1 atmosphere for every 10 m of water depth.

■ How many atmospheres of pressure would be exerted on a microbe living in the Mariana Trench at a depth of 10 000 m?

☐ Each 10 m increase in depth is equivalent to a rise in pressure of 1 atm, so at 10 000 m, the pressure would be equivalent to about 1000 atmospheres.

Microbes that grow optimally under high pressure are called barophiles (weight-loving) and, as usual, there are groups which thrive at different optimum pressures. They are sometimes called piezophiles, which means 'pressure-loving'. Moderate barophiles grow optimally at 400 atm, while extreme barophiles grow optimally above 700 atm and cannot grow below 500 atm. The ranges of these organisms are shown in Figure 6.11.

■ How would you interpret the description 'barotolerant' as applied to a microbe?

☐ It means that the microbe can tolerate high pressure, but does not need high pressure to grow.

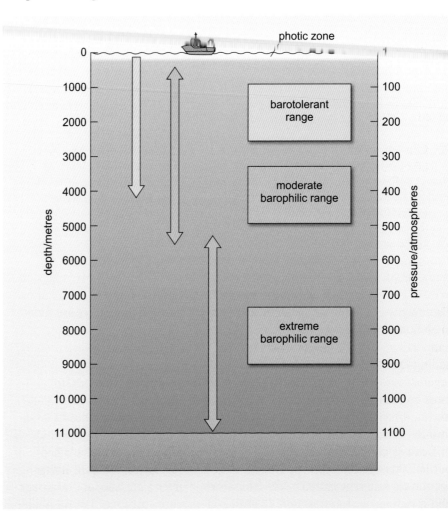

Figure 6.11   The range of depths and pressures in the deep ocean environment in which groups of microbes can live. Light penetrates only a small region below the surface layer, creating a photic zone where photosynthetic microbes are found. Barotolerant microbes, barophilic microbes and extreme barophiles are restricted to the depth ranges shown by the arrows in the diagram.

The main effect of pressure on microbes is on the plasma membrane. Pressure squashes the membrane, pushing the fat molecules closer together.

Question 6.9

Based on the information about the composition of plasma membranes in Section 6.2.1, would you expect the plasma membranes of barophiles to contain more or less saturated fats than those of similar species living near the ocean surface?

In order to study extremophiles in detail, they need to be cultured in the laboratory by techniques described in *Laboratory methods 6.1*.

Laboratory methods 6.1   Growing extremophiles

As extremophiles prefer to live in extreme conditions, culturing them in the laboratory can be challenging. Many extremophiles can be grown by changing or supplementing the media they are grown in to create conditions favourable for their growth. For example, acidophiles can be grown in media where acid is used to create a low pH. The iron-oxidising bacterium *Acidithiobacillus ferrooxidans*, which grows in mine spoil and is an acidophile, prefers to grow at a pH below 3.0 and hydrochloric acid is added to its culture media.

■ Can you suggest how a psychrophile can be encouraged to grow in the laboratory?

☐ Psychrophiles prefer to grow at low temperatures, so no special additions are needed to the culture media in which they grow. Instead the temperature of the media must be kept low and this is usually accomplished by placing the Petri dishes in a standard refrigerator in the laboratory. They often grow much more slowly than other bacteria, so patience is needed.

Thermophiles and hyperthermophiles are grown at high temperatures in an incubator, either in broth or on types of agar that can tolerate high temperatures. Metallophiles can also be grown in the laboratory by adding metals at high concentration to their media. The most difficult organisms to grow are the barophiles, as all manipulations and culturing must be done at high pressure. This is accomplished using pressure vessels in which spreading of plates and collecting of colonies can be done through a viewing window into the vessel. Samples of barophiles are also difficult to collect since they must be retrieved from the deep subsurface of the Earth by drilling or by collecting them from the deep oceans using robotic exploration vehicles sent from ships, and then kept under pressure at all times.

One of the more interesting groups of organisms to try to cultivate are the Archaea as they represent some of the microbes most tolerant of extremes. Archaea have membranes that are different from the bacteria in that their chemical composition makes them tolerant to many antibiotics used to kill bacteria. By adding antibiotics to the media, bacteria can be preferentially killed allowing Archaea to grow. If the medium is also held at a high temperature, thermophilic Archaea will reproduce quickly and so can be isolated. As an aside, no Archaea are known that cause human disease, so the antibiotic resistance of Archaea has no implications for human health. Why this is so is not known. It is possible that most Archaea, being extremophiles, have never had the chance to evolve to cause disease in humans, although an increasing number of Archaea are also being found to live in normal environments, so the lack of human diseases caused by Archaea remains something of a mystery.

Because of the difficulties in growing extremophiles it is not uncommon for particular microbiology laboratories to specialise in studying only a limited number of extremophile species and to develop significant expertise in the culturing and isolation of them.

6.5   Microbes in very salty environments

When water first accumulated on the surface of the Earth, sodium ions were dissolved out of the rocks of the Earth's crust and chloride ions were added from gases like hydrogen chloride, which were emitted from volcanoes (look back to Box 4.2 for basic information about ions). Together these two ions, sodium Na^+ and chloride Cl^-, made the water salty. Subsequently other ions, such as potassium, calcium and magnesium, have been added to seawater as they have been dissolved by streams and rivers and carried down to the sea. And carbonate ions have been added by carbon dioxide from the atmosphere dissolving in the seawater. So if seawater is evaporated, the solid left is mostly sodium chloride (common salt, or table salt) but other salts such as calcium carbonate and magnesium chloride are present too. Although oceans are salty, there are so many microbes (and other organisms) living in them, that seawater is considered to be a normal environment. However, there are environments much saltier (more saline) than the open oceans, and these are the ones that contain the salt-loving microbes, the halophiles.

■ From general knowledge, do you know any areas of water which are more salty than the oceans?

☐ You may have thought of the Dead Sea, and there are also salt lakes in Utah, USA, in the Andes and elsewhere.

These environments are particularly salty because they are in hot areas where the rate of evaporation is high. As the water evaporates, the ions dissolved in it from surrounding rocks are left behind and so the water becomes increasingly salty – its salinity increases.

■ Why will high salinity be a problem for the microbes? You may find it useful to look back to the ways of preserving food in Section 4.1.1.

☐   Salt tends to draw water out of food, and would draw it out of microbes too, so that the microbes would be deprived of sufficient water for the normal metabolic reactions to go on inside them.

The process of water moving through a selectively permeable membrane, such as the plasma membrane of a microbe, from a less salty area to a more salty area is called osmosis. In fresh water, the inside of a microbe is more salty than the outside, and so water would tend to move (diffuse) into the microbe (Figure 6.12a). If the outside is more salty, then water moves from inside the microbe to the outside (Figure 6.12b) and the microbe becomes dehydrated, unless it has some special mechanism to prevent the dehydration. In fact, osmosis does not depend only on the presence of ions which form salts; dissolved molecules like sugar can play a similar role (which is why fruit can be preserved by adding sugar to make jam – see Section 4.1.1). Water diffuses through a selectively permeable membrane from a region of low concentration of dissolved molecules to a region of high concentration.

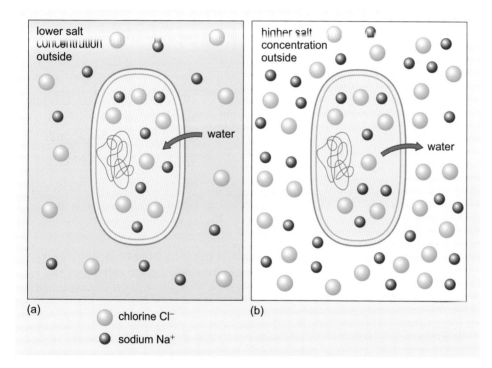

chlorine Cl⁻

sodium Na⁺

Figure 6.12   The process of osmosis occurs through the selectively permeable membrane of a microbe. (a) When a microbe is in a fluid which has a lower salt concentration than the inside of the microbe, water will diffuse through the membrane into the cell. (b) When a microbe is in a fluid which has a higher salt concentration than the inside of the microbe, water will diffuse through the membrane out of the cell.

Halophilic microbes have evolved two slightly different ways of coping with the dehydration that would naturally occur in very salty water. The main group of halophiles use some of their energy to make extra molecules in their cells so that overall the concentration of molecules inside the cell is equal to or greater than in the very salty water outside. With this adaptation, osmosis works in the microbe's favour, i.e. water is drawn in and dehydration is avoided. The extra molecules can be different kinds of sugars and amino acids (the building blocks of proteins) and there are other less well-known substances too. Three other small groups of microbes, not closely related to one another, use a different method. They selectively accumulate sufficient potassium ions (K^+) to make the concentration of dissolved molecules similar inside the cell to the salty water outside. However, since potassium ions are similar to the sodium ions (Na^+) of salt itself, significant modifications have first to be made to the enzyme systems and the other proteins in the cells to allow them still to function as the potassium ions will interact with the enzyme's amino acids. Another problem in very salty conditions is that plasma membranes are affected and so some halophiles have rather different fats in their membranes from those described in Box 6.2, such that the membranes are only stable in salty conditions.

■ Thinking just about osmosis, what would happen to a halophilic microbe that was placed in fresh water?

☐ The inside of the microbe would have a much higher concentration of dissolved molecules than the outside water, and so water would rush into the microbe. The microbe cell would then be forced to expand and after a few minutes, it might burst.

Halophilic communities are found not only in the salty lakes and seas mentioned above, but also in human-made ponds in hot countries, called solar saltern crystalliser ponds, into which salty water (often seawater but not always) is pumped and then allowed to evaporate, so that the salt can be harvested for commercial uses. An example of such ponds in California, USA, is illustrated in Figure 6.13.

Figure 6.13   An aerial view of a solar saltern crystalliser pond in San Francisco Bay, USA.

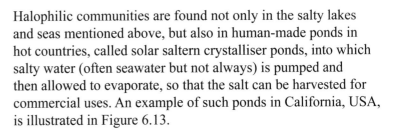

Question 6.10

Based on what you read about psychrophiles in Section 6.2.1, how could you explain the colours seen in the salt ponds in Figure 6.13?

As mentioned in Chapter 4, salt has been used in the food industry for centuries to protect food from spoilage. Although this process is indeed effective at killing most microbes, halophilic microbes have been isolated from salt-treated food and in some cases the shelf-life of the food is limited owing to microbial spoilage by halophilic microbes. Finally, the most surprising place where halophilic microbes have been found is in the nasal cavities of desert iguanas. Because they live in a very dry environment, these lizards often need to get rid of salts, to prevent their bodies becoming too salty. They do so by producing a very salty secretion from their noses and it is in these secretions that a halophilic species of *Bacillus* has been found.

6.6   Microbes and radiation

Perhaps one of the most extraordinary discoveries in microbiology was that some microbes are resistant to levels of ionising radiation which would rapidly be fatal to other living things. Ionising radiation is a term that covers a range of high-energy particles that can cause damage to biological material. There are not too many natural environments on the Earth that have high radiation levels, except for some natural deposits of uranium, but there are many human-made environments that have high levels of radiation, such as nuclear power plants and areas in hospitals where radiotherapy is administered to cancer patients, for example. Radiotherapy is used because it is a way of killing cancer cells. The main effect that it has is to damage the cell's genome by breaking up the molecules of DNA into small fragments.

■   Why might damaging the DNA in this way prove fatal for a cell?

☐   DNA carries the code for all the proteins, including the enzymes, that the cell needs to make. If the DNA is broken up, it cannot function properly to make the proteins, and the cell will die.

It would be reasonable to expect that microbes would be killed in the same way by ionising radiation. Additionally, because such radiation is relatively rare in the natural environment, it would be surprising if any microbes had evolved with a particular radiation tolerance. However, in 1956, the first radio-tolerant microbe was found during an experiment to discover if canned food could be sterilised, i.e. if all the microbes could be killed, by exposing it to a type of radiation known as gamma radiation. A tin of meat was exposed to a dose of such radiation that was thought to kill all known forms of life. However, this did not stop bacterial decay of the meat, and subsequently a bacterium named *Deinococcus radiodurans* (meaning 'marvellous berry that withstands radiation') was isolated from the meat (Figure 6.14). Subsequent studies showed that it could resist a dose of radiation at least 500 times the lethal dose for a human.

When *D. radiodurans* is exposed to high levels of radiation, its DNA is severely damaged, as expected. However, it survives and continues to grow. Its secret seems to be that it has several copies of its genome in each cell. This means that if particular genes are damaged, other copies of the same gene can continue to function. It also has very efficient DNA-repair mechanisms, which can match the shattered pieces of DNA and splice them back together again in the correct way so that they continue to function. It seems that its special systems evolved, not to resist radiation, but to resist drying out (desiccation) which can have a similar effect on DNA. *D. radiodurans* is very resistant to desiccation and also to chemicals which would kill most other species. So it is not just an extremophile, but, using the prefix poly-, which means 'many', it could be called a polyextremophile.

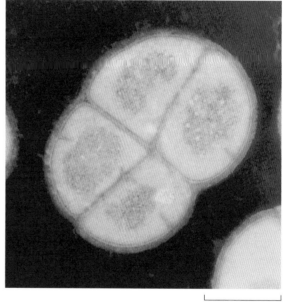

1 µm

Figure 6.14   False-colour TEM of *Deinococcus radiodurans*.

6.7   Polyextremophiles

Polyextremophiles are the 'superheroes' of the microbial world. They are microbes that are able to live in environments that are extreme in more than one way, such as a hot alkaline spring with both high temperature and high pH.

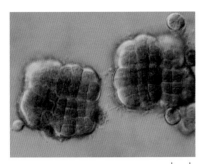

L────┘
10 μm

Figure 6.15 False-colour light micrograph of the polyextremophile *Chroococcidiopsis*.

Chroococcidiopsis (Figure 6.15) is a desiccation-tolerant, radiation-resistant cyanobacterium that is found in many places on Earth. It has been isolated from hot springs, hypersaline habitats, hot arid deserts and the frozen wastes of Antarctica. In many of these places, it is the only living organism present. *Chroococcidiopsis* can be present as individual cells or it may occur in colonies, as shown in Figure 6.15. In the natural environment it often lives in cavities in rocks, or forms biofilms at the rock–soil interface. It copes with the stress of desiccation by developing a special thick outside coat, within which it can survive for many years until conditions improve. This is similar to a spore, but it is not quite as hardy. *Chroococcidiopsis* cells which have been dried for five years have started growing when provided with appropriate conditions again in the laboratory. Some species of *Chroococcidiopsis* have been found living amongst the salt crystals in natural rock salt deposits.

■ Which adjectives would you use to describe *Chroococcidiopsis*?

☐ It is definitely a polyextremophile. It is radio-tolerant (resistant to radiation) and halophilic (salt-loving). It can cope with hot and cold environments and so is thermotolerant and psychrotolerant. It is also tolerant to drying out.

Activity 6.2   Using the digital microscope to examine extremophilic photosynthetic microbes

The estimated time for this activity is 30 minutes.

In this activity you will use the digital microscope to look at some other cyanobacteria that live in the extreme environment of the coastal cliffs in the UK.

You will find the detailed instructions for this activity in the Activities section of the course website.

Having looked at microbes which live in extreme environments, you will return in the next chapter to some much more down-to-earth microbes that nevertheless play vital roles in the survival of life on Earth.

Question 6.11

In no more than a couple of sentences for each, explain the relevance of the following terms to a discussion on extremophiles:

(a) *Taq* polymerase

(b) alkalinophile

(c) phospholipid bilayer

(d) carotenoid pigment

(e) bioleaching.

Question 6.12

Extreme conditions affect all parts of microbes to some extent. Put ticks in the appropriate boxes in Table 6.2 to indicate the main parts of the cell that would be affected by each of the extreme conditions.

Table 6.2 Parts of the cell affected by extreme conditions.

Part of cell	Extremes of:				
	temperature	pH	pressure	salinity	radiation
DNA					
enzymes (proteins)					
plasma membrane					
cytosol					

Summary of Chapter 6

- Many environments that would be unbearable to other living organisms are places where microbes can survive and in some cases, thrive.

- Extreme conditions that microbes can grow in include temperature extremes, extremes of pressure and pH, high heavy-metal concentrations and high salinity. Each extreme requires certain specific adaptations to the cell's structure or its components. One of the most important of these is having enzymes that can carry out biochemical reactions in the cells in spite of extremes.

- The composition of a microbe's plasma membrane can affect its tolerance to extremes of temperature and pressure.

- Some microbes can tolerate multiple extremes and are known as polyextremophiles. Many natural environments subject microbes to more than one extreme condition.

Chapter 7
Microbes run the world

7.1 Introduction

In this course so far, you have been introduced to most of the roles that microbes play.

■ Thinking back over what has been covered, list the positive and negative impacts of microbes in the world.

☐ Here are some things you may have thought of:

Positive: they help in the production of many sorts of human food and drink (Chapter 4); they help in the sequencing of genomes and the study of life in extreme environments (Chapters 3 and 6); they are important in the treatment of sewage (Chapter 4); they can be used to produce pharmaceuticals (Chapter 4); they help us to digest food (Chapter 5).

Negative: they cause many diseases (Chapters 1, 3 and 5); they cause the decay of human food (Chapter 4).

You may or may not feel that microbes overall do more harm than good to the human race. However, they have one vital role in the environmental processes that allow all life to continue on Earth. This role, which has only been touched on so far, leads to the title of this chapter. Because of their crucial role in the cycling of many important chemical elements essential for other forms of life, it is no exaggeration to say that 'Microbes run the world'. In relation to the movement of elements around the our planet, it is useful to divide the Earth up into four spheres – the atmosphere, the biosphere (all living things), the hydrosphere (oceans, rivers, lakes, ice, etc.) and the geosphere (soil, rocks, etc.).

■ Name at least one substance that humans need from each of these spheres to live in modern society.

☐ From the atmosphere, we need oxygen to breathe. We get our food – all our organic compounds – from the biosphere. The hydrosphere provides water, for drinking, washing, sanitation, etc. The geosphere provides ore which can be processed into metals, fossil fuels such as coal and oil, and it is the place where the plants, which we use for food, can grow.

Very many chemical elements move naturally between one of these spheres and another, and often between parts of the same sphere, known as reservoirs, such as between the surface ocean and the deep ocean. If they did not, then the reservoirs would, over time, become depleted in particular elements. For example, if the oxygen in the atmosphere was gradually removed by the process of respiration and none was ever returned, then eventually the level would fall so much that those organisms in the biosphere dependent on oxygen for respiration would all die out. Different chemical elements move between the reservoirs in the different spheres at different rates. For example, oxygen cycles rapidly between the atmosphere and biosphere, whereas carbon trapped in carbonate rocks such as limestone, cycles only very slowly back from the geosphere into the hydrosphere, when the rock dissolves in water. This chapter concentrates on the role played by microbes in the cycling of a number of important elements between the various reservoirs. All of life as we know it depends on the element carbon (C). Leaving aside water, the vast majority of the other molecules in living things, known as organic molecules, contain carbon and so the carbon cycle is the first to be considered.

7.2   Microbes and the carbon cycle

7.2.1   Overview of the carbon cycle

Activity 7.1   Reading Table 7.1

The estimated time for this activity is 15 minutes.

There is a great deal of information in Table 7.1. This activity takes you through its more important features and gives you general advice about reading tables of data.

Table 7.1 Major reservoirs of the global carbon cycle, showing the amount and major form of carbon, the percentage of the global total mass of carbon and the mean residence time of carbon for each reservoir.

Reservoir	Mass of carbon/10^{12} kg	Major form of carbon	Percentage of total mass of carbon	Mean residence time/years
living things	560	organic carbon (living)	0.0011	4.7
atmosphere	800	carbon dioxide	0.0016	3.6
soil	1500	organic carbon (non-living)	0.003	25
surface ocean	1000	dissolved carbon	0.002	7.9
deep ocean	37 000	dissolved carbon	0.07	1000
ocean sediment	3000	carbonate carbon; organic carbon	0.006	5000
rock	50 000 000	carbonate carbon; organic carbon	99.91	200 000 000

■ Whenever you meet a new table, the first question you should ask yourself is 'What is this table about?' Where do you find that information?

☐ The information you need is in the caption – 'Table 7.1 Major reservoirs …' etc.

■ The caption gives you some information, but then you need to look at the headings of the columns and the rows. Start with the first column (on the left-hand side). Which reservoirs belong to each of the four spheres listed earlier?

☐ The first column is headed Reservoir and the column gives a list of each of the different places where carbon might be found. These names form the headings for the rows. The living things row belongs to the biosphere. The atmosphere is straightforward. The soil, ocean sediment and rock belong to the geosphere. The surface ocean and deep ocean belong to the hydrosphere.

■ You may have noticed that freshwater bodies (lakes, rivers, etc.) are not included in this table. Why might that be?

☐ The amount of carbon that they hold is extremely small compared with the other reservoirs listed here, and so, since the caption refers to 'Major reservoirs', freshwater reservoirs are omitted, but they are part of the hydrosphere.

■ Now look at the numbers in the 'Mass of carbon' column. How many times more carbon is there in the ocean sediment than the surface ocean? Roughly, how many times more is in the deep ocean compared with the ocean sediment?

☐ There is 3 times more carbon in the ocean sediment than in the surface ocean (3000 units compared with 1000) and there is over 10 times more carbon in the deep ocean compared with the ocean sediment (37 000 units compared with 3000). You may have calculated that more accurately as 12 times more, but that is not necessary when making a rough comparison of values.

■ To identify the actual amounts of carbon involved, you need to look at the units which belong to each value in the table. As long as the units are the same for each value, the table looks much less cluttered if these are put in the heading of the column. What would the amount of carbon in living things be, including the units?

☐ The value is 560 and the units are 10^{12} kg, so the whole amount would be written as 560×10^{12} kg, which would be spoken as '560 times 10 to the twelve kilograms', where 10^{12} means 10 multiplied by itself 12 times, which would be 10 000 000 000 000, or 10 thousand billion. If you would like to understand more about expressing large numbers using powers-of-ten notation, you should access Section 7 of the Maths skills ebook on the course website. However, for the purposes of this course, it is sufficient to realise that 10^{12} kg is an unimaginably huge amount of carbon. By writing the numbers this way, with the same units for all the values in the table, it is possible to compare the values much more easily than if each number was written out in full.

■ The next column is headed 'Major form of carbon' and gives the form in which carbon is present in each reservoir. There will be more about that later. This is followed by a column headed 'Percentage of total mass of carbon'. What does this heading mean in relation to the values in the column? Where is the vast majority of carbon found?

☐ The values indicate the percentage of the total mass of carbon that is found in each of the reservoirs. So if you add up these values, you should find that the result is very close to 100%. The vast majority of carbon, actually 99.91%, is found in rocks, as carbonate carbon and organic carbon.

■ Now look at the heading of the final column and explain what the values in this column mean.

☐ This column gives the mean residence time in years, that is, the time on average that a carbon atom spends in each of the reservoirs. You will notice that carbon stays in the living things, atmosphere, soil and surface ocean reservoirs for 25 years or less. For example, a carbon atom remains in a living thing for 4.7 years on average. If the carbon atom is in a leaf, it may remain there for only a few weeks or months; if it is in a piece of wood, it may remain there for decades or even centuries. Carbon remains in the deep ocean, ocean sediment and rock reservoirs for between 1000 years and 200 million years.

Currently, microbes are mostly in the living-things reservoir and the surface oceans, but you may be surprised to know that most of the carbon in the ocean sediment and rock reservoirs is there because of the action of microbes, as you will learn later.

7.2.2 Microbes in the surface oceans

The surface ocean is that part of the ocean down to about 100–200 m depth and is the layer that can be penetrated by sunlight (the photic zone in Figure 6.11) and is mixed by wind and wave action which allows air to come into contact with water in this layer.

■ Look back to Table 7.1. What is the major form of carbon in the surface oceans?

☐ It is dissolved carbon.

Dissolved carbon is in the form of carbon dioxide CO_2, which is soluble in water. When some is removed, more dissolves, so that the amount present remains roughly constant.

Some carbon in the surface oceans exists as organic carbon in the small, mostly microscopic, free-floating organisms which live in the surface waters of the oceans. These are called plankton, divided into phytoplankton, which photosynthesise like plants, and zooplankton which obtain their food by other means. Phytoplankton, mostly cyanobacteria and single-celled algae, contain the green pigment chlorophyll and remove CO_2 from the water for use in photosynthesis (Equation 1.4). There are about 5000 species of phytoplankton whose total mass is greater than that of all the marine animals put together.

DM Activity 6.2

■ Which of the phytoplankton are eukaryotes and which are prokaryotes, and what is the difference between them? You may find it useful to look back to the phylogenetic tree of life in Figure 2.3.

☐ The cyanobacteria are prokaryotes, with a circular loop of DNA in the cytosol of the cells, while the algae are eukaryotes where the DNA molecules are present in the form of chromosomes stored in the nucleus of each cell.

Calculations indicate that photosynthesis by microbes in the oceans is responsible for about one-half of the photosynthesis performed on Earth today, making the oceans just as important as land plants in removing carbon dioxide from the atmosphere and fixing it into organic material. Figure 7.1 is a satellite image of the Earth showing the areas where most of the photosynthesis is occurring.

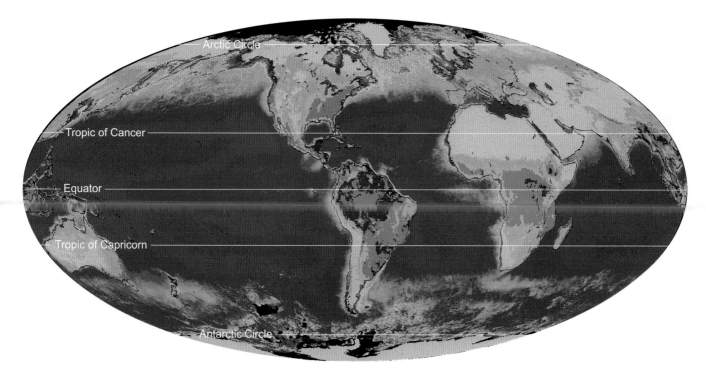

Figure 7.1 Satellite image of the Earth showing the concentration of chlorophyll on land and in surface waters, and therefore the regions where most photosynthesis is occurring. On land the highest concentrations are in dark green. In the oceans the highest concentrations are bright red, followed by yellow, green and blue, with the lowest concentrations being purplish-red.

Question 7.1

(a) Identify on Figure 7.1 the three major land areas where there is the greatest concentration of chlorophyll, and so where most photosynthesis is occurring on land.

(b) From your general knowledge, what sort of vegetation is present in these areas?

(c) Contrary to what you might have expected, chlorophyll, and therefore photosynthesis, is not evenly spread throughout the oceans. Can you suggest any possible reasons for this uneven distribution?

To be able to photosynthesise effectively, phytoplankton need to be able to float close to the surface during the day. Some cyanobacteria have gas bubbles (vacuoles) in their cells, which make them buoyant. Many of the algae produce distinctive and exquisitely beautiful projections from their cells, constructed of calcium carbonate ($CaCO_3$) or silica. The purpose of these structures is still highly controversial, but one proposal is that they might be used by the microbe to become heavier and so sink in the water to regions where there may be more nutrients. They may also have a role in support and in defence from predators that might otherwise eat them. Figure 7.2 shows some examples of these phytoplankton. Diatoms and dinoflagellates (Figure 7.2a) are more common in temperate and cold oceans, while coccolithophores (Figure 7.2b) are more common in tropical seas.

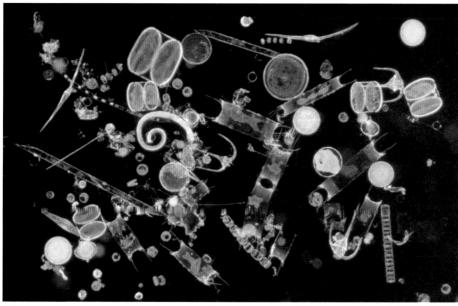
(a)

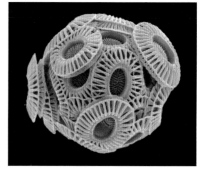
(b)

Figure 7.2   (a) A collection of phytoplankton, mainly diatoms and dinoflagellates. The diatoms include elongate and round species and some that form chains. The small, pale algae are dinoflagellates, as are the distinctive ones with three spines, which belong to the genus *Ceratium*. The field of view is 1.25 mm across. (b) A specimen of the coccolithophore *Emiliania huxlei*, showing the tiny plates of calcium carbonate, called coccoliths, which surround the algal cell. The coccolithophore is about 5 µm across.

■   If it were possible to follow a carbon atom, taken in as a molecule of carbon dioxide by a coccolithophore, it could later be found in two quite different sorts of compounds. What are they?

☐   The carbon can be converted into organic compounds: carbohydrates initially in photosynthesis and then into other organic molecules, such as proteins and fats needed by the algal cell. Alternatively, the carbon could be used in producing a molecule of calcium carbonate, to build one of the coccoliths (tiny plates surrounding the cell).

The phytoplankton are called autotrophs or primary producers, since they are at the bottom of the food chain. They use carbon dioxide from the air and fix the carbon into organic compounds that are then available as food for other organisms in the biosphere. The organic compounds in phytoplankton can be used as food by zooplankton. The zooplankton may either prey on living phytoplankton, or other zooplankton, or consume their dead remains. The zooplankton are heterotrophs, or consumers. As well as microbes, the zooplankton include adults of small marine invertebrates (animals without backbones, such as copepods, like tiny shrimps) and larvae of many other marine invertebrates (starfish, crabs, etc.). Amongst these zooplankton microbes are bacteria and some protozoa.

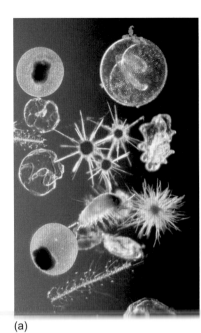

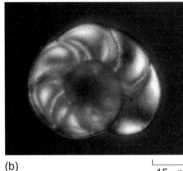

(a)

(b)

15 μm

Figure 7.3 (a) A group of planktonic organisms, mainly zooplankton. In the centre of the image is a group of spiny radiolarians. There are two hairy chains of diatoms, one on the far left and one at the bottom. The field of view is about 0.6 mm across. (For interest, below the radiolarians is the larva of a crustacean, possibly a crab, and below that, a female copepod with two egg sacs attached to the left, partly hidden by the crustacean larva. The two round objects on the left-hand side are fish eggs.) (b) A foraminiferan *Operculina ammanoides* with an elegant chambered shell.

The protozoa include foraminifera and radiolaria (Figure 7.3), which, like some of the phytoplankton, also have beautiful solid structures (sometimes called shells or tests), often made of calcium carbonate. They engulf their food using a technique similar to that used by phagocytic white blood cells (Section 5.3). Up to one-third of the prokaryotes in the oceans belong to a single bacterial species called *Pelagibacter ubique*, phylum Proteobacteria (Figure 7.4). On occasions, several million of these bacteria per millilitre of seawater have been found (1 teaspoon has a volume of about 5 millilitres) and this could make them the most common living thing and amongst the smallest of the free-living cells on Earth. They appear to play a major role in cycling not only carbon in the oceans, but also nitrogen and sulfur.

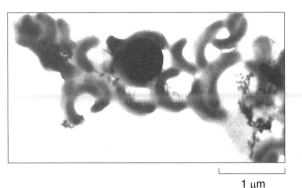

1 μm

Figure 7.4 A group of *Pelagibacter ubique* cells showing their boomerang shape.

Question 7.2

Figures 7.2, 7.3 and 7.4 show representatives of microbes found in the surface ocean plankton. Using the information in the figures and their captions, calculate the approximate sizes of the microbes in Table 7.2 and then complete the table. The size of the bubonic plague microbe *Yersinia pestis* is given for comparison.

Table 7.2 Comparison of the sizes of various microbes.

Microbe	Size/μm
radiolarian (include the spines)	
dinoflagellate (use *Ceratium* from Figure 7.2a)	
diatom (use a round one from Figure 7.2a)	
foraminiferan	
coccolithophore	
Yersinia pestis	1
Pelagibacter ubique	

Question 7.3

Study carefully Figure 7.5 and its caption. This illustrates some of the processes by which carbon is cycled by microbes in the surface ocean. In the following paragraph, all the names of compounds containing carbon atoms, namely carbon dioxide, sugar, organic compounds and calcium carbonate, have been removed. Replace them in the correct spaces to provide a concise written summary of the processes.

_____ dissolves from the atmosphere into seawater. It is taken in by phytoplankton and used in photosynthesis, and some of the carbon atoms become part of _____ molecules and then other _____ in the phytoplankton. Some are released back into the seawater as _____ in the respiration of the phytoplankton and eventually may return to the atmosphere. Other carbon atoms may become part of 'skeletons' made of _____ in some foraminifera and coccolithophores. The phytoplankton may be consumed by zooplankton, which use the _____ as food and release the carbon back into the seawater as _____ in respiration. Some of the carbon atoms from the food will become part of the _____ in the bodies of the zooplankton and others may be made into _____ if they have 'skeletons'. The phytoplankton or zooplankton that die are consumed by other zooplankton and the carbon atoms are recycled back into the water in _____. Small amounts of carbon, including the skeletons, escape the recycling and fall to the sea floor in small particles.

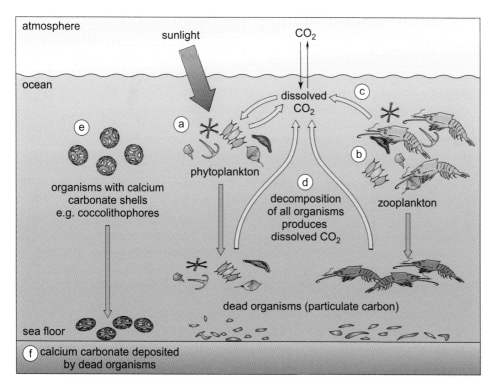

Figure 7.5   Pictorial representation of the cycling of carbon in the surface ocean by microbes. (a) Phytoplankton form organic carbon from water and dissolved carbon dioxide through photosynthesis. (b) Phytoplankton are consumed by zooplankton and other organisms. (c) These organisms respire giving out CO_2. Eventually they die and decompose. (d) Some of the carbon from dead and decomposing organisms is returned to dissolved carbon (here shown as CO_2) to be used again in photosynthesis. A small amount of organic carbon escapes dissolution and drifts downwards in small particles. Organisms with calcium carbonate skeletons such as coccolithophores (e) die and contribute their skeletons to deposits on the sea floor (f).

7.2.3   The carbon cycle on land

A similar fate awaits the carbon which is taken in as carbon dioxide by land plants. The organic compounds produced can be used by the plant for respiration or they can be eaten by animals, and used by them for respiration, both of which return the carbon dioxide to the air. Or the plants may die and the organic compounds will then become part of the soil on which the plant was growing.

■ What part can microbes, including fungi, then play in recycling the carbon?

☐ The microbes in the soil can use the dead plant material as their food and release the carbon dioxide back into the atmosphere.

In *Laboratory methods 7.1* you can read more about how fungi can be cultured in the laboratory so that microbiologists can investigate how they break down carbon compounds.

Laboratory methods 7.1   Cultivating fungi and preventing their growth

Fungi have many important roles to play in decomposition and other nutrient cycles in soil and water. It is therefore essential that microbiologists can isolate them in the laboratory to be able to study their biochemistry and the chemical transformations they make.

■ Can you think of a way in which fungi might be separated from bacteria? Rereading *Laboratory methods 6.1* will give you a clue.

☐ If antibiotics are added to a culture of microbes, the bacteria will be killed and the fungi will preferentially grow.

DM Activity 3.2

Most fungi are heterotrophs, which means that they use organic matter as a source of nutrients and energy. For this reason many of them are cultured on agar plates containing extracts of malt or other organic-rich substances. Fungi are also grown in nutrient broth made from extracts of beef.

Fungi present a particular problem for microbiologists because they form spores, which can very easily contaminate a laboratory and prove very difficult to remove once they become dispersed. As you read in Chapter 3 about the discovery of penicillin, fungi often cause contamination and frequently microbiologists are just as much at pains to stop fungi growing as to try and culture them.

■ What difference between fungi and bacteria might you try and exploit if you wanted to culture bacteria, but stop fungi from growing and contaminating your cultures?

☐ Fungi are eukaryotes and bacteria are prokaryotes and so any chemical that kills only eukaryotes could be used to prevent fungi from growing on agar plates which were intended for culturing bacteria.

One effective antifungal compound is cycloheximide which can be added to agar to stop the growth of fungi. Cycloheximide specifically inhibits the synthesis of proteins in eukaryotes by interfering with their ribosomes which take part in assembling proteins. Interestingly, the chemical was first discovered in a bacterium, *Streptomyces griseus*, and may be a type of natural antifungal compound used by bacteria to reduce competition for food in the natural environment.

There can be hundreds of millions of microbes of thousands of species in a teaspoon of soil. Some of them, along with some of the microbes in fresh water, are photosynthetic and take up carbon dioxide from the air to make sugar and other organic compounds, some of which they then use in respiration.

■ Are these microbes autotrophs or heterotrophs?

☐ They are autotrophs (primary producers) since they are at the bottom of the food chain.

Those microbes in the soil which use dead organic (plant and animal) material as food, using the processes of aerobic respiration, anaerobic respiration or fermentation (Equations 1.2, 1.3 and 1.4) are the heterotrophs.

7.2.4   The carbon cycle in the past

During some periods of Earth history, huge quantities of carbon dioxide have been removed from the atmosphere, and the carbon has been stored in a different form, buried within the Earth's crust. Some of that carbon is now found either on the surface of the Earth, or close enough to the surface for humans to be able to recover it.

■ From general knowledge, can you suggest what form that carbon is in now?

☐ You probably thought of it being present as coal and oil, and you may also have thought of natural gas and possibly carbonate rocks like limestone and chalk.

You may be surprised to know that the activities of microbes played an important part in the production of all but one of these substances.

The black organic material that we call coal is the result of compression of primitive trees and other vegetation which grew in vast ancient swamps about 300–350 million years ago, in what has been appropriately named the Carboniferous Period. When the plants died, their remains sank into the swampy water and were soon buried by sediments (sand and mud) and gradually compressed and heated by the mass of material on top of them. Chemical changes took place to convert the organic molecules into almost pure carbon in some sorts of coal. So coal was not formed by microbes.

However, most of the carbon that is now present in oil and natural gas was originally organic compounds in planktonic microbes that lived in the ancient oceans. When these microbes died, some of their remains sank to the sea floor (as shown in Figure 7.5). Over millions of years, they became covered with sediment and then compressed and buried deeper within the Earth's crust. Eventually, the heat and pressure at depth caused the organic matter to change chemically and oil and gas were formed. It is thought that a burial depth of about 5 km is needed for oil production. At greater depths, and so higher temperatures, gas, consisting of up to 90% methane, is formed. It is thought that most of our oil and gas has been produced from the remains of microbes that lived between 10 million and 160 million years ago.

Limestone and chalk are different forms of $CaCO_3$ that were also most commonly produced by marine plankton that accumulated on the sea floor, but this time it is their calcium carbonate 'skeletons' that have accumulated to form the rock. For example, the limestone that was used to build the pyramids in Egypt is made almost entirely of the skeletons of foraminifera (Figure 7.3b) and the chalk forming the White Cliffs of Dover is made of the coccoliths of coccolithophores (Figure 7.2b). The coccoliths that now make up the chalk cliffs accumulated at the bottom of a warm tropical sea about 136 million years ago, when the land was dominated by the dinosaurs. The whole sea floor as far as the Baltic Sea was covered with a very thick layer of coccoliths, to such an extent that even now there is more than 100 m thickness of chalk. Over time, the shifting land masses of Europe and changing sea levels brought the top of the chalk layer above sea level. Because the chalk is so soft, the ocean was able to erode away the land in places, and form what is now the English Channel.

7.2.5   Methanogens

There is one important type of autotrophic bacteria that has not yet been mentioned, a group of the Archaea called methanogens (Figure 7.6, and also see the phylogenetic tree in Figure 2.3). These obligate anaerobes take up carbon dioxide, combine it with hydrogen gas (H_2) and produce the gas methane (CH_4) and water in anaerobic conditions. The hydrogen gas is produced by certain other microbes when they break down organic material in anaerobic conditions.

■   Assuming that the organic material produced by methanogens is the sugar glucose $C_6H_{12}O_6$, write the chemical equation to show this reaction.

☐   The equation is:

$$CO_2 + H_2 \longrightarrow C_6H_{12}O_6 + CH_4 + H_2O$$
carbon dioxide + hydrogen $\longrightarrow$ glucose + methane + water

When this equation is balanced (with difficulty), it becomes:

$$12CO_2 + 36H_2 \longrightarrow C_6H_{12}O_6 + 6CH_4 + 18H_2O \qquad \text{(Equation 7.1)}$$

Methanogens most commonly live in anaerobic environments such as bogs and marshes, where the methane produced is called marsh gas. They also colonise landfill sites, where waste is buried, and often produce so much methane that the gas has to be allowed to escape to the atmosphere using open-topped vertical

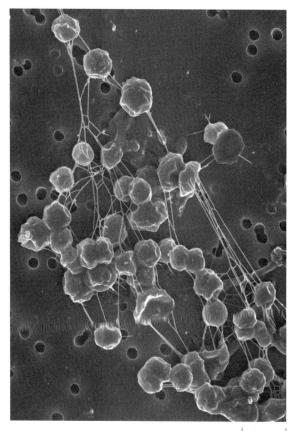

2 μm

Figure 7.6 A group of methanogens. The threads are secretions from the bacteria.

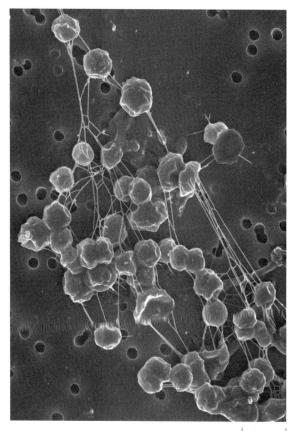

pipes sunk deep into the waste. Without these, there would be a risk of the gas building up sufficiently to cause an explosion. Methanogens are also found in the digestive system of many mammals, including ourselves, but particularly in ruminants, which add a significant amount of methane annually to the atmosphere. Some methanogens are found deep underground, where they use hydrogen that is produced by the breakdown of water by heat or by radiation. They have also been found in desert soil and in ice-core samples from a depth of 3 km in a Greenland glacier.

Question 7.4

Identify and correct any errors in the following statements about methanogens.

(a) Methanogens live in wet places and respire aerobically.

(b) Most natural gas found in conjunction with oil, has been produced by methanogens.

(c) All methanogens are extremophiles

(d) Methanogens perform a type of photosynthesis and therefore contain chlorophyll.

(e) Methanogens cause the decomposition of waste in landfill sites, producing methane.

Methanogens have been the subject of much study from scientists trying to understand the carbon cycle, because methane is about 20 times more potent as a greenhouse gas than is carbon dioxide. Both gases, along with others, absorb outgoing heat radiation from the Earth and trap it within the atmosphere, so warming the air and the ground below, resulting in detectable global warming. So any changes in the balance of microbes on the Earth that result in more methane being produced, could have important consequences for future climate. Understanding the carbon cycle and the role that microbes have in it is therefore vital to an understanding of the long-term climate of the planet.

7.2.6 Summary of the carbon cycle

Activity 7.2 The carbon cycle today

The estimated time for this activity is 30 minutes.

Figure 7.7 shows a pictorial representation of the carbon cycle as it is occurring now, including man's influence on it, with each of the transfers marked by a lettered arrow. Note that the tree symbol is representative of *all* photosynthesising organisms on land, including microbes. The respiration of animals on land makes only a small contribution to the overall carbon cycle so is not shown. The following questions test your understanding of those processes in which microbes are involved.

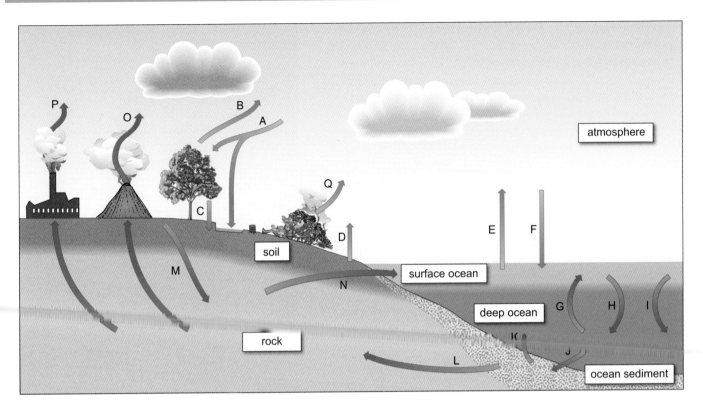

Figure 7.7 Pictorial representation of today's carbon cycle.

(a) Which arrow would include the intake of carbon dioxide in photosynthesis by microbes on land, such as those which live in the soil and in fresh water?

(b) Which arrow would include the various types of microbial respiration that release carbon dioxide into the air?

(c) Which arrow represents the breakdown of organic matter in the soil, mainly by the respiration of microbes, so releasing carbon dioxide back into the atmosphere?

(d) Identify the pair of arrows that represents (i) the uptake of carbon dioxide into the surface waters which is then taken in by photosynthetic microbes and converted into their carbon compounds (in the areas of sea coloured red, yellow and green in Figure 7.1) and (ii) the release of carbon dioxide from the surface waters of the oceans, due to the respiration of microbes and other organisms living there.

(e) There are two arrows which could represent the particles which are the remains of microbes, and which contain carbon, both organic carbon and carbon in the form of carbonate skeletons (coccoliths, etc.) falling towards the bottom of the ocean. Choose the one that is later alphabetically!

(f) Which arrow shows the microbial remains from (e) collecting on the ocean floor?

(g) Not all these particles remain on the ocean floor. Below a depth of about 4 km, depending on temperature, calcium carbonate particles dissolve in seawater. However the organic compounds remain. Which type of microbe would be involved in the breakdown of carbon in organic compounds on the floor of the deep oceans? Which arrow shows the results of their work?

(h) Arrow L indicates burial of those particles which are not broken down, and their eventual conversion into rock. What types of rock can be formed, and which other substances might be generated too?

(i) Describe a possible route for a carbon atom to travel from entering the leaf of a tree, which subsequently falls to the ground, into a limestone sediment (calcium carbonate) at the bottom of a shallow sea, including the molecule(s) in which the carbon is incorporated at each stage and the role of microbes in the processes. Your answer should be around 200–250 words.

Note: the remaining arrows in Figure 7.7 do not involve microbes directly, but to complete your understanding of the carbon cycle, you might like to see how many of these you can identify. You can check your answers with Table 7.6 in the answer to the activity which lists all the arrows and the processes they represent.

Activity 7.3 Fungi in the carbon cycle

The estimated time for this activity is 15 minutes.

In this activity you will watch a short video sequence about the role of fungi in the carbon cycle. The detailed notes for the activity, including some questions, are in the Activities section of the course website.

7.3 Microbes and the nitrogen cycle

Although carbon is an essential component of all the organic molecules in living things, many organic molecules also contain nitrogen atoms.

- ■ Which molecules have you already met that contain nitrogen? (Box 4.1 will be helpful.)

- ☐ Nitrogen atoms are present in all amino acids (for example glycine, whose formula is NH_2CH_2COOH). Amino acids are the sub-units which make up all proteins, including enzymes, without which life could not continue. (Chlorophyll also contains nitrogen atoms.)

The largest reservoir of nitrogen on Earth is found in the atmosphere, which is composed of about 78% nitrogen gas (N_2). Although every time we breathe in, our lungs receive a lot of nitrogen, it just leaves our body again when we breathe out. There is no way that humans can use the nitrogen in the air to make any of the nitrogen-containing compounds that we need. We need to obtain our nitrogen from the food that we eat, mostly the protein in our diet. However, nitrogen must somehow get into the biosphere from the atmosphere, so that it can then be cycled through organisms in the biosphere. And again, the organisms that can do this are the microbes. Some species of bacteria have the ability to take up nitrogen gas from the atmosphere and convert it into other compounds of nitrogen. This is called nitrogen fixation. There are many other processes involved in the cycling of nitrogen, and some areas are not yet fully understood, but microbes play a vital part in many of them. Although microbes are the only living organisms that can fix atmospheric nitrogen, smaller amounts of nitrogen can reach the ground through natural phenomenon. The electrical discharge in a flash of lightning causes nitrogen and oxygen to react in the atmosphere, to produce nitrogen oxides (NO and NO_2). Rain can wash these down to the Earth's surface soil to make nitrates, which act as fertiliser, though the amount is quite small. The other major pathway of nitrogen fixation on the Earth today is the result of human activity. Industrial methods have been developed for combining nitrogen gas (N_2) and hydrogen gas (H_2) to form ammonia (NH_3), which can then be used as plant fertiliser (and also to make explosives). This process, called the Haber–Bosch process after

German chemists Fritz Haber and Carl Bosch who later received Nobel Prizes for their work, today fixes as much nitrogen from the atmosphere as the natural nitrogen fixation process.

■ Write the chemical equation for the reaction between nitrogen and hydrogen to produce ammonia.

☐ The equation is:

nitrogen + hydrogen $\longrightarrow$ ammonia

$N_2 + H_2 \longrightarrow NH_3$

which when balanced becomes

$N_2 + 3H_2 \longrightarrow 2NH_3$ (Equation 7.2)

Box 7.1 introduces some other forms of nitrogen.

Box 7.1 Ions containing nitrogen

You may recall from Box 4.2 that water, H_2O, can split into two charged particles, H^+ and OH^-. These are ions, a hydrogen ion and a hydroxide ion, respectively. Acids in water can also split into ions, and it is the number of hydrogen ions produced that determines the acidity or pH of the solution. Other substances can form ions too, and there are several nitrogen-containing ions which are involved in the nitrogen cycle.

When ammonia dissolves in water, it forms ammonium hydroxide which then splits into ions by the following process:

$NH_3 + H_2O \longrightarrow NH_4OH \longrightarrow NH_4^+ + OH^-$

The NH_4^+ ion is called an ammonium ion.

■ Hydroxide (OH^-) ions are produced too. Will this result in an acid or an alkaline solution? Will the pH value of such a solution be high or low?

☐ As explained in Box 4.2, solutions containing more hydroxide ions than hydrogen ions are alkaline and they have pH values greater than 7. Assuming that the water originally had a pH of 7, there will be far more OH^- ions around than H^+ as a result of the introduction of ammonia so the solution will now be alkaline.

There are two other important ions containing nitrogen, called nitrate ions NO_3^- and nitrite ions NO_2^-. It is possible for microbes to convert ammonium ions into nitrite ions and then into nitrate ions, by some complex chemistry. Both nitrate and nitrite ions are soluble in water and common in soil. Most plants obtain the nitrogen needed for their proteins, and for making chlorophyll, by taking up nitrate or ammonium ions in the water absorbed through their roots. Farmers and gardeners often add fertiliser containing nitrates to the soil and for a particularly high dose of nitrogen, ammonium nitrate NH_4NO_3 can be used.

7.3.1   The nitrogen cycle on land

Figure 7.8 shows a diagrammatic representation of the nitrogen cycle on land and you will need to study it carefully and refer to it during this section.

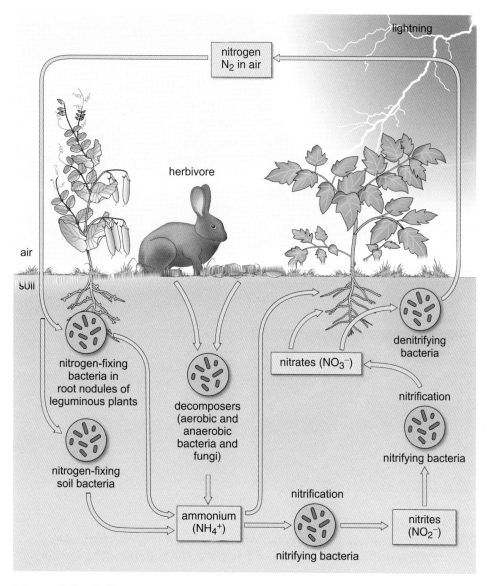

Figure 7.8   A diagrammatic representation of the nitrogen cycle on land (not to scale).

■   From Figure 7.8, identify the two places where nitrogen-fixing bacteria are found. Remember these are bacteria that can take up nitrogen from the atmosphere and fix it into their own nitrogen-containing molecules.

☐   There are nitrogen-fixing bacteria in the soil and in the root nodules of leguminous plants.

Leguminous plants, or legumes, are those that have seeds in pods, and belong to the family Fabaceae. Common examples are peas, beans, lentils, clover, lupins and peanuts. In nodules (small swellings) attached to their roots, they harbour colonies of bacteria belonging to the genus *Rhizobium*, phylum Proteobacteria (Figure 7.9). The bacteria benefit by being protected inside the nodules and they are provided with an anaerobic environment, which is essential for the functioning of those enzymes in the bacteria that are involved in nitrogen fixation. By having these nodules, the legumes can grow better in poor soils than can ordinary plants.

■ Explain why legumes are able to grow better in poor (unfertilised) soils than other plants.

☐ All plants need nitrogen to make important molecules, particularly chlorophyll and proteins. Most plants have to take up the nitrogen in the form of nitrate or ammonium from the soil. If the soil is short of these ions, and no fertiliser is added, the plants will not grow well. Legumes, on the other hand, have a readily available source of nitrogen fixed by the bacteria in their root nodules and this allows them to grow well and produce healthy green leaves.

This type of association between two organisms, the legumes and *Rhizobium*, where they co-exist and each gains an advantage from the other is called mutualism, a type of symbiosis where both partners gain from the relationship.

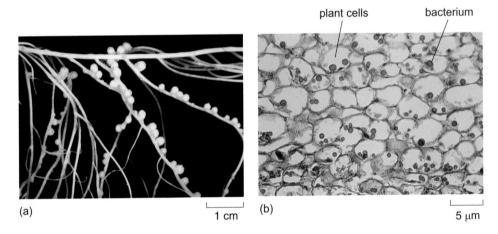

plant cells   bacterium

(a)   1 cm   (b)   5 µm

Figure 7.9   (a) Nodules containing nitrogen-fixing *Rhizobium* on the roots of a pea plant. (b) Light micrograph of the cells in the nodule of a legume root, colonised by *Rhizobium*. The bacteria appear as tiny round structures inside cells. The microscope slide has been stained red to show the structures more clearly.

Question 7.5

Explain why farmers often plant a crop of clover in one of their fields and then plough it into the soil at the end of the season.

Despite the fact that approximately 170 million tonnes of nitrogen are removed from the atmosphere each year by nitrogen-fixing bacteria, and fixed into nitrogen compounds in the soil, nitrogen still remains the nutrient which is most often deficient in the world's soils. Since many legumes are important agricultural crops, there has been considerable work on *Rhizobium* to try to increase the amount of nitrogen fixation that goes on. However, it has not proved easy because the bacteria are unable to fix nitrogen outside the nodules. Research also continues to try to transfer, by genetic engineering, the ability to fix nitrogen to bacteria which currently do not have the ability. Some cyanobacteria that live in the soil outside root nodules, are also able to fix nitrogen.

In Figure 7.8 the nitrogen-fixing soil bacteria are shown as being deep in the soil where there is less oxygen and that the nitrogen is first fixed into ammonium (NH_4^+) ions. These ions can be taken in and used directly by plants (and also by microbes, which of course need nitrogen for their own proteins, etc.). However, it is easy for ammonium ions to revert to ammonia gas and so the nitrogen would be lost again from the soil back to the atmosphere. Luckily, there are microbes which use the ammonium ions and convert them to more stable forms of nitrogen.

■ Use Figure 7.8 to identify which ions are produced in the next two stages and which microbes are involved.

☐ The first stage in the process of nitrification involves the conversion of ammonium ions to nitrite ions (nitrites) NO_2^- and the second involves the conversion of nitrite ions to nitrate ions (nitrates) NO_3^-. The microbes involved are called nitrifying bacteria.

Nitrifying bacteria use these inorganic nitrogen compounds as a source of energy and are therefore classed as chemolithotrophs (Section 6.2.2). Examples of nitrifying bacteria are *Nitrospira* and *Nitrobacter*, which are very common in soils, marine environments and freshwater lakes, wherever there is some ammonia to provide them with energy. When organisms die, and decay by the action of bacteria and fungi, the nitrogen present in their tissues is released into the soil as ammonium ions, which can then again be converted into nitrates and nitrites by nitrifying bacteria, so keeping the nitrogen cycling within the soil (Figure 7.8).

Unfortunately for the health of the soil and the plants growing in it, there are also bacteria which return nitrogen to the atmosphere. These are generally anaerobes, and live in waterlogged soils, or in ocean sediments. They are called denitrifying bacteria (Figure 7.8) and they transform nitrate back into nitrogen gas, thus completing the nitrogen cycle.

■ How might a farmer prevent this denitrifying activity which removes valuable nitrogen from the soil in the fields?

□ Improving the drainage of fields would help, as there would then be less waterlogged soil in which the denitrifying bacteria could live. Similarly, ploughing the fields would allow oxygen to reach deeper into the soil, again providing an inhospitable environment for the anaerobic bacteria.

But there is another complication. Some microbes have been found that can mix the products of the nitrogen cycle to carry out denitrification. These anammox (anaerobic ammonia oxidation) microbes combine ammonium ions with nitrate ions to form nitrogen gas. Like other denitrifying reactions, this occurs under anaerobic conditions in sediments in lakes and the ocean. It can be summarised by the following equation:

ammonium ions + nitrite ions $\longrightarrow$ nitrogen gas + water

$$NH_4^+ + NO_2^- \longrightarrow N_2 + 2H_2O$$ (Equation 7.3)

The significance of this reaction is that it increases the diversity of microbes that take part in denitrification and the range of environments in which this important process occurs. New research also shows how beneficial denitrifying bacteria may be for the environment. In 2005, German researchers discovered that the process of denitrification involves the use of nitrous oxide gas (N_2O) as one intermediate product to help microbes convert nitrate into nitrogen gas. Nitrous oxide is another greenhouse gas (slightly more effective than carbon dioxide, but less than methane). By converting nitrous oxide into nitrogen gas, these bacteria could be an important method for naturally removing nitrous oxide from the atmosphere and therefore could conceivably play a role in reducing global warming.

Question 7.6

List the five main types of bacteria that take part in the nitrogen cycle on land and state, in a sentence each, their roles.

7.3.2   The nitrogen cycle in the oceans

Not surprisingly, organisms in the oceans require nitrogen for their proteins just as much as land plants and animals do. Some nitrogen from the land reaches the sea via rivers and run-off from the land surface in the form of nitrates, and this tends to encourage growth of marine organisms around coasts. There are also nitrogen-fixing bacteria in the oceans which use nitrogen gas from the air, in a similar way to those in root nodules and in the soil, and fix it as ammonia. The nitrogen fixation occurs in special compartments within cells where the nitrogen-fixing enzymes are kept free of oxygen. Then nitrifying bacteria convert the ammonia to nitrite and then nitrate. The nitrates can be absorbed from the water by phytoplankton, which use the nitrogen atoms to make their essential organic molecules containing nitrogen (chlorophyll, proteins, etc.). The nitrogen becomes available to all species when the phytoplankton are eaten by zooplankton, which are in turn eaten by animals further up the food chain. After death, the particles of organic matter containing the nitrogen may fall through the water, and may either settle to the sea floor, where the nitrogen is out of reach, or upwelling ocean currents may carry them back to the surface where they can be broken down to ammonium ions again by decomposers in the zooplankton. As in the soil, denitrifying bacteria can convert nitrates in the water back into nitrogen gas which escapes to the atmosphere.

Question 7.7

Based on the paragraph above, complete the flow chart in Figure 7.10 showing the nitrogen cycle in the oceans by labelling the arrows with the organisms or processes involved.

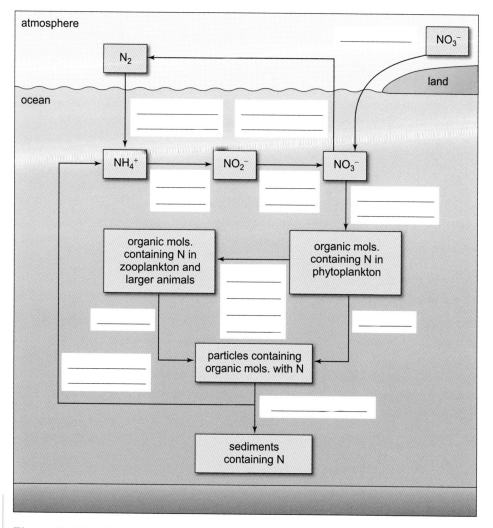

Figure 7.10   The nitrogen cycle in the oceans; to be completed in Question 7.7.

7.4   Microbes and the sulfur cycle

Sulfur is another vital element for living organisms, since it is needed – along with nitrogen and carbon – for the manufacture of some of the amino acids such as cysteine (Section 4.2), essential for some proteins. The most common form

Figure 7.11 Purple sulfur bacteria seen as a layer just below the surface of coastal sand where conditions are anaerobic. The plastic white spoon gives the scale.

of sulfur in the biosphere is sulfate ions (SO_4^{2-}). However, it also occurs in volcanic regions as the element sulfur (S), a yellowish powder, and as the gas hydrogen sulfide (H_2S) (Section 4.2) which smells of rotten eggs. It is also found in another gas in the air, sulfur dioxide (SO_2). This is one of the gases emitted when fossil fuels are burned, particularly in power stations. When dissolved in water, SO_2 can produce sulfuric acid which is responsible for the damage caused to the ecosystems of some lakes, and the damage to some forests, from so-called acid rain. Microbes play vital roles in the transformation of sulfur from one form to another.

Green and purple sulfur bacteria (Figure 7.11) (Proteobacteria) photosynthesise using hydrogen sulfide, H_2S, in place of water, H_2O, and in the process they produce the element sulfur.

■ Based on the equation for the normal type of photosynthesis (Equation 1.4 and 4.12), write down a chemical equation for this type of photosynthesis using hydrogen sulfide. Note that water is a by-product on the right hand side.

□ The equation is:

carbon dioxide + hydrogen sulfide + energy from Sun $\longrightarrow$ organic compounds (glucose) + sulfur + water

$CO_2 + H_2S + \text{energy from Sun} \longrightarrow C_6H_{12}O_6 + S + H_2O$

which, when balanced, becomes

$6CO_2 + 12H_2S + \text{energy from Sun} \longrightarrow C_6H_{12}O_6 + 12S + 6H_2O$ (Equation 7.4)

The sulfur itself can be used as a source of energy and converted to sulfate by sulfur-oxidising bacteria. As with the nitrogen cycle, if the sulfur cycle only operated in this one direction the biosphere would soon have a lot of sulfate, but few other forms of sulfur. The sulfate can be recycled into sulfur and hydrogen sulfide by anaerobic microbes, called sulfate-reducing bacteria, in a process analogous to denitrification.

■ Where might you expect to find these anaerobic microbes?

□ Like the denitrification microbes, they occur in waterlogged soils. These microbes are responsible for the rotten-eggs smell sometimes detectable in bogs and marshes and if you dig down into coastal mud and sand. They are also found even deeper underground and in deep-sea sediments.

Question 7.8

Write out the names and chemical formulae of three different chemicals in which sulfur can be found in the environment, omitting sulfur dioxide, starting with the one with the most hydrogen and ending with the one with the most oxygen. Indicate, using labelled arrows, which of the conversions from one to another can be achieved by microbes and say which microbes are involved.

7.5   Microbes and the phosphorus cycle

Phosphorus is yet another chemical element that plays an important role in all living organisms, generally in the form of phosphate ions (PO_4^{3-}). Phosphate is an essential component of DNA and RNA. The sides of the DNA 'ladder' are shown in Figure 1.10 as alternating pentagons and circles. The pentagons represent sugar (ribose) molecules and the circles represent phosphates. Phosphate ions are also fundamental to the molecules that store energy in cells, adenosine diphosphate (ADP) and adenosine triphosphate (ATP). Reactions that produce energy, like respiration, generate ATP by linking a third phosphate group to ADP. ATP is a high-energy molecule and can be broken down again to provide energy for activities in the cell, such as the movement of flagella in microbes. In animals, phosphates are also important in the structure of bones and teeth.

Phosphate ions are found in rocks, though generally in very low concentrations. At the surface of the Earth, these rocks are broken down by weathering and the phosphates are slowly released into soil and water. They can then be taken into microbes, algae and plants and eventually consumed by animals in their food. When organisms die, their remains are decomposed by microbes and the phosphate is once again available for intake by living organisms. Some phosphate in the ocean can eventually settle to the ocean floor and become reincorporated into the rocks of the geosphere.

Humans have had a profound effect on the natural cycling of phosphorus on Earth. Through mining of those rare rocks that contain significant phosphate, we free a much larger amount of phosphorus from the geosphere than would ever be released by natural processes. Much of this phosphorus is used in industrial applications and as fertiliser for plant crops. Because phosphorus is a limiting element for biological growth, particularly in plants, farmers can increase crop yields by adding phosphate fertiliser. However, a high proportion of phosphorus in fertilisers is then carried from the land and into waterways by drainage, elevating phosphorus levels in lakes, rivers and oceans. As phosphorus becomes abundant in these systems it causes an excessive growth of microbes, such as algae, and can cause lakes and ponds to become overgrown.

- ■ Excessive growth of microbes increases the BOD (Section 4.3). What is BOD and what problems are caused if it is high?

- ☐ BOD is biological oxygen demand. If there is excessive growth of aerobic microbes, then much of the dissolved oxygen in the water will be used up in their respiration, leaving insufficient for other organisms, such as invertebrates and fish, which will die.

Microbial populations perform a number of key roles in the phosphorus cycle, primarily by processing forms of phosphorus that are of no use to other living organisms so that the phosphorus becomes accessible to the biosphere. As mentioned, phosphorus is released from rocks by weathering. This takes place in two ways, physical and chemical. Physical weathering occurs through interactions between the rock and the Earth's atmosphere, such as wind erosion

5 mm

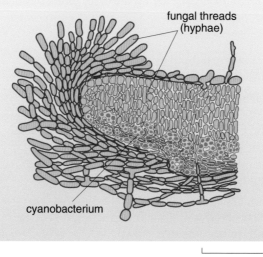

1 cm

Figure 7.12 Two species of lichen found on rocky shores.

or the breakdown of rock in water. Chemical weathering occurs through chemical reactions. Microbes can play a role in both of these processes. By growing inside cracks and microscopic spaces in rocks, microbes can apply physical pressure to the rock itself and help break it apart. They can also produce acids and other compounds that take part in the chemical weathering of rocks and break them down. Lichens (Figure 7.12) can be very important in this weathering process.

Although lichens look like a single organism, and function as though they are, they are in fact made of two different organisms. The main body of a lichen is a fungus, but within the fungal body there is a layer of microbial cells of photosynthetic algae or cyanobacteria, depending on the species of lichen (Figure 7.13). Both partners benefit from this. Fungi cannot photosynthesise but can absorb the products of photosynthesis made by the algae or cyanobacteria to use in their respiration to produce energy. These cells, in return, are protected by the body of the fungus from excessive solar radiation and from drying out. As a result, the lichen can thrive in extremely harsh environments, such as on bare rock, where neither of the individual species could survive on their own. Lichens come in many shapes and colours and are often some of the first organisms to take part in breaking down rock and releasing phosphorus.

DM Slide 6.8

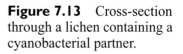

fungal threads (hyphae)

cyanobacterium

50 μm

Figure 7.13 Cross-section through a lichen containing a cyanobacterial partner.

DM Slides 2.2 and 2.5

Many microbes, particularly the Actinobacteria (Figure 4.10), have particular abilities to remove phosphorus from rocks and rock particles in the soil, by the production of acids. Unsurprisingly, like the nitrogen-fixing bacteria, these bacteria have had a great deal of attention from agriculturalists who see an opportunity to accelerate phosphorus release into fields by inoculating soils with these bacteria.

Question 7.9

As far as the four spheres of the Earth are concerned, there is a fundamental difference between the phosphorus cycle and the other three cycles so far considered, carbon, nitrogen and sulfur. What is the difference?

7.6 Other important chemical cycles

The four cycles discussed above – carbon, nitrogen, sulfur and phosphorus – are the most important, and the most studied cycles. However, every chemical element used by organisms in the biosphere must undergo some amount of cycling in the environment, otherwise life on Earth would run out of the molecules it needs. In particular, oxygen needs to be cycled between the biosphere and atmosphere, to allow organisms such as ourselves to respire aerobically. It appears that the first oxygen was released into the atmosphere by the activities of early microbes, probably cyanobacteria, as you will learn in Chapter 8.

Hydrogen is the most abundant chemical element in the Universe, but on Earth it rarely occurs in significant quantities as a gas (H_2). However, it is present in most of the molecules vital for life, particularly with oxygen in water and this makes it hard to separate the hydrogen cycle from the oxygen cycle. Some microbes do produce gaseous hydrogen (as mentioned in Section 7.2.5) and, since hydrogen produced this way would be a clean fuel, there is currently considerable scientific interest in the process. Algae have been found to produce hydrogen as a product of photosynthesis when in the dark in aerobic conditions, particularly if they are deprived of sulfur. Microbial fuel cells are currently being developed to produce hydrogen commercially.

Question 7.10

Identify and correct any errors in the following statements.

(a) Carbon is fixed into organic molecules by decomposers.

(b) Nitrogen fixation results in the formation of nitrate compounds.

(c) Denitrification causes nitrogen gas to be removed from the atmosphere.

(d) Sulfate reducers play an important role in the production of hydrogen sulfide gas.

(e) Phosphorus is acquired by most microbes by fixing it from the atmosphere.

Question 7.11

Complete Table 7.3 to show the form(s) in which the various elements are found in the various spheres, including the chemical formulae where appropriate.

Table 7.3 Forms in which elements are found on Earth. (To be completed in Question 7.11.)

Element	Atmosphere	Biosphere	Hydrosphere	Geosphere
carbon				
nitrogen				
sulfur				
phosphorus				

Summary of Chapter 7

- Microbes play a central role in cycling many elements on the Earth. This occurs through the main reservoirs of the geosphere, atmosphere, hydrosphere and biosphere. For many chemical reactions there are microbes that can drive the reaction either way.

- The carbon cycle is one of the most important cycles on the Earth. Over 99% of carbon is locked up in carbonate rocks and buried organic carbon, but the rest is cycled through life in photosynthesis, respiration and decomposition, amongst other processes. These processes are not merely useful, but absolutely essential for the rest of life on the Earth.

- The fixation of nitrogen gas from the atmosphere can only be carried out by microbes and so the nitrogen used by all other organisms, including plants, depends upon microbes.

- Other essential elements that are required by the biosphere are cycled by microbes, including sulfur and phosphorus. Some microbes can photosynthesise using sulfur. Phosphorus cycling by microbes primarily involves the release of phosphorus by the breakdown of rocks in weathering reactions.

Chapter 8
Life beyond the Earth

Before considering perhaps one of the biggest questions in contemporary science – Is there life beyond Earth? – it is necessary to look back at how and when life came into being on the Earth, at the conditions present then and at what sort of life it was. It is then possible to investigate whether similar conditions might exist elsewhere in the Solar System, or on planets around any of the other many billions of stars elsewhere in our galaxy and beyond, and consider the possibility that we are not alone in the Universe. This is the science of astrobiology.

8.1   The development of life on Earth

8.1.1   Going back in time

The gradual development of life on Earth is recorded in the fossils seen in rocks. Modern humans, *Homo sapiens*, originated in East Africa probably about 200 000 years ago, one-fifth of a million years ago. The first species placed in the genus *Homo*, an early ancestor of modern man called *Homo habilis*, appeared about 2.5 million years (Ma, short for 'mega-anna', plural of mega-annum) ago. The dinosaurs died out about 65 Ma ago, probably in the aftermath of a meteorite impact with the Earth. The first fossilised four-legged land animals have been dated at about 350 Ma ago, at a time when huge swampy forests were common on Earth.

■   Thinking back to the carbon cycle (Section 7.2.4), what happened to the vegetation from those swampy forests in Carboniferous times?

☐   The vegetation was buried by sediment, compressed and heated and eventually was converted into the coal that is used today.

Going back through more and more ancient rocks, the only fossils found are those of simpler animals and plants, some of which are entirely different from anything seen today. The first organisms made of more than one cell (multicellular organisms) appeared about 600 Ma ago. Prior to that, there were only single-celled microbes.

The oldest fossils visible to the naked eye are called stromatolites and are a type of microbial mat. It is known that stromatolites were made by bacteria, because they are still forming in a few coastal regions today. They are flat, rounded mounds formed when sediment (particles of mud and sand) is trapped by colonies of bacteria, including cyanobacteria. Figure 8.1 shows both modern stromatolites, growing now in Western Australia, and fossils of ancient stromatolites, around 2400 Ma old. Structures that look like stromatolites have been reported in rocks up to 3500 Ma old. In Section 2.6.1, you met cyanobacteria as components of microbial mats in other environments such as hot springs and in ponds.

(a)   (b)   1 cm

Figure 8.1   (a) Modern stromatolites in Shark Bay, Western Australia. The flat, rounded mounds are up to about 1 m across, and around 30 cm high. (b) A section through a fossil stromatolite from rocks in Argentina about 2400 Ma old.

Question 8.1

Which of the following statements about present-day stromatolites is incorrect?

(a) Stromatolites are layers of microbes that make use of different environments at different depths in the mat to grow.

(b) The top layer of stromatolites is often dominated by photosynthetic microbes.

(c) Stromatolites will always have fermentation occurring within them.

(d) Stromatolites are layers of microbes that trap sediment between them.

Microscopic examination of ancient stromatolites reveals fossils of the microbes themselves, single cells and groups of cells, sometimes in chains. Figure 8.2 shows a comparison of some living and some ancient cyanobacteria, so that you can see how similar they are. Earlier rocks, dated at about 3400 Ma, contain molecules left over from the decay of microbial organisms, probably cyanobacteria, although the actual cells are no longer visible.

■ How might the cyanobacteria, which are photosynthetic microbes, have changed the composition of the atmosphere?

☐ The process of photosynthesis (Equations 1.4 and 4.12) generates oxygen and so once cyanobacteria were present they would have started to add oxygen to the atmosphere.

DM Activity 6.2   In fact, it is almost certain that microbes, including the cyanobacteria, were the source of the original atmospheric oxygen that allowed all the aerobic species to begin to develop. It is a sobering thought to realise that the human race would not be here without the activities of early microbes.

Figure 8.2   Comparison of living and fossil cyanobacteria. (a), (c) and (e) are from stromatolites growing today in Mexico; (b), (d) and (f) are from rocks in the former Soviet Union. (b) is 950 Ma old; (d) is 850 Ma old and (f) is 1550 Ma old.

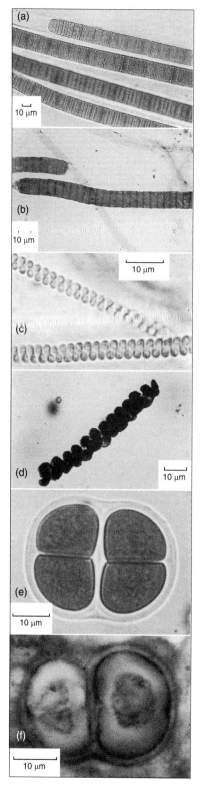

8.1.2   The first microbes

Since there is chemical evidence for microbes in rocks 3400 Ma old, the first microbes must have appeared at some point before that time. Conditions on the Earth then were very different from the conditions now. The Earth was created from material that gathered together in the early Solar System, eventually forming a ball of molten rock about 4600 Ma ago. By about 4100 Ma, there was a solid rocky crust, though there was almost certainly much more volcanic activity than there is now. There was also much more icy and rocky material circulating in the Solar System, and that produced a regular hail of asteroids and comets onto the newly forming surface of the Earth. Nitrogen was present in the atmosphere, together with other gases belched out by volcanoes, amongst which were, as now, carbon dioxide and water. Some water was also almost certainly delivered by comets. Because conditions were so hostile, it is likely that no life existed on Earth before 3900 Ma

■ How long did it take until microbes were definitely present?

☐ Since it seems likely that microbes were alive 3400 Ma ago, there was a period of 500 Ma (from 3900 Ma to 3400 Ma) and at some time during this period, the first microbes appeared.

■ Look back at Figure 2.3. Where would you place the very first microbes on the phylogenetic tree of life?

☐ They would be right at the bottom of the 'trunk', before any of the 'branches' began.

The tree shown in Figure 2.3 has been constructed using information from rDNA studies (Section 5.2.1), which indicates how closely related the different species are. You will see that there is quite some distance between the base of the tree and the branch that includes the cyanobacteria. This indicates that there must have been a number of species before the cyanobacteria, going right back to the one original organism which was the ancestor of all species.

This common ancestor of all microbes, and, in fact, of all life on Earth today, is known as the last universal common ancestor (LUCA). Life for the LUCA was hard. The volcanic activity and asteroid and comet bombardment created unstable conditions, causing dramatic local temperature changes. Much of the Earth was probably hotter than it is today. There was certainly no oxygen in the atmosphere, so the LUCA must have been an anaerobe. Oxygen gas (composed of two oxygen atoms, O_2) is the source of ozone (formed from three oxygen atoms, O_3).

Currently the ozone layer, high in the atmosphere, absorbs much of the incoming ultraviolet radiation from the Sun, which can cause damage to the genetic material of cells in the same way as other forms of ionising radiation. There would have been no ozone layer to protect the LUCA.

Question 8.2

How would you describe a microbe that could withstand high temperatures and high levels of radiation?

Exactly how the LUCA derived its energy and the compounds needed to construct its cells is more difficult to know. Organic materials can be produced in comets as they travel around the Solar System and it may be that cometary impacts on the early Earth provided the organic compounds used by the LUCA. There is some evidence that the LUCA may have been a chemolithotroph, using energy from rocks, possibly at hydrothermal vents in the oceans (Section 6.2.2). It is even possible, that the LUCA, or close relatives of that species, might still be living there today.

8.1.3 Before the LUCA

Even though it was the first organism, the LUCA was complex. It consisted of everything needed for a cell to survive and reproduce in a very harsh environment, such as enzymes, proteins, lipids, carbohydrates, etc. The probability that all these formed together and assembled themselves into a living cell by chance is so small as to be inconceivable. It seems much more likely that the origins of the LUCA were a step-wise development from simple chemicals. The reality is that scientists just don't know how this could have occurred. Scientists have successfully managed to make amino acids and nucleic acids from simple carbon building blocks in the laboratory, but nobody has yet worked out how these molecules would assemble into a self-replicating organism.

A more imaginative theory for the origins of life is the panspermia hypothesis, which proposes that the LUCA originated beyond the Earth. This alien LUCA emerged on its home planet and some of the microbes were subsequently blasted away from the surface by a meteor impact. The LUCA then spent time floating around in space until it landed on the early Earth. Meteorites made of material from the surface of Mars have been found on Earth, so this is not impossible. It has also been found that some microbes can survive enormous impact pressures, so the hypothesis cannot be rejected completely.

- ■ What is the problem with using the panspermia idea as a method of explaining the origin of life?

- ☐ It does not get away from the problem of how the LUCA evolved on its planet of origin. It does not get any nearer to the answer of how the first living organism evolved in the first place, it just moves the problem somewhere else.

8.2   Life elsewhere in our Solar System

Although microbes are adaptable and amazingly resilient, they do require certain basic conditions to be able to live. If these conditions are present elsewhere in the Solar System, then there is a chance that life could exist there.

■ What are the essential requirements for life as we know it?

☐ All living things require energy, liquid water and a source of carbon (Section 1.8.1).

The Earth is just the right distance from the Sun for water to be present as a liquid.

■ What three types of energy sources are available for microbes on Earth?

☐ They can use energy from the Sun, for photosynthesis. They can extract energy from organic molecules such as sugars, by aerobic respiration, fermentation and anaerobic respiration. They can use inorganic compounds, such as iron, nitrogen and sulfur compounds.

In the following sections, the conditions present on a selection of the bodies in our Solar System will be examined, to see whether there is any chance that life could exist, or could have existed anytime in the past. Figure 8.3 gives the names and the relative sizes of the planets and will be useful for reference as you work through the remainder of the chapter.

8.3   Mercury, Venus and the Moon

■ Using Figure 8.3, describe the positions of Mercury, Venus and the Moon in relation to the Earth and the Sun.

☐ Mercury and Venus lie between the Sun and the Earth, with Mercury closest to the Sun. They both orbit the Sun, whereas the Moon orbits the Earth, so the Moon is sometimes closer to the Sun than is the Earth and sometimes further away.

Since Mercury is close to the Sun, it is likely to be much hotter than the Earth and, in fact, the part of Mercury's surface that faces the Sun reaches about 470 °C and it freezes to –190 °C when facing away. These temperatures are too severe for even the most extreme thermophiles and psychrophiles found on Earth to survive, and with no atmosphere and no water, there is no possibility of life on Mercury. Venus, however, looks slightly more promising.

Venus is approximately the same size as Earth, but orbits the Sun at an average distance of 108 million kilometres compared to the Earth's average of 146 million kilometres. So the temperature would be expected to be higher than that of Earth, but it turns out to be much hotter than the distance would indicate. This is because the atmosphere of Venus is 97% carbon dioxide, with just a small amount of nitrogen. Carbon dioxide is a greenhouse gas and so traps heat within the atmosphere and keeps the surface temperature at 464 °C, similar to that of

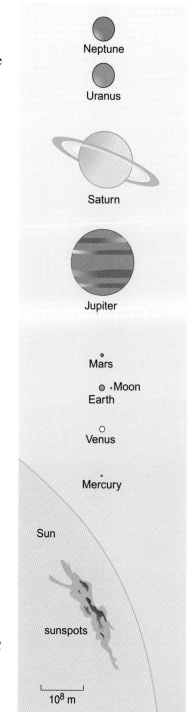

Figure 8.3 The relative sizes of the Sun and the planets. The planets are shown in order of increasing distance from the Sun, but the distances between the various bodies are not to scale; they are separated by far greater distances than are shown.

Mercury and beyond the limits of even the most hardened hyperthermophile. The surface of Venus cannot be seen by cameras using visible wavelengths of light because the atmosphere contains very dense clouds. There are very small amounts of water in the atmosphere, but the clouds are mostly composed of droplets of sulfuric acid. At about 50 km above the surface, the temperature is much more hospitable, at about 70 °C, and the pressure is similar to that on the Earth's surface. So, conditions could be possible for the survival of a particularly hardy acid-tolerant thermophile.

Studies of the atmosphere of Venus by the Russian Venera spacecraft and the American Pioneer and Magellan probes found traces of hydrogen sulfide (H_2S) and sulfur dioxide (SO_2) in the atmosphere. These two gases react very quickly with one another and so are never normally found together unless something is producing them. Even more mysterious is the presence of another gas called carbonyl sulfide (COS).

■ What elements make up the gas carbonyl sulfide?

⊓ The gas consists of one atom of carbon, one of oxygen and one of sulfur.

This gas is difficult to produce chemically but is produced by living things, so it has sometimes been considered to be an indicator of biological activity. However, there is no evidence of other organic material on the surface or in the atmosphere of Venus, and it is generally accepted that life does not exist on Venus. The COS is probably the product of chemical reactions in the atmosphere that are not at present fully understood.

The Moon is also considered unlikely to have any life of its own. There is no atmosphere and no water and there are huge fluctuations in temperature, from 123 °C to –233 °C.

■ By how many degrees does the Moon's surface temperature vary?

☐ The temperature ranges from 123 °C above freezing point down to 233 °C below freezing point. That is a total range of 123 °C + 233 °C = 356 °C.

All spacecraft now leaving the Earth are carefully sterilised before launch to avoid any possible contamination of other environments with Earth microbes. However, this has not always been the case. Surveyor 3 was launched to the Moon in April 1967 and was exposed to the lunar surface for the following 31 months, prior to the arrival of the Apollo 12 manned mission. Apollo 12 landed only about 160 metres from Surveyor 3 and members of the crew were able to retrieve several pieces of the Surveyor, including the TV camera and associated electrical cables, the sample scoop, and two pieces of aluminium tubing (Figure 8.4). These items were returned to Earth and analysed to determine how they were affected by exposure to the lunar environment. Within a piece of foam from inside the TV camera, living cells of *Streptococcus mitis*, a bacterium common in the human mouth, were found. This was originally used as evidence that microbes can survive in the hostile lunar environment.

Figure 8.4 An astronaut on the Moon from Apollo 12 (which can be seen in the distance) removing parts from the Surveyor 3 spacecraft.

■ If you were told that the camera had been handled by astronauts during and after collection on the Moon and by engineers after its return to Earth, why might you be sceptical about these claims?

☐ Without suitable precautions (described in Activity 2.2), it is very easy for samples to be contaminated by microbes from other sources, such as people handling the samples.

In fact, the camera was not stored in a sealed metal container for its return from the Moon, but in a nylon bag, so it could very well have been contaminated by microbes from the environment inside the Apollo 12 capsule. Furthermore, the Surveyor programme scientist in charge of the camera parts, subsequently stated that a member of his staff reported a 'breach of sterile procedure', where an implement being used to scrape samples off part of the Surveyor had been placed on a non-sterile laboratory bench, before being used. Microbes could have been picked up from the bench or from the breath of those carrying out the sample collection. Since the Surveyor 3 camera was subsequently exposed to normal terrestrial conditions (and is now on display in the Smithsonian Air and Space Museum in Washington DC), the tests cannot be repeated.

■ Why are scientists particularly interested to find out whether microbes can survive away from their normal conditions on Earth?

☐ If it is found that they can, then this would provide support for the panspermia hypothesis (Section 8.1.3), that the first life could have arrived on Earth from elsewhere in space.

In summary, it seems very unlikely that life exists on Mercury, Venus or the Moon. However, things may be different on Mars.

8.4 Mars

Mars is the planet which, for hundreds of years, has been the focus of interest as a possible home for extraterrestrial life. Interest has moved on from science-fiction stories of intelligent inhabitants, to looking for evidence of subsurface microbes living there now, or in the past.

The average temperatures on Mars today are much below those on Earth. At the equator the daily temperatures range from –100 °C to +20 °C with temperatures at the poles reaching as low as –125 °C during the winter. Mars has an atmospheric composition much like Venus, consisting of 95% CO_2 and 3% N_2 with trace amounts of oxygen, water and methane, but the atmosphere is very thin compared to that on Venus and Earth. The atmospheric pressure is about one-hundredth of that on Earth, and any liquid water on the surface would instantly evaporate or freeze. It is very difficult for water to be liquid on the surface of Mars. Additionally, ionising radiation (Section 6.6) from space bombards the surface of Mars after passing through the very thin atmosphere, and there is no ozone layer to provide protection from ultraviolet radiation. As well as the protection provided by the atmosphere on Earth, the Earth's magnetic field also traps many incoming high-energy particles and prevents them from reaching the surface. When the particles collide, they produce vivid coloured lights, seen as the aurorae – the northern and southern lights. On Mars there is no significant magnetic field to trap these particles and they can therefore impact on the surface.

Question 8.3

Which molecule in any microbe that might, for example, be transported to Mars by a spacecraft from Earth, would be most crucially affected by radiation?

8.4.1 Mars in the past

Earth and Mars (and the rest of the planets) formed around the same time about 4600 Ma ago.

■ Based on the information about the Earth in Section 8.1.2, what could you predict about the early atmosphere of Mars? How might conditions differ from those on Earth?

□ The Earth's early atmosphere is thought to have consisted of nitrogen, carbon dioxide and water, and the Martian atmosphere was probably similar. However, because Mars is further from the Sun, you might expect the surface temperature to have been lower than on Earth.

Since life evolved on Earth (or possibly arrived from elsewhere via the panspermia process), then if conditions were similar on Mars, there is no reason why life should not have arisen (or arrived) there too.

■ Looking back to Figure 8.3, what is the additional difference between Mars and Earth not so far mentioned?

☐ Mars is significantly smaller than Earth.

In fact, Mars is only about half as big as the Earth (the diameter of Mars is about 6800 km while Earth is over 12 700 km across). This size difference had major effects on the processes that occurred on the planet after its formation.

■ How does the ratio of the surface area to volume of Mars compare with that of the Earth? You may need to look back to Section 1.9, particularly Question 1.7, when a similar question about small and large microbes was investigated.

☐ The conclusion from Question 1.7 was that 'The ratio of surface area to volume is much bigger for a small microbe than for a large one'. This is just as valid for planets as it is for microbes. Mars has a much larger surface area to volume ratio than Earth.

Because of this relatively greater surface area, once it had been formed as a planet, Mars cooled down much faster than Earth and became less geologically active. The smaller size of the planet also meant that it had weaker gravity and so was less able to hold onto atmospheric gases, which is just one of many factors that contributed to the thin atmosphere Mars has today.

Water may also be frozen in the planetary crust. So, it is estimated that by 3500 Ma ago, the surface of Mars had been transformed into one which was inhospitable for life.

Question 8.4

Based on the information about how long it took for life to appear on Earth, was there sufficient time for life to have appeared on Mars by similar processes, at least on its surface?

8.4.2   Searching for life on Mars

The answer to Question 8.4 indicates that there was time for life to develop on Mars. Detailed photographs of Mars provide very good evidence that wetter conditions did once exist on Mars, as shown in Figure 8.5. Although conditions are probably now too hostile for life to survive on the surface, it could still exist below the surface, perhaps using water deep in the crust.

In late 1975, two Viking landers were launched to Mars and the following year they became the first human-made objects to land successfully on the Martian surface. To ensure that no Earth microbes could contaminate Mars, both craft were baked to sterilise them in a giant purpose-built oven. The landers, which arrived on opposite sides of the planet, were each equipped with a suite of scientific instruments designed to detect the activity of microbes within the Martian soil, using three different experiments.

Figure 8.5   An ancient valley on Mars photographed by the European Space Agency's Mars Express. The deposits in the valley were probably laid down by water. The area is 100 km across.

The first of these was a carbon assimilation experiment, which tested for the intake of atmospheric carbon dioxide (CO_2), or carbon monoxide (CO), and its incorporation into organic molecules.

■ Which microbial metabolic processes could this experiment reveal?

☐ The intake of CO_2 into organic compounds can be accomplished by autotrophs that use CO_2 as their source of carbon. So this experiment was designed to look for life taking up its essential carbon.

The plan was to scoop up some Martian soil into a special chamber which contained CO_2 and CO, and then to see if any of the molecules of gas were absorbed. To be able to identify whether this had happened, the gas molecules were 'labelled' by being made with radioactive carbon, called carbon-14. If any of the labelled gases were absorbed by microbes in the soil and converted into organic compounds, the soil would, after a time, become radioactive. When strongly heated, the organic compounds would break down and the radioactive carbon would be released again, and could be measured with a detector (similar to a Geiger counter). To the great excitement of the scientists working on the project, carbon was indeed absorbed into the soil, just as though microbes were present. However, whenever an experiment like this is performed, it is necessary to devise another experiment which acts as a control. In this case the control experiment would test whether the same results could be obtained without a biological explanation.

■ What would be an appropriate control in this situation?

☐ If a sample of Martian soil were heated to a sufficiently high temperature to kill any microbes present before being exposed to the gases, then it should not take up any of the gases containing the radioactive carbon.

This control experiment was performed, with the soil heated to 175 °C. However, the radioactive gases were still absorbed. So there must have been some physical process, unconnected with the presence of life, which was causing the uptake of the gases by the soil. So this first experiment did not provide support for the presence of life on Mars.

The second experiment was a gas exchange experiment. A Martian soil sample was placed into another test chamber and the Martian atmosphere was replaced by the gas helium, which is inert (it does not take part in any reactions), so any other gases detected must have been produced by something happening within the soil. The soil was then exposed to water and a variety of nutrients, a selection of amino acids, salts, vitamins and nucleotide bases from DNA, brought from Earth. Any gases released from the soil after addition of these nutrients were then analysed, by an instrument called a gas chromatograph, which can detect the gases oxygen, carbon dioxide, nitrogen, hydrogen and methane. If microbes were present, it was expected that some gases would be produced by their metabolic processes.

■ What control could be used for this experiment?

☐ A second soil sample could be collected, but only water and no nutrients could be added. The amount of gas produced would be expected to be different in the control if microbes were at work in the soil.

Again, initial results looked promising, since oxygen was given off by the soil when it was exposed to the nutrients. But the same disappointment occurred when the control results were studied, since exactly the same amount of oxygen was given off when only water was added with no nutrients. So some non-biological process must have been responsible.

In the third and final experiment, organic carbon compounds commonly used by Earth microbes, again labelled with radioactive carbon, were put into contact with Martian soil in another test chamber that contained a simulated Martian atmosphere.

■ What sort of microbial process would use organic compounds in the anaerobic conditions of Mars?

☐ Perhaps the most likely type of metabolic reactions which would have been detected in this experiment are fermentation and anaerobic respiration, both of which use organic compounds. As there is very little oxygen on Mars, aerobic respiration would have been very unlikely.

It was hoped that if any microbes in the soil were metabolising these nutrients, then radioactive gases would be emitted as a by-product. A positive result would be detection of radioactive gas in the chamber upon addition of the nutrients, and the amount of gas should increase as time went by and the microbes continued to use the nutrients. Eventually, the amount of gas being produced would level off as the organisms used up all the remaining nutrients. This is exactly what was observed. Radioactive gas was produced by the soil on contact with the labelled nutrients and the amount of gas increased and then levelled off with time, just as would be expected if there were microbes in the soil. In this experiment, controls seemed to give some support to the hypothesis of microbial activity. Heating the soil to 50 °C reduced the amount of radioactive gas produced and heating to 160 °C completely stopped any production. Although these results sound very positive, they have to be taken alongside the negative results from the previous experiments, and overall scientists concluded that there could have been some chemical explanation for these results, not involving living organisms. The results did not conclusively point to the presence of life on Mars.

One experiment that was not part of the set of biology experiments, but still yielded results related to possible life on Mars, was an instrument to measure the abundance of organic chemicals within the soil. The instrument was very sensitive, but the only organic compounds found in the Martian soil by this device were solvents used to clean the instrument itself before it was launched. So, although initial results from the biological results supported the presence of life on Mars, the controls did not, and no organic molecules were found in the soil. The conclusion was that life on Mars was not detected by the Viking landers, but that may not be the end of the story.

There is now clear evidence that water-ice does occur on the surface of Mars (Figure 8.6) and it seems very likely that ice also occurs below the surface. If these subsurface ice deposits were heated by volcanic activity, it is plausible that water could be created under the surface today. Microbes below the surface would be shielded from most of the radiation present at the surface. So investigations continue and some of these are experimental, as described in *Laboratory methods 8.1*.

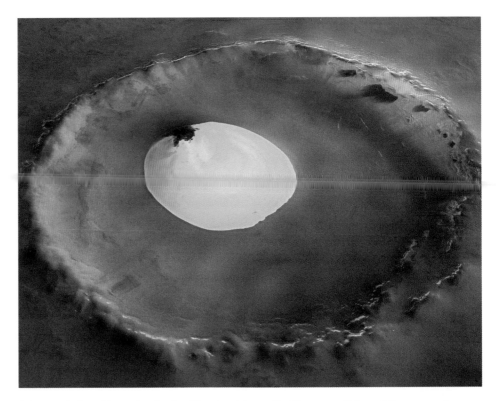

Figure 8.6 Water-ice in the Vastitas Borealis Crater on Mars. The crater is 35 km wide. The image was taken by Europe's Mars Express in 2005.

Question 8.5

The Viking experiments were designed in the 1970s long before the information you learnt in Chapter 6 on extremophiles was known. Briefly explain how knowledge of chemolithotrophy would change the way such an experiment would be designed today.

Laboratory methods 8.1   Mars simulation chamber

Microbiologists are not completely reduced to speculation when it comes to trying to study the survival of microbes on Mars. Laboratory experiments to investigate how well microbes might survive are done using a Mars simulation chamber (Figure 8.7). This is a pressure vessel in which cultures and other microbiological samples can be placed. A powerful vacuum pump is connected to it, allowing the pressure to be reduced to the atmospheric pressure found on the surface of Mars. The various landers have made detailed temperature measurements on the surface of the planet, and the temperatures in the chamber can be adjusted to reproduce these exactly. The large amount of ultraviolet (UV) radiation on Mars can be simulated by using xenon-arc lamps whose light is shone in through quartz windows (quartz is transparent to UV). Computer control makes it possible to simulate daily and seasonal changes in all the environmental factors. So with the Mars simulation chamber, microbiologists are able to study whether any microbes that might contaminate spacecraft could survive on the Martian surface, and to investigate possible conditions for Martian life, if it exists.

chamber for samples with
simulated Martian conditions   quartz window   tube leading to
vacuum pump

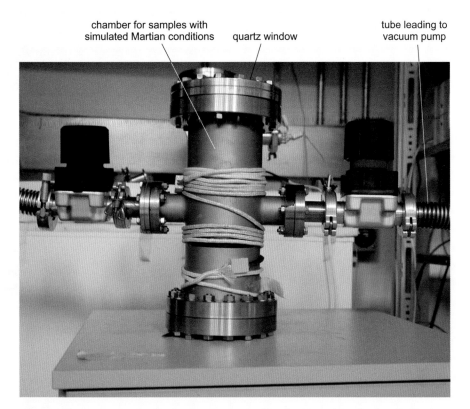

Figure 8.7   A Mars simulation chamber. The chamber is 60 cm high and pipes to the left and right of it feed in and extract simulated Martian atmosphere.

The surface of the Moon could also be studied using a Mars simulation chamber. However, an even stronger vacuum pump would be required to get down to the vacuum experienced on the Moon, which is even more extreme than the very low pressure on Mars. The Moon can also get very hot on the side facing the Sun, which could only be simulated with additional modifications to the chamber. However, in principle any planet can be simulated in the laboratory using a simulation chamber that can achieve the right pressure, temperature and radiation conditions.

One of the reasons why scientists continue to be optimistic about life on other planets is the remarkable diversity of reactions from which microbes can get energy.

■ Look back to Section 6.3, particularly Equation 6.1, and explain briefly how *Thiobacillus ferrooxidans* obtains its energy.

☐ This microbe uses iron-containing minerals, such as iron sulfide, which it combines with oxygen (and water) to produce the energy it needs for life.

Iron is found in all volcanic rocks on Earth and is the fourth most common element. On Mars too there is plenty of iron in the crust (this iron gives Mars its reddish colour) but only trace amounts of oxygen. However, iron can also be oxidised with nitrate to produce energy. Scientists do not yet know whether nitrates can be formed, or are present, on Mars, so it is difficult to assess the chances that chemolithotrophic iron microbes are present there.

8.4.3 The ALH84001 meteorite

After the Viking lander experiments, the hope of finding life on Mars diminished, until the capacity of the extremophiles was realised and a particular Martian meteorite was found. About 4500 Ma ago, when the planets were young, it appears that a volcano erupted on Mars, magma flowed out and eventually cooled to form a solid lava field. At this time, Mars, like Earth, was being subjected to bombardment by rocky materials from around the Solar System. The rock of the lava field was cracked and fissured by these impacts. Flood water filled the cracks until about 3000 Ma ago when the planet dried and became the parched desert that it is today. About 16 Ma ago the fractured lava field was hit by an impact which blasted pieces of rock off the planet and into orbit around the Sun. A small piece of that Martian rock – barely the size of a potato – spent the next 16 million years orbiting the Sun and occasionally crossing the orbit of the Earth. About 13 000 years ago Earth and the meteorite met. The meteorite crashed into Antarctica where it was quickly buried in ice and snow. In 1984, cycling of the ice returned the meteorite to the surface and it was discovered by a team of meteorite hunters in the Allan Hills region of Antarctica. It was designated ALH84001 (Figure 8.8).

Detailed studies of this meteorite revealed some remarkable structures which led to press reports that a relic of past life on Mars had been found. In the time when water was present in and around the Martian lava field, they said, life had evolved and here was the evidence.

The evidence that was presented was as follows:

1   Globules of carbonate were found, and these bore a striking resemblance to terrestrial microbial fossils.

2   Inside these carbonate globules were tiny particles of the iron compound, magnetite. The size, composition and structure of these particles are typical

1 cm

Figure 8.8 The ALH84001 meteorite.

of magnetite molecules formed in chains within the cells of terrestrial magnetotactic bacteria, such as *Magnetospirillum magnetotacticum* (Figure 8.9). The term magnetotactic means that these bacteria use the iron compound, magnetite, like a compass to orientate themselves according to the Earth's magnetic field. The exact purpose of lining up along magnetic fields is unknown but the magnetite inclusions may help to guide cells in lakes and ponds down towards nutrient-containing sediments since the magnetic field tends to dip downwards into the Earth except near the Equator.

3   A particular class of organic molecules, called polyaromatic hydrocarbons (PAH), that are typical waste products of certain terrestrial microbes, were present in the fissures of the rock, closely associated with the microbe-shaped carbonate globules.

4   As well as the magnetite, the rock also contained iron sulfide. The three compounds, magnetite, iron sulfide and carbonate are not all stable under any one physical condition and thus they should not exist together. They could however exist together if they had been produced by one or more types of living organism.

magnetite particles

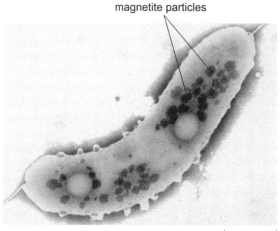

250 nm

Figure 8.9 A cell of *Magnetospirillum magnetotacticum*, containing magnetite particles.

The suspected fossils were ovoid structures 20 nm to 100 nm long. They resemble fossilised small bacteria (Figure 8.10).

■ How does this size compare with that of the bubonic plague microbe, *Yersinia pestis*?

☐ *Y. pestis* is about 1 μm in size (Chapter 1 and Table 7.2 in Question 7.2). Since 1000 nm = 1 μm the structures inside the meteorite are between 10 and 50 times smaller than this.

It is not yet certain whether a microbe of this size would be large enough to contain all the essential molecules (DNA, proteins, etc.) needed for life. And since the original announcement was made, the evidence has been heavily disputed. For every theory that supported biological origins, a contrary non-biological theory was given. Carbonate globules can be formed by chemical reactions in water. Magnetite, although produced by some bacteria, is also produced chemically in the natural environment. Many of the PAHs can also be produced in the environment without the involvement of microbes. Therefore the evidence in ALH04001 is as inconclusive as the Viking lander results.

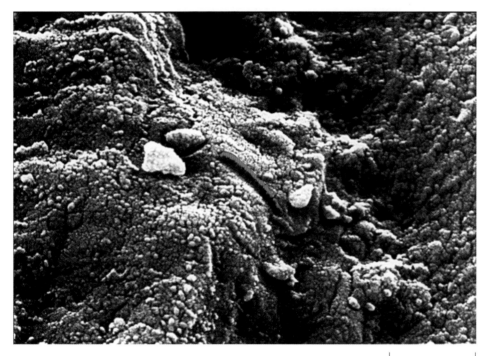

200 nm

Figure 8.10 ALH84001 'microfossils'. The tube-like structure (highlighted red) in the centre is 0.2 μm long.

Activity 8.1　Life on Mars

The estimated time for this activity is 30 minutes.

In this activity you will watch some video sequences that consider whether the conditions on Mars may be hospitable for life. The detailed notes for the activity, including some questions, are in the Activities section of the course website.

8.5 The gas giants

You will see from Figure 8.3, that moving out from Mars, the next two planets are huge. They are the gas giants, Jupiter and Saturn. Jupiter is 11 times the diameter of Earth, and two-and-half times the mass of all the other planets and their moons (natural satellites) combined. There is some metal and rock buried within the core of both Jupiter and Saturn, but they are mostly made up of hydrogen, helium and compounds containing hydrogen such as water, methane, and ammonia. The next two planets, Uranus and Neptune, have greater amounts of ammonia, methane and water than Jupiter and Saturn, and are termed ice giants. For the most part there is no clear separation between surface and atmosphere on any of these four giant planets.

The temperature at the top of Jupiter's clouds is about −145 °C and the temperature increases with depth below the clouds, reaching about 20 °C ('room temperature') at a depth where the atmospheric pressure is about 10 times as great as it is on Earth. Scientists have speculated that if Jupiter has any form of life, it would reside at this level, where there is probably liquid water present. The problem for the microbes would be to remain at this level. The internal heat of the planet warms the lower part of the atmosphere and it rises by convection, while the cold atmosphere at the top sinks. This sets up enormous vertical winds in the atmosphere of Jupiter, travelling upwards and downwards at about 600 km per hour. The highest wind speeds on Earth in hurricanes rarely exceed about one-third of this value. It is hard to contemplate how microbes could remain at roughly the same level in the atmosphere under these conditions.

8.6 Life on other moons

Although the Earth's Moon is too inhospitable for life to survive, the moons of other planets have different conditions, and some of them look quite promising in the search for life.

8.6.1 Europa

- What is the main effect that the Earth's Moon has on the Earth?

- ☐ The gravitational attraction between the Moon and the Earth causes the water in the oceans to be moved around the Earth forming the tides.

In fact, it is possible to measure changes in the height of the land too (land tides), but since land is much less easily moved than water, these are minute and only measurable with very accurate instruments. The Moon experiences similar slight flexing of its surface due to the gravitational pull of the Earth. Now consider a much bigger planet like Jupiter and its moons, of which there are over

Figure 8.11 A collage of the four large moons of Jupiter, from left to right, Ganymede, Callisto, Io and Europa, to the correct relative sizes. The radius of Europa is 1565 km, similar in size to our own Moon (1737 km).

60, including the four largest, Ganymede, Callisto, Io and Europa (Figure 8.11). Of these, Europa is the most intriguing in terms of the possibility of life.

The gravitational effect of the huge mass of Jupiter causes significant flexing of the surface of Europa. This causes warming in an analogous way to the heating of a squash ball when it is continually squashed as it hits the players' racquets and the sides of the court. The amount of heat released within Europa may be sufficient to maintain an ocean of liquid water, containing twice the volume of water that is in the Earth's oceans, beneath Europa's icy crust. This presence of liquid water places Europa among the highest priority targets for astrobiologists and has led to considerable speculation about the possibility of life there.

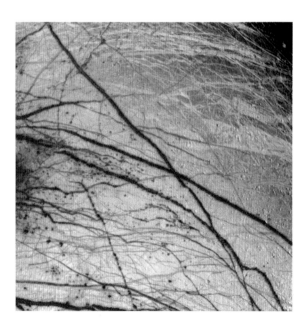

Figure 8.12 Cracks on the surface of Europa. The region shown is about 700 km across.

Europa has no atmosphere and its crust of ice, which may be between 10 km and 100 km thick is therefore directly exposed to open space. It is surprisingly smooth; if it were to be scaled down to a few centimetres in diameter, it would be ten times smoother than a squash ball. The surface is not, however, perfect. It is cracked by the gravitational forces of Jupiter. The cracks are shown in the photograph of part of Europa's surface in Figure 8.12.

Three possible sources of energy have been suggested for microbes living on Europa: photosynthesis, chemical energy from hydrothermal vents, and organic compounds produced by the effects of high-energy particles.

■ What problem would photosynthetic microbes have in the ocean of Europa?

☐ The thick ice sheet (10–100 km) would be likely to block out sunlight from reaching the ocean.

However, along the cracks, it might be possible for the faint light from the very distant Sun to penetrate more deeply and photosynthetic organisms living in these cracks just might be able to use sunlight. The energy available for photosynthesis on Europa has been estimated to be nearly a hundred times greater than energy available from other possible sources. It has been wildly speculated that the reddish–brown coloration visible in some of Europa's cracks may be due to colonies of photosynthetic microbes.

The second possible source of energy is chemical energy from possible hydrothermal vents on the floor of Europa's ocean, where it lies on top of the rocky core. The tidal forces, as well as keeping water liquid, will buckle the core and may heat it sufficiently for hydrothermal vents to form. There could be life around these vents, similar to the vents in the oceans of Earth (Section 6.2.2).

The final possibility for life on Europa depends on an unusual source of energy. Europa orbits within the magnetic field of Jupiter which channels high-energy particles produced from the Sun and elsewhere in the galaxy, onto Europa's surface. The interactions of these particles with material on Europa could produce oxygen from the frozen water and organic compounds from the trapped CO_2. These would eventually escape from within the ice and could reach the subsurface ocean, providing the essentials for autotrophic microbes in the ocean.

With such a thick surface layer of ice the exploration of Europa would be difficult, even without the vast distance from Earth. So unfortunately it will be a long time before any questions about life on Europa are answered.

However, scientists are getting some idea about how they might drill into Europa from studying Lake Vostok, one of many subglacial lakes trapped under the ice sheets in Antarctica. The lake is buried almost 4 km deep in the ice and is 250 km long and 50 km wide. Samples have yet to be taken from inside the lake itself, but by drilling within a few hundred metres of the lake scientists have been able to show that the ice above the lake contains micro-organisms. Within the lake itself, there may be microbes which have been isolated from others on Earth for possibly 500 000 years. When drilling continues, it will be particularly important not to contaminate the environment of the lake with anything used in the drilling process. The techniques that are being developed might one day be used on Europa.

8.6.2   Titan

■ Titan is a moon of Saturn. Use Figure 8.3 to identify whether it will be closer or more distant from the Sun than Europa?

☐ Since Saturn's orbit is further from the Sun than Jupiter, Titan will also be further away.

Titan receives only 1% of the light received on Earth and it is very cold. However, some peculiar processes are taking place there. For instance, there is an abundance of organic compounds within the thick orange atmosphere and liquid methane appears to rain down producing methane lakes and oceans across the moon. Titan seems to have a roughly equal mixture of water-ice and rock. The Cassini–Huygens mission to the Saturn system dropped a probe into Titan in 2005 and much of what is known about this moon was discovered by instruments on this probe. The surface of Titan is much too cold to maintain liquid water but it is possible that pockets of liquid water can occur in deeper rocks which are tidally heated. This region, particularly if it also contains methane and other hydrocarbons, might be a possible home for microbes. Again, it is likely to be many years before any further evidence can be obtained.

Question 8.6

The three requirements for life as we know it, are energy, liquid water and a carbon source. How could each of these be obtained by microbes on Europa and Titan?

8.7   Extrasolar planets

A Roman Catholic monk, Giordano Bruno, in 1584, was one of the first to contemplate the possibility that there may be planets similar to Earth, orbiting distant stars. In the book *On the Infinite Universe and Worlds* he wrote:

> 'There are countless suns and countless Earths all rotating around their suns in exactly the same way as the seven planets of our system. We only see suns because they are the largest bodies and are luminous, but their planets remain invisible to us because they are smaller and non-luminous. The countless worlds in the universe are no worse and no less inhabitable than our Earth.'

He was ridiculed at the time and eventually burned at the stake and it was not until 1995 – over 400 years later – that Bruno's work was vindicated by the discovery of the first planet beyond our Solar System. Hundreds of extrasolar planets are now known and many more are being discovered, literally on a weekly basis. These exoplanets cannot be directly observed even with the most powerful telescopes, since the adjacent star is just too bright. So astronomers have to use more sophisticated strategies.

Even though exoplanets are tiny compared to their accompanying stars (suns), they still exert a gravitation pull on everything around them, including their star. This pull makes the star wobble and the wobble can be observed from Earth as changes in the wavelength of light being emitted from the star. This is an example of the phenomenon known as Doppler shift. A second method of detection, the transit method, is based on the fact that if a planet is orbiting a star, it may occasionally pass in front of the star, as observed from the Earth. This produces a periodic dimming of the light received from the star, which is detectable on Earth. Although detecting exoplanets is fascinating, there is an even greater problem in detecting whether there is any microbial life on such planets.

■   What product of microbial activity could possibly be detectable from a long distance away?

☐   One product of microbial activity is gases, such as oxygen produced by photosynthesis, which build up in the atmosphere and might be detected by powerful enough instruments.

Gases can be detected in the atmospheres of planets because they tend to absorb particular wavelengths of light and so cause a characteristic change in the light spectrum being given off from a planet. If it is possible to block out the bright light from the star and collect just the light from the planet, then it would be possible to identify whether there were any gases present that might be associated with microbial activity. This is the approach that scientists plan to take in examining distant planets for life. One of the most promising gases is oxygen from photosynthesis because large amounts of oxygen in the atmosphere can only be sustained by life. No geological process is known to be able to produce large quantities of oxygen. Some microbes produce methane (the methanogens Section 7.2.5), but unlike oxygen, large quantities of methane can be released by geological processes. It is not therefore such a good marker for life, but if it was present with oxygen it could well indicate biological processes. Another gas produced by microbes is nitrogen, produced by denitrification (Section 7.3.1). However nitrogen is present in many planetary atmospheres, including our own which is 78% nitrogen, and so it could easily be at high concentrations without biological activity. The same problem exists with CO_2, which is produced by microbes, but can also be present in a planetary atmosphere without biological activity. So oxygen remains one of the most favoured biological signatures.

The search for microbial life on planets orbiting distant stars is one of the most exciting areas of modern microbiology. If gases produced by microbes were detected outside the Earth, scientists would know that the empire of the microbes extends to the far reaches of the Universe, even if these so-called microbes were in fact unique and unrelated to the microbes known on the Earth. If the gases are never detected, then perhaps the empire of the microbes remains confined to an unusual planet called Earth. Either way, the search reminds us that microbiology is a universal science.

Summary of Chapter 8

- Microbes are thought to have evolved on the Earth at the latest by 3.8 billion years ago. They probably appeared in the space of about 400 million years.

- For at least 3 billion years there were nothing but microbes on the Earth. Organisms made up of more than one cell (multicellular) only appeared about 600 million years ago.

- Many locations in the Solar System are too extreme for life, at least as we understand it. These include the planets Mercury and Venus.

- Some planets appear to have plausible conditions for life. Mars is one such location and during its early history when water was more abundant it may have had conditions conducive to life. Jupiter's moon, Europa, is another location with liquid water.

- One of the most tantalising prospects for finding life elsewhere is the detection of gases produced by life in the atmospheres of planets orbiting distant stars.

Questions: answers and comments

Question 1.1

Pollen grains, sperms and red blood cells are not organisms themselves, but are specialised parts of larger organisms. Microbes typically are not visible to the unaided eye at any stage of their life cycle, though when they collect in large numbers they most certainly are visible, as you will see later in the course.

Question 1.2

Since 1 mm = 1000 μm, then 0.8 mm = 0.8 × 1000 μm = 800 μm.

If 400 microbes measure 800 μm, then each microbe must be (800/400) μm long = 2 μm. So, each microbe would be 2 μm long.

Question 1.3

The microbe *Y. pestis* measures about 23 mm in Figure 1.1b, which is 23 000 μm. Its actual size is 1 μm and so to make it appear 23 000 times bigger, then it must have been magnified about 23 000 times for this image.

Question 1.4

(a) Most of the microbes in Figure 1.7a are up to about one-quarter as long as the 10 μm scale bar. They are about 2.5 μm long. The microbes in Figure 1.7b are depicted between about 6 mm and 8 mm long, as measured with a ruler. They have been magnified 3000 times, so are actually 3000 times smaller than this. Since 6 mm = 6000 μm, the actual size of the smaller microbes is (6000/3000) μm = 2 μm. The larger microbes are (8000/3000) μm = 2.7 μm.

(A typical light microscope will not magnify this much. This image has been enlarged for the purposes of the question.)

(b) The sizes are quite close, but it is difficult to be exact since the microbes vary in size.

(c) The advantage of using the scale bar is that if you copied the image into a different document and changed the size, the scale bar would change too. If you doubled the size of the picture of the microbe, the scale bar would appear twice as long, but would still have the same relationship to the microbe as before. However, if you gave a numerical magnification, then you would have to recalculate it each time the size of the image was changed.

Question 1.5

Each amino acid needs a sequence of 3 bases, so a total of 3 × 120 = 360 bases would be needed, together with a 'stop' triplet at the end.

Question 1.6

(a) Each *Y. pestis* is about 1 μm long, so 4096 of them would form a row 4096 μm long. There are 1000 μm in 1 mm, so this line would be just over 4 mm long.

(b) It takes 24 hours for a line about 4 mm to be produced. In another 2 hours, the number would have doubled, so they could form a line 8 mm long. After 28 hours, the line would be 16 mm long. And it would take another 2 hours, making a total time of 30 hours, to form a line 32 mm long.

Question 1.7

(a) The volume of the smaller microbe (*Y. pestis*) is 1 μm × 1 μm × 1 μm = 1 μm³.

The volume of the larger microbe (*H. walsbyi*) is 5 μm × 5 μm × 5 μm = 125 μm³.

(b) The surface area of one face of the smaller microbe is 1 μm × 1 μm = 1 μm².

A cube has 6 faces, so the total area of the surface of the smaller microbe is 6 × 1 μm² = 6 μm².

The surface area of one face of the larger microbe is 5 μm × 5 μm = 25 μm².

So the total surface area of the larger microbe is 6 × 25 μm² = 150 μm².

(c) So, for the smaller microbe, the ratio of the surface area to the volume is 6 : 1.

And, for the larger microbe, the ratio of the surface area to the volume is 150 : 125. The surface area is numerically only just bigger than the volume, and, expressed in the same way as the ratio above, it would be 1.2 : 1.

Question 1.8

See Table 1.3.

Table 1.3 Disease/illness-causing microbes (completed Table 1.1).

Disease/illness caused	Name of microbe
anthrax	*Bacillus anthracis*
diarrhoea and fever	*Clostridium difficile*
food poisoning	*Escherichia coli*
wound infections	*Staphylococcus aureus*
bubonic plague	*Yersinia pestis*

Question 1.9

Here is a possible answer, though you might have expressed your comparisons in a rather different way:

(i) Binary fission involves one cell dividing into two, while in sexual reproduction two specialised reproductive cells (egg and sperm) fuse together.

(ii) Binary fission does not require the finding of a mate.

(iii) Binary fission produces two identical cells; sexual reproduction produces offspring which are different from the parents and usually different from each other.

Question 1.10

See Table 1.4.

Table 1.4 Processes that occur in living organisms. (Completed Table 1.2.)

	Photosynthesis	**Aerobic respiration**	**Anaerobic respiration**
green plants	✓	✓	
animals		✓	
microbes	✓	✓	✓

Question 1.11

(a) False. Disease-causing microbes can be called 'bugs', but bugs are actually a group of insects. The word 'germs' implies that microbes cause disease and many of them do not, such as *Haloquadratum walsbyi* (Figure 1.3) and *Thiomargarita namibiensis* (Figure 1.4).

(b) True. *Yersinia pestis* is the microbe which causes bubonic plague and is carried in the saliva of the flea *Xenopsylla cheopis*.

(c) False. Bacilli are rod-shaped (cylindrical) bacteria, while cocci are the round ones. There is no special name for square bacteria, since there are so few of that shape.

(d) False. Bacteria have a single circular loop piece of DNA, sometimes called a bacterial chromosome, but they do not have a set of chromosomes.

Question 2.1

(a) The aseptic technique is used to prevent contamination by unwanted microbes. The technique also prevents microbes from the culture being studied from getting out into the surroundings, an essential precaution if they are pathogenic (disease-causing).

(b) The media are put into an autoclave (a laboratory version of a pressure cooker) and heated to 121 °C for about 15 minutes. This kills common microbes. Special tape is put on the items in the autoclave which changes colour when they have been maintained at the required temperature for the time needed.

Question 2.2

(a) An inoculum is a sample of microbes that have been added to the culture medium. In this case, they have been placed using a wire loop onto the surface of an agar plate.

(b) The microbes are streaked out so that eventually single microbes are deposited onto the agar surface, which then form discrete colonies after culturing. Since each of these colonies is derived by binary fission from one microbe, all the cells in such a colony should be identical.

(c) Microbial colonies are characterised by shape, size, colour, texture and smell. Clearly with pathogenic bacteria, smell should not be used!

Question 2.3

(a) One of the bottles of culture medium was labelled 'Blood base agar' which is used for many microbes associated with humans. Blood is used because it is a rich source of nutrients for the microbes. The red colour is due to the haemoglobin which is found in red blood cells.

(b) When large numbers of microbes have grown in a broth, the broth becomes cloudy or turbid.

Question 2.4

(a) The first step is to ensure that the slide is sterile, which is done by passing the slide through the Bunsen flame to kill any microbes that might be present. A drop of water is then put on the slide and the culture is mixed into the water to give an emulsion. If the emulsion is too thick, the stained microbes would be piled on top of one another and individual ones would be impossible to see under the microscope. They need to be spread out as a dilute emulsion. The emulsion is left to dry at room temperature and then passed gently through the Bunsen flame to fix the microbes to the slide, without heating it too much as this would burst the cells. The microbes can then be stained without being washed off the slide.

(b) Rod-shaped bacteria are called bacilli, and round ones are cocci. These terms were introduced in Section 1.4, but now you know how to pronounce them!

Question 2.5

In streak plates, the microbes are spread out in individual lines across the surface of the agar, whereas in a spread plate, they are spread evenly all over the surface of the agar.

Question 2.6

A bacterial lawn is produced by using a swab (or spreader) to spread a culture all over the surface of a plate. Small discs of paper each containing one antibiotic are positioned on the surface of the agar and the antibiotic then diffuses (spreads) outwards from the paper into the agar. If the antibiotic is effective against the microbial species, then it will be unable to grow where the antibiotic is present, and the agar surface will remain clear. The size of the clear circle is a measure of the effectiveness of each antibiotic against that species.

Question 2.7

If the microbe moves straight upwards at 100 µm per second, it will travel 1 mm (1000 µm) in 10 seconds. So, if buried to a depth of 50 mm, it would take 50×10 seconds $= 500$ seconds or just over 8 minutes to reach the surface. Of course, in reality, it would take much longer, since it would only be able to move when environmental conditions were suitable and it will not move in an exactly straight line.

Question 2.8

Taking 20 µm (20 000 nm) as a typical length of a flagellum, and using 20 nm as its diameter, then a flagellum is about 1000 times longer than its diameter.

Question 2.9

Figure 2.16 gives a completed version of Figure 2.14.

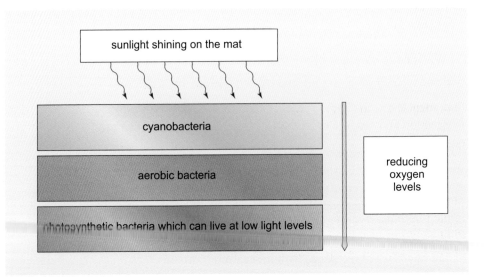

Figure 2.16 A labelled section through a typical microbial mat; a completed version of Figure 2.14.

Question 2.10

Different species of microbe can appear very similar, so appearance is not a certain way of classifying microbes. Because they mostly divide by binary fission, the other way of identifying species in plants and animals – that they can breed together and produce offspring that can themselves breed – cannot be used. So the only way of confirming their identity would be to analyse their DNA. Identical, or virtually identical, DNA would confirm that they did indeed belong to the same species.

Question 2.11

Anaerobic microbes are those which do not need oxygen for respiration. They would preferentially grow below the surface of an agar plate, so it would be appropriate to use a 'pour plate' where the microbes were mixed with the liquid agar which was then allowed to solidify. You may have considered that pouring the agar into a flat Petri dish with a large surface area exposed to the oxygen in the air, might be far from ideal for anaerobic microbes and it might be better to allow the agar to solidify in a tall thin glass container. The microbes could also be cultured in a broth in a glass flask. Again, for anaerobic microbes, it would be best to fill the flask completely with the broth, and cover the top in some way, so that as little air as possible was in contact with the surface.

Question 2.12

Here is the completed paragraph with the required words in italics:

There are two types of projection used for moving that can be found on the surface of different microbes, long ones called *flagella* and short ones called *pili*. When a microbe with *flagella* finds itself in an unsuitable environment, the direction of *rotation* of the *flagella* changes and the microbe *tumbles*. Spiral-shaped bacteria called *spirochaetes* have *flagella* located between the *plasma* membrane and the cell *wall*. Microbes with short projections move in a manner called *twitching*.

Question 2.13

Statement (b) is false; statements (a), (c) and (d) are true.

Statement (b) is false in two ways. Microbes need to be very close to one another to be able to communicate and the process that they use is called quorum (not quantum) sensing.

Question 2.14

Since the picture was probably taken in daylight, at least some of the microbes in the microbial mat are likely to be undergoing the process of photosynthesis. Photosynthesis produces oxygen and if it proceeds faster than the process of aerobic respiration which uses it up, then bubbles of oxygen form (Section 2.6.1).

Question 3.1

(a) Dental plaque is a biofilm, containing microbes, which forms on the surface of teeth.

(b) The drawings show rod-shaped bacilli (A, B and F), round cocci (E), and corkscrew spirillum (G).

(c) The dotted line probably indicates that van Leeuwenhoek saw the microbe moving between C and D, though his microscope would not be powerful enough to see what caused the movement.

Question 3.2

Applying each of Koch's postulates in turn to the disease of the silkworm caterpillars:

1   There would need to be evidence that all of the caterpillars that died were infected with the fungus, and that the spores were present in all of them. It should not be possible to culture the fungus from healthy caterpillars.

2   It should be possible to obtain the spores from the infected caterpillars, and grow a pure culture of the fungus, on a suitable growth medium. (It might be quite difficult to do this, since the fungus might be hard to culture outside living organisms.)

3   Assuming the fungus could be cultured, it should be possible to infect healthy caterpillars with the fungus and they should then succumb to the same disease.

4 It should be possible to obtain fungal spores from these newly infected caterpillars and again grow these in a culture.

If all these four conditions were met, this would be confirmation that the disease was caused by fungal spores.

Question 3.3

There are various ways of answering this question, depending on your definition of life. If something is alive, you might expect it to grow (by taking in raw materials and having a source of energy) and to reproduce. There are other characteristics you might have chosen too, like having an organised internal structure. (a) Bacteria meet all these criteria. They can grow and reproduce, and they have an organised internal structure. (b) Viruses have an organised internal structure, and reproduce (inside other cells), but they do not grow, in the sense of getting bigger. They are a fixed size when found outside cells and when inside cells they become disassembled, and then more components are made, and assembled into new (full-size) viruses. Living things also adapt and evolve to environmental conditions, which is another characteristic of being 'alive'. Both bacteria and viruses evolve, so by this criterion they could be viewed as being alive. The debate continues!

Question 3.4

The plates referred to here are Petri dishes containing a layer of agar gel, with appropriate nutrients in it, as required by the microbe being cultured, in this case *S. aureus*. A small sample of the microbe would be picked up on a sterilised wire loop and spread onto the surface of the agar in parallel streaks, in several directions on the plate. This spreads out individual microbes, which each then develops into a colony. (*75 words*)

Question 3.5

There are likely to be many fungal (and possibly bacterial) spores for which tomato soup does not provide the ideal conditions to grow. For example, some species may need more sugar or less sugar in their environment; they may need other substances, such as vitamins, which are not present in tomato soup; they may be species that grow very slowly and so do not produce a visible colony in the time available; they may need to grow in the dark, or in cool conditions, or where there is no oxygen. You may be able to think of other reasons too. Since none of these species will form a visible colony, despite their spores being present, the number calculated will almost certainly be less than the total number of spores in the air above the soup.

Question 3.6

See Table 3.3.

Table 3.3 Completed version of Table 3.2 showing the lead scientists and the century in which each milestone in microbiology was reached.

Milestone in microbiology	Lead scientist	Century
Development of the first compound microscope	Hooke	17th
Improvements in the microscope to allow magnification up to ×200	van Leeuwenhoek	17th
Cowpox used for vaccination against smallpox	Jenner	18th
Final refutation of the theory of spontaneous generation	Pasteur	19th
First description of *Bacillus* and classification of microbes	Cohn	19th
First link between microbes and diseases (based on work on anthrax)	Koch	19th
Discovery of viruses	Beijerinck	19th
Discovery of first antibiotics	Fleming	20th
Sequencing of first microbial genome	Venter	20th

Question 3.7

(a) An enzyme is the name for a protein that speeds up chemical reactions which would otherwise go too slowly to be useful (Section 3.7).

(b) A substance produced by one microbe to kill another is an antibiotic (Section 3.7.2).

(c) A medium of a particular composition and with specific conditions of incubation which favour the growth of particular types or species of bacteria is an enrichment medium (Section 3.8).

(d) A substance which can join bases together to make a new strand of DNA is the enzyme DNA polymerase (Section 3.9).

(e) The process of finding out the exact order of the bases in the genetic material of a species is DNA sequencing or genome sequencing (Section 3.9).

Question 3.8

If all four of Koch's postulates must be satisfied before the microbe can be accepted as the cause of a disease (Section 3.5), then, because it cannot be cultured, *Mycobacterium leprae* fails to meet postulates 2, 3 and 4, and so cannot be accepted as the cause. However, this literal interpretation of the postulates is no longer accepted and in fact it has proved possible to culture the leprosy bacillus in other animals. It can be grown in the footpads of mice, and in nine-banded armadillos, which, like humans, are susceptible to leprosy.

Question 3.9

(a) The depth of air in the container is 6 cm, since the container is 10 cm deep and the soup depth is 4 cm.

So, the volume of air in the container above the soup would be

$$20 \text{ cm} \times 10 \text{ cm} \times 6 \text{ cm} = 1200 \text{ cm}^3.$$

Since there are 1 million cm^3 in 1 m^3, the volume of air in the container in m^3 would be

$$(1200/1000\ 000)\ m^3 = 0.0012\ m^3.$$

There were 13 colonies, so at least 13 spores must have been present in the air (probably more, see answer to Question 3.5).

So the number of spores per m^3 would be $13/0.0012 = 10\ 833$.

So, to the nearest hundred, there must be at least 10 800 spores per cubic metre of air.

(b) A kitchen 4 m long, 3 m wide and 2.5 m high would have a volume of $4\ m \times 3\ m \times 2.5\ m = 30\ m^3$ (ignoring space taken up by furniture).

So, if there are 10 800 spores per cubic metre of air, the total number of spores in the kitchen would be

$$(10\ 800\ \text{spores per}\ m^3) \times 30\ m^3 = 324\ 000\ \text{spores}.$$

That is quite an amazingly large number!

Strictly speaking, the value 10 833 spores per cubic metre should have been used in this calculation, to avoid errors which occur when you do subsequent calculations with numbers that have been rounded. This would give you a result of 325 000 spores in the kitchen.

Question 4.1

Eggs, tea and ice cream are the three that do not involve microbes.

It is possible to consider a hen's egg, either unfertilised or fertilised but before incubation, to be a single cell, but a rather special and large one, certainly too big to be considered a microbe!

When tea leaves are picked, they are allowed to wilt and undergo other changes, before being heated and dried. These changes are called 'fermentation' in the tea industry, but they depend only on the enzymes already in the tea leaves, which begin to break down the cells of the leaves, so they are not true fermentation involving microbes. Ice cream is made from dairy products such as cream and milk, together with flavourings and sweeteners. Should one of the flavourings be vanilla, then microbes may be involved in the traditional processes of curing the vanilla pods to produce the characteristic flavour.

All the other items depend on microbes in some way, as you will discover as you work through this chapter.

Question 4.2

The equation becomes:

$$C_6H_{12}O_6 + O_2 \longrightarrow CO_2 + H_2O + \text{energy}$$

If you have tried to balance the equation, here is the balanced version:

$$C_6H_{12}O_6 + 6O_2 \longrightarrow 6CO_2 + 6H_2O + \text{energy} \qquad \text{(Equation 4.4)}$$

This is the equation for aerobic respiration (cf. Equation 1.1).

Question 4.3

Acetobacter breaks down alcohol, using oxygen, to give acetic acid. So the word equation is:

$$\text{alcohol} + \text{oxygen} \longrightarrow \text{acetic acid} + \text{water} + \text{energy} \qquad \text{(Equation 4.5)}$$

and the chemical equation is:

$$CH_3CH_2OH + O_2 \longrightarrow CH_3COOH + H_2O + \text{energy} \qquad \text{(Equation 4.6)}$$

This is a balanced equation since there are the same number of each type of atom, C, H and O, on each side of the equation. Now add these equations to Table 4.1 in Activity 4.1.

Question 4.4

In anaerobic conditions, *Leuconostoc* uses glucose to produce lactic acid, so the word equation would be:

$$\text{glucose} \longrightarrow \text{lactic acid} + \text{energy} \qquad \text{(Equation 4.7)}$$

The corresponding chemical equation is:

$$C_6H_{12}O_6 \longrightarrow CH_3CHOHCOOH + \text{energy}$$

Adding up the atoms in lactic acid gives $C_3H_6O_3$. You will notice that a molecule of glucose has exactly twice as many of each type of atom, so in this fermentation process, each glucose molecule splits into exactly two molecules of lactic acid. The balanced equation is:

$$C_6H_{12}O_6 \longrightarrow 2CH_3CHOHCOOH + \text{energy} \qquad \text{(Equation 4.8)}$$

Add Equations 4.7 and 4.8 to Table 4.1 in Activity 4.1.

Question 4.5

Microbes can be killed by heat. For example, the yeast *Saccharomyces*, used in making bread, is killed when the bread is baked.

They can be killed by alcohol. For example, the yeasts used in making wine and brewing beer, are killed when the alcohol content reaches a certain level.

Microbes can be killed by acid (low pH). When producing pickled cabbage (sauerkraut) or pickled cucumbers, the *Leuconostoc* bacteria are killed when the acidity reaches a certain level below pH 5.

Question 4.6

(a) Most microbes are sensitive to temperature (see Activity 2.2) and so will be killed by being heated to 70 °C for 30 minutes. This will prevent unwanted microbes present in the raw milk being involved in the cheese production process.

(b) The microbes are round, so they are cocci, and as the name suggests, they belong to the genus *Streptococcus*. If the microbes had been rod-shaped, they would have been bacilli, belonging to the genus *Lactobacillus*.

(c) The word equation for the production of lactic acid from lactose is:

$$\text{lactose} + \text{water} \longrightarrow \text{lactic acid} + \text{energy} \qquad \text{(Equation 4.9)}$$

And the equation using the molecular formulae is:

$$C_{12}H_{22}O_{11} + H_2O \longrightarrow CH_3CHOHCOOH + \text{energy}$$

which when balanced becomes

$$C_{12}H_{22}O_{11} + H_2O \longrightarrow 4CH_3CHOHCOOH + \text{energy} \qquad \text{(Equation 4.10)}$$

Add Equations 4.9 and 4.10 to Table 4.1 in Activity 4.1.

Question 4.7

The equation for the breakdown of lactic acid with oxygen by *Propionibacter* to produce carbon dioxide and water is:

$$CH_3CHOHCOOH + O_2 \longrightarrow CO_2 + H_2O + \text{energy}$$

When balanced, this becomes.

$$CH_3CHOHCOOH + 3O_2 \longrightarrow 3CO_2 + 3H_2O + \text{energy} \qquad \text{(Equation 4.11)}$$

Now add the word equation and balanced chemical equation to Table 4.1 in Activity 4.1.

Question 4.8

Step 1: actinomycin affects the copying of DNA.

Step 2: neither of the antibiotics listed disrupt the actual process of cell division, though ultimately, those antibiotics which affect protein production and DNA copying will inevitably prevent the cells from dividing.

Step 3: beta-lactams such as penicillin and ampicillin, disrupt the cell's ability to produce proteins, as do gentamicin and erythromycin.

Question 4.9

(a) CH_3OH is an alcohol, since it ends in an OH group, like ethanol (Box 4.1). This is methanol, found in methylated spirits and in some vehicle windscreen washer fluids.

(b) HOOCCOOH is an organic acid, since it has a COOH group, like acetic acid (Box 4.1). In fact, this compound is just composed of two COOH groups, written back to back. It is called oxalic acid and is found in various foods, including rhubarb and tea leaves.

(c) NH_2CHCH_3COOH has both a COOH and an NH_2 group making it an amino acid (like glycine in Section 4.2). If you said it was an acid, then that's correct too.

Question 4.10

Using formulae, the equation for photosynthesis is

$$CO_2 + H_2O + \text{energy from Sun} \longrightarrow C_6H_{12}O_6 + O_2$$

When this is balanced, it becomes

$$6CO_2 + 6H_2O + \text{energy from Sun} \longrightarrow C_6H_{12}O_6 + 6O_2 \quad \text{(Equation 4.12)}$$

You may have noticed that this is the exact reverse of the equation for aerobic respiration

$$C_6H_{12}O_6 + 6O_2 \longrightarrow 6CO_2 + 6H_2O + \text{energy} \quad \text{(Equation 4.4)}$$

You should now add Equations 1.4 and 4.12 to the final row in Table 4.1, thus completing Activity 4.1.

Question 4.11

If air was not excluded from the container of cabbage, it is most likely that the bacteria would respire aerobically, and so would produce just carbon dioxide and water, instead of the acid, according to this equation:

$$C_6H_{12}O_6 + 6O_2 \longrightarrow 6CO_2 + 6H_2O + \text{energy} \quad \text{(Equation 4.4)}$$

The cabbage would not have the sour taste, which results from the acid production, but might taste slightly fizzy due to the bubbles of carbon dioxide trapped in the jar in which it is stored. The production of acid creates an environment which is inhospitable to most other microbes, so the food can be kept for several months. However, in the absence of this acid, other microbes from the air could colonise the cabbage, and would probably render it inedible in a very short time.

Question 4.12

Plasmodium is the microbe which causes malaria. An effective drug against malaria is artemisinin. It has been possible to introduce some of the genes from the plant, sweet wormwood, which produces this drug, into *E. coli*, by genetic engineering. *E. coli* can then be used to produce large quantities of the precursor of artemisinin, which is called amorphadiene. In the laboratory, this can be converted to artemisinin.

Question 5.1

Statements A, B, D and E are correct.

In statement C, the Y-shaped molecules are antibodies, not antigens. The correct version should read:

C Lymphocytes are part of the adaptive immune system and carry Y-shaped *antibodies* on their surface.

In statement F, the cells which come in to destroy the pathogens are phagocytes, not lymphocytes. The correct version should read:

F When the antigens on a pathogen have been recognised by antibodies, and antibody–antigen complexes have been formed, then *phagocytes* come in to destroy the pathogens.

You might find it useful to correct the words in the original Question 5.1 to provide a useful summary of the immune system.

Question 5.2

By various techniques, such as heating the bacteria, subjecting them to other environmental stresses or passing them through a whole series of animals, it would be possible to produce a less virulent strain of *Clostridium tetani* which could be used in a vaccine. When injected, this would carry the same antigens on its surface as the virulent form. The antigens would be recognised by the antibodies on the surface of one of the lymphocytes, which would then divide rapidly to produce many more lymphocytes. These would release antibodies into the bloodstream which would bind to the bacterial vaccine. When a normal virulent strain of *C. tetani* infected the body, the blood would contain the appropriate lymphocytes and antibodies which would be able to destroy the microbe before it could cause an infection

Question 5.3

Streptococcus pyogenes is found in one-tenth of the population, so that means that 10 people in every hundred would carry it *Streptococcus pneumoniae* occurs in one-fifth of the population, which is 20 in every hundred individuals and *Clostridium difficile* is found in 3% of the population, 3 in every hundred people. So if each person only carried one species, then 33 people in every hundred (33%) of the population would be infected with one of the three species. In fact, probably some people will carry two, and a few might be harbouring all three, so the number of infected people is likely to be less than 33 in every hundred. As long as the people carrying these microbes have immune systems which are functioning efficiently, they are not taking antibiotics and they do not have any wounds or similar injuries, the microbes are kept under control and do not multiply and cause disease. However, when patients are admitted to hospital they are increasingly screened (tested) for these microbes so that precautions can be taken to prevent the spread of infection.

Question 5.4

Both processes involve DNA from two individuals. In conjugation, two cells come together and one extends a pilus. In sexual reproduction, two individuals come together and mate. However, in conjugation, the main part of the DNA (the genomic DNA) is not usually involved; a subsidiary piece, called a plasmid, is usually transferred. In sexual reproduction, half of the DNA of one individual is combined with half from the other, so that the offspring has characteristics of both parents.

Question 5.5

These are the two obvious differences.

1   Conjugation requires the presence of another microbe, whereas transformation does not need any other living cells to be present, just the DNA.

2   Conjugation generally transfers plasmid DNA only. In transformation, the foreign DNA could be derived from many different sources and is taken up as naked DNA from the environment.

Additionally, in conjugation, the DNA transfer is usually successful. The transformation process may not be successful as the DNA fragment taken up may be destroyed in the cell.

Question 5.6

All the figures which include microbes in this chapter have been taken using an electron microscope. Figure 5.4 shows a phagocyte ingesting anthrax bacteria in which the three-dimensional appearance is very clear. The scale bars on Figures 5.7 and 5.8 indicate that the images have been magnified about 2000 times and 3000 times, respectively. These are much higher magnifications than would be possible with a light microscope, so these are SEM images too. Figure 5.9b shows details of pili that would not be visible with a light microscope. Figure 5.3, while not strictly a picture of microbes, since it shows red and white blood cells, is also taken with an SEM. Figure 5.11 shows a slice through a virus, so this is a TEM image. Figure 5.15 is also a set of images through slices of tissue and virus. It is a set of false-coloured TEM images.

Question 5.7

Here is the completed paragraph with the required words in italics:

Viruses consist of a strand of genetic material, either *DNA* or *RNA*, surrounded by a protein *coat* or *capsid* which *protects* it. All the *genes* needed to make new *viruses* are present in the *nucleic acid* but the *replication* process can only take place when the virus is inside a *host* cell. Viruses *hijack* the host cell's *biochemical* processes to make new *copies* of themselves which then burst out of the host cell.

Question 5.8

Comparing microbes P and Q, there are 11 differences in the sequence of bases. The number of differences between microbe P and microbe R is only 4, while there are 13 differences between microbes Q and R. So, microbes P and R are most closely related since their DNA sequences are most similar. Microbe Q is more closely related to microbe P than to microbe R, because there are only 11 differences between Q and P whereas there are 13 differences between Q and R.

Question 5.9

The errors are shown in italics in the square brackets below.

The phagocytes form part of a system that is identical in all people and is called the adaptive [this should be *innate*] immune system. However, it is the innate [this should be *adaptive*] immune system that allows the human body to respond very rapidly to microbes that it has encountered before. The immune system uses a type of white blood cell called lypophytes, [this should be *lymphocytes*] which have chemical receptors on their surfaces that can bind to any materials which are foreign to the body. The basis of the unique recognition of different microbes is the antibody system. Antibodies are U-shaped [this should be *Y-shaped*] proteins, with the two prongs made up of small chains of enzymes [this should be *amino acids*] that can be arranged in an enormous number of different ways to recognise the antigens on the surfaces of different foreign microbes.

Question 5.10

Since flu is caused by a viral infection, it would normally not be appropriate to give antibiotics, since they have no effect on viruses. Excessive use of antibiotics can lead to an imbalance in the natural population of commensal bacteria in the body, and so can result in an illness developing. It can also increase the possibility of resistant strains of bacteria developing. However, antibiotics might be appropriate if the flu has led to a secondary bacterial infection.

Question 5.11

(a) The BTV8 virus would be injected into fertilised chicken eggs and allowed to grow and replicate in the cells. It would then be passed through more eggs until the virus was weakened and would no longer cause the disease in susceptible animals. The virus could then be used in a vaccine.

(b) The vaccination will introduce antigens from the virus into the body of the vaccinated animals. The adaptive immune system will be stimulated and antibodies will be produced by the lymphocytes and released into the blood. If the animal then encounters the virus, the immune system will be ready to deal with it, the antibodies will immediately link to the antigens on the virus, so that it can be destroyed by phagocytes before causing the disease.

(c) Viruses need to attach to particular cells in the animal in order for the cells to be infected and the disease to develop. In those animals which are unaffected, the receptors on the cells are presumably not appropriate for the viruses to bind to and so they cannot grow and reproduce.

(d) The disease is spread by midges that carry the virus from one animal to another. It is necessary for all farmers to vaccinate their animals so that some animals do not continue to harbour the disease and allow it to be spread by midges to other unvaccinated animals.

Question 6.1

(a) Since the normal temperature of the human body is 37 °C, the microbe which is most likely to live inside the body is Microbe B whose optimum temperature is 39 °C. In fact, Microbe B is *Escherichia coli*, found in the human gut.

(b) Water boils at 100 °C. Microbe E, with an optimum temperature of 106 °C is the only one that could survive in boiling water. The top temperature for Microbe D is about 97 °C, so it would not survive in boiling water.

(c) Microbe B, *E. coli*, has the largest range, from about 8 °C to 47 °C, a range of about 39 °C. This helps to explain why it is so common and can live, for example, in meat on display in a butcher's shop.

(d) Its optimum temperature is given as 39 °C, and its range is between about 8 °C and about 47 °C. So it can grow for about 31 °C below its optimum temperature, but only about 8 °C above.

(e) Microbe A can only survive between about 12 °C and about minus 5 °C (−5 °C), so its range is about 17 °C.

(f) At low temperatures, all chemical reactions go much more slowly than at higher temperatures. So even at its optimum temperature, Microbe A can only grow very slowly compared to other microbes.

Question 6.2

Statements B, D, E and F are correct. Statement A is not wholly correct because there can be other components of the cell such as a cell wall, outer membrane and capsule outside the plasma membrane (Figure 1.8). Statement C is incorrect because the chromosome is made of DNA, not RNA.

Question 6.3

1 DNA: weak bonds between the two chains break and the double helix falls apart.

2 Enzymes: weak bonds holding the molecule in shape break and the molecule unravels, so the shape of the active site is lost and the enzyme stops functioning.

3 Plasma membranes: the fats become soft, the proteins are affected and unwanted substances can enter the cell, while essential substances escape from it.

Question 6.4

Those microbes with optimal temperatures below 15 °C are psychrophiles. Those which live at medium temperatures (between 15 °C and 40 °C) are mesophiles. Thermophiles thrive at temperatures between 40 °C and 80 °C and those that live above 80 °C are called hyperthermophiles (D and E). If your completed Table 6.1 is not correct, make sure you amend it as you will need to refer to it later.

Question 6.5

It is important for a psychrophile which lives at very low temperatures that its plasma membrane does not become too stiff and so it is likely to have many more unsaturated tails, with one or more double bonds in them, than the plasma membrane of a mesophile which lives at higher temperatures.

Question 6.6

(a) An acidic environment is likely to kill many of the microbes (all the neutrophiles and alkalinophiles) which are ingested in the food, some of which might otherwise cause illness.

(b) Acids affect the stability of the weak bonds in proteins, so when foods containing protein are eaten, the stomach acid will cause the proteins to unravel. This in fact makes it easier for them to be digested by the stomach enzymes.

Question 6.7

The equations would be:

urea + water $\longrightarrow$ carbon dioxide + ammonia

$$(NH_2)_2CO + H_2O \longrightarrow CO_2 + NH_3$$

When balanced to ensure the same number of each type of atom on each side of the equation, it becomes:

$$(NH_2)_2CO + H_2O \longrightarrow CO_2 + 2NH_3$$

Question 6.8

The equation for the breakdown of iron sulfide by the action of *T. ferrooxidans*, with the names of the substances written in the same sequence on the line below the chemical formulae, is as follows:

$$FeS_2 + 3O_2 + 2H_2O \longrightarrow Fe + 2H_2SO_4 + energy$$

iron sulfide (pyrite) + oxygen + water $\longrightarrow$ iron + sulfuric acid + energy

Question 6.9

When the pressure is higher, the molecules are pushed closer together. Saturated fats already pack very closely together since their carbon chains are straight and so if they were pressed any more closely, they would tend to make the membrane very stiff and it would not function properly. Unsaturated fats, on the other hand, pack much more loosely due to kinks in the carbon chains. High pressure would push the chains closer together but the membrane would still be relatively flexible. You would therefore expect many fewer saturated fats in the membranes of barophiles, and this is in fact the case when the membranes are analysed.

Question 6.10

The reddish colours are likely to be caused by pigments in huge quantities of halophilic microbes living in the salt ponds. The psychrophiles, which live in snow, produce coloured pigments like this to absorb the solar radiation that would otherwise damage their cells, and so it would be reasonable to conclude that the pigments of halophiles serve a similar purpose and this is thought to be the case.

Question 6.11

You may have chosen to make slightly different points from these, but these are examples of what you might have written.

(a) *Taq* polymerase is a thermostable enzyme produced by the thermophile, *Thermus aquaticus*, to enable it to replicate DNA at high temperatures. One important commercial use of this enzyme is in the polymerase chain reaction (PCR) which makes multiple copies of DNA, for use in genetic fingerprinting.

(b) An alkalinophile is a microbe which prefers to grow at an alkaline pH, i.e. where the pH value is significantly greater than 7. High pH values are found in some volcanic environments.

(c) Plasma membranes are made of a phospholipid bilayer, two layers of phospholipids with their tails pointing inwards and their heads on the outside. Those phospholipids with unsaturated tails pack less closely than those with saturated tails and so make the membrane less rigid.

(d) Carotenoid pigments are found in some extremophiles, where they absorb some of the radiation from the Sun, protecting the cell contents from damage.

(e) Bioleaching is the process of extracting minerals from crushed ores using the acidophile bacterium, *Acidithiobacillus ferrooxidans*. The microbes use metal sulfides as their source of energy and so release metals and sulfuric acid.

Question 6.12

See Table 6.3.

Table 6.3 Parts of the cell affected by extreme conditions. A completed version of Table 6.2.

Part of cell	Extremes of:				
	temperature	pH	pressure	salinity	radiation
DNA	✓	✓			✓
enzymes (proteins)	✓	✓		✓*	✓
plasma membrane	✓		✓	✓	
cytosol		✓	✓	✓	

*Although not mentioned in the text, salinity does affect enzymes, by affecting the folding of the protein molecules and therefore the shape of the active site.

Question 7.1

(a) On land, the major areas of photosynthesis are in South America, central and southern Africa and south-east Asia.

(b) These are areas of rain forest, where rainfall and temperature are both high, and there is plenty of sunlight, so conditions are favourable for photosynthesis.

(c) It is less easy to correlate the amounts of chlorophyll detected in the oceans with climate zones. The regions with highest concentration are along coasts (especially off river mouths) and at higher latitudes. Nutrients such as nitrogen, phosphates and iron are carried into coastal seas by rivers but do not reach far out into the open oceans and this limits the population of phytoplankton in these regions and therefore the overall amount of photosynthesis. Water also tends to upwell along coastlines as it meets land, bringing nutrients with it and favouring photosynthesis.

Question 7.2

Radiolarian: The picture in Figure 7.3a is about 50 mm across and that represents 0.6 mm, so the magnification is 50/0.6 times = about 80 times. The largest radiolarian with its spines is about 20 mm across. Its actual size would be $20 \times 1000/80$ µm across = 250 µm.

Dinoflagellate: The picture in Figure 7.2a is 120 mm across. If that represents 1.25 mm, then everything is magnified roughly 100 times. The images of *Ceratium* in Figure 7.2a are about 15 mm long, so the actual *Ceratium* would be 100 times smaller, i.e. 150 µm long.

Diatom: As before in Figure 7.2a everything is magnified by about 100 times. The largest round diatom measures about 12 mm across, so the actual diatom would be 100 times smaller than this, i.e. 12/100 mm, or $12 \times 1000/100$ µm across, which is 120 µm.

Foraminiferan: The scale bar in Figure 7.3b represents 15 µm. Measuring the length of that, and the width of the foraminiferan, shows it to be 3.5 times larger than the scale bar, so that is just over 50 µm.

Coccolithophore: The size is given in the caption to Figure 7.2b as 5 µm.

Pelagibacter ubique: The scale bar on Figure 7.4 shows that one cell is about 1 µm long.

See Table 7.4. Don't worry if your values are slightly different from these.

Table 7.4 Comparison of the sizes of various microbes (completed Table 7.2).

Microbe	Size/µm
radiolarian (include the spines)	250
dinoflagellate (use *Ceratium* from Figure 7.2a)	150
diatom (use a round one from Figure 7.2a)	120
foraminiferan	50
coccolithophore	5
Yersinia pestis	1
Pelagibacter ubique	1

Question 7.3

Here is the completed paragraph with the missing words in italics.

Carbon dioxide dissolves from the atmosphere into seawater. It is taken in by phytoplankton and used in photosynthesis, and some of the carbon atoms become part of *sugar* molecules and then other *organic compounds* in the phytoplankton. Some are released back into the seawater as *carbon dioxide* in the respiration of the phytoplankton and eventually may return to the atmosphere. Other carbon atoms may become part of 'skeletons' made of *calcium carbonate* in some foraminifera and coccolithophores. The phytoplankton may be consumed by zooplankton, which use the *organic compounds* as food and release the carbon back into the seawater as *carbon dioxide* in respiration. Some of the carbon atoms from the food will become part of the *organic compounds* in the bodies of the zooplankton and others may be made into *calcium carbonate* if they have 'skeletons'. The phytoplankton or zooplankton that die are consumed by other zooplankton and the carbon atoms are recycled back into the water in *carbon dioxide*. Small amounts of carbon, including the skeletons, escape the recycling and fall to the sea floor in small particles.

Question 7.4

There are errors in all the statements about methanogens.

(a) Some methanogens do live in wet places, but they are obligate anaerobes and so cannot survive if oxygen is present. They cannot respire aerobically.

(b) Most natural gas is formed by chemical changes which occur to the remains of dead microbes buried deep below the Earth's surface (Section 7.2.1). It is not produced by methanogens.

(c) Those methanogens which live deep underground, within ice cores or in the desert, could be considered as extremophiles. As anaerobic conditions are extreme to humans, then most methanogens could be considered to be extremophiles.

(d) Although the reaction which methanogens perform is somewhat similar to photosynthesis, in that it uses carbon dioxide and produces sugars, it does not take place in the presence of light and so the microbes do not need chlorophyll.

(e) Methanogens do produce methane in landfill sites, but they are actually using the hydrogen produced by other types of microbes that are causing the decomposition, rather than themselves digesting the waste.

Question 7.5

Clover is a legume and therefore has nodules on its roots containing the bacterium *Rhizobium*. These bacteria fix nitrogen from the air and provide nitrogen for the use of the clover plants. If, at the end of the season, the clover is ploughed in, the nitrogen compounds in the clover will remain in the soil and provide fertiliser for the next crop. It is often called 'green manure'.

Question 7.6

The bacteria that take part in the nitrogen cycle are as follows:

1 Nitrogen-fixing bacteria. Found in the soil or in root nodules of legumes, they fix atmospheric nitrogen N_2 into ammonium ions NH_4^+.

2 Decomposers. These break down dead plants and other waste in the soil, and convert the nitrogen components in the dead matter or waste to ammonium ions.

3 Nitrifying bacteria. These convert ammonium ions to nitrite ions, NO_2^-, and then convert the nitrites to nitrate ions, NO_3^-.

4 Denitrifying bacteria. In anaerobic conditions these convert nitrates back into nitrogen gas which is released to the atmosphere.

5 Anammox bacteria. These combine ammonium ions with nitrate ions to form nitrogen gas which escapes to the atmosphere. These bacteria are also denitrifyers.

Question 7.7

See Figure 7.14.

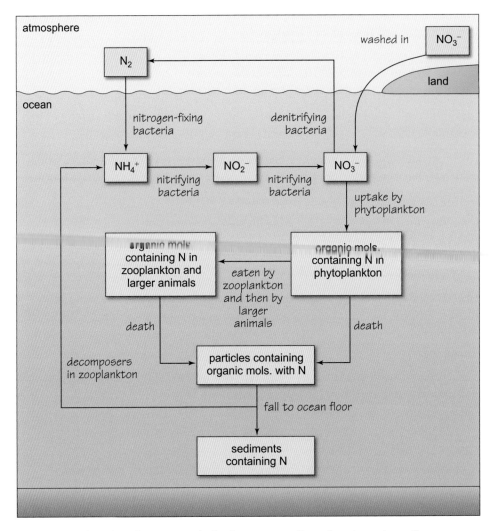

Figure 7.14 The nitrogen cycle in the oceans. Completed version of Figure 7.10.

Question 7.8

Here are the forms of sulfur and the bacteria involved in their conversions:

$$H_2S \xrightleftharpoons[\substack{\text{anaerobic sulfate-reducing}\\\text{bacteria}}]{\substack{\text{purple and green}\\\text{sulfur bacteria}}} S \xrightleftharpoons[\substack{\text{anaerobic sulfate-reducing}\\\text{bacteria}}]{\substack{\text{sulfur-oxidising}\\\text{bacteria}}} SO_4^{2-}$$

where H_2S is hydrogen sulfide, S is the element sulfur and SO_4^- is sulfate ion.

Question 7.9

Carbon, nitrogen and sulfur cycle through all four 'spheres' (atmosphere, biosphere, hydrosphere and the geosphere). Phosphorus is not found in the atmosphere (except perhaps as tiny amounts in dust) and only cycles through the other three spheres.

Question 7.10

(a) This statement is false. Carbon is fixed into organic carbon by autotrophs. The process is the opposite of decomposition because it involves the formation of organic molecules not their decomposition (Section 7.2.2).

(b) This is correct, although the first products of nitrogen fixation are ammonium ions. These are transformed (via nitrites) into nitrates by nitrifying bacteria (Section 7.3.1).

(c) This statement is false. Denitrification is the process of releasing nitrogen gas back into the atmosphere, not taking it up (Section 7.3.1).

(d) This statement is correct. Sulfate reducers produce hydrogen sulfide gas (Section 7.4).

(e) This statement is incorrect. Phosphorus is primarily found in phosphate compounds in rocks and does not exist in a gas in the atmosphere (Section 7.5).

Question 7.11

See Table 7.5.

Table 7.5 Forms in which elements are found on Earth. Completed Table 7.3.

Element	Atmosphere	Biosphere	Hydrosphere	Geosphere
carbon	carbon dioxide CO_2	organic molecules and carbonate skeletons	dissolved carbon dioxide CO_2	carbonate rocks, coal, oil, gas, etc.
nitrogen	mostly nitrogen N_2, small amounts of NO and NO_2	organic molecules containing N such as proteins and chlorophyll	ammonium ions NH_4^+, nitrite ions NO_2^-, nitrate ions NO_3^-	in soil: ammonium ions NH_4^+, nitrite ions NO_2^-, nitrate ions NO_3^-
sulfur	sulfur dioxide SO_2 and hydrogen sulfide H_2S	organic molecules containing S, such as some amino acids	sulfate ions SO_4^{2-}	sulfur S and sulfate ions SO_4^{2-} in soil
phosphorus	–	DNA, RNA, ATP and ADP	phosphate ions PO_4^{3-}	phosphate ions PO_4^{3-} in rocks and soil

Question 8.1

(a) This statement is correct. A stromatolite is essentially a microbial mat or biofilm made up of different layers of microbes that makes use of different environments at different depths in the mat to grow (Section 2.6.1).

(b) This is correct. Photosynthetic microbes will live on or near the surface of stromatolites so that they can use sunlight as a source of energy.

(c) This statement is incorrect. Stromatolites do not always have fermentation occurring within them. Often the inside of a stromatolite does have anaerobic conditions, but there is no reason why fermentation needs to occur.

(d) This statement is correct. Stromatolites are layers of microbes that trap particles of mud and sand.

Question 8.2

A microbe which can grow at high temperatures is called a thermophile, or possibly a hyperthermophile and one that can cope with radiation is called radio-tolerant (Sections 6.2 and 6.6). Organisms that can tolerate more than one sort of extreme condition are called polyextremophiles (Section 6.7).

Question 8.3

The most important molecule affected by radiation is DNA (Section 6.6) because it carries the code for all the proteins that are required for microbes to grow and reproduce. So any contaminant microbes on a spacecraft that lands on Mars are likely to be killed very quickly, unless they are somehow shielded deep inside the spacecraft, where they might survive for longer.

Question 8.4

It has been estimated that conditions on Earth were too hostile before about 3900 Ma for life to develop due to volcanic activity and bombardment by asteroids and comets (Section 8.1.2). Life probably was present by about 3400 Ma. So, it seems that the time required for life to appear was no more than 500 Ma. If similar timescales apply on Mars, then conditions there would also have been too hostile before about 3900 Ma, and they became too hostile again, due to the very low temperature, at about 3500 Ma. That leaves a window of 400 Ma, about the same period of time as on Earth. So, it appears that there was plenty of time for life to have appeared on Mars.

Question 8.5

Chemolithotrophy is the ability to obtain energy from inorganic sources, such as hydrogen sulfide and iron. Knowledge of this mode of energy acquisition might encourage the design of experiments that are not so focused on the use of organic compounds as an energy source but instead might try to feed hypothetical microbes with inorganic sources of energy suitable for chemolithotrophs.

Question 8.6

Microbes could plausibly obtain energy on Europa by using light for photosynthesis, or chemical energy from hydrothermal vents or by breaking down organic compounds produced by the effects of high-energy particles. On Titan, microbes could be chemolithotrophs, gaining energy from simple molecules such as those containing sulfur, iron or nitrogen. However, Titan's temperature is almost certainly too low for life, at least on its surface.

Liquid water exists on Europa underneath the thick layer of ice, while it could be present on Titan deep in its subsurface, heated by tidal effects from its parent planet Saturn.

It is thought that interactions between incoming high-energy particles and simple molecules such as carbon dioxide and water on Europa, could produce organic molecules. On Titan, there are organic compounds in the atmosphere, and these would provide a source of carbon for microbes, but again, the temperatures on Titan are probably too low for life.

Activities: answers and comments

Answers to the DVD activities will be found on the course website.

Activity 2.2

The answers to Questions 2.1 to 2.6 can be found above in *Questions: answers and comments*.

Activity 3.1

Comments on *Analysis of results*:

Table 3.4 shows the results of the investigation carried out by a member of the S171 Course Team.

Table 3.4 Sample results from Activity 3.1.

	Total number of colonies after 10 days	Number of different types of colony	Observations on colony types
Container 1 closed at once	4	2	3 small white colonies, each only a few mm across, and one green one.
Container 2 open in kitchen for 2 hours	About 10	About 4	The colonies were large (several cm across each) and merging into one another. There were 5 light-green ones with dark-green centres; 2 bright yellow ones; 1 white one which was forming quite a deep mound and 2 pale jelly-like ones.

(a) If there were colonies in Container 1, it is most likely that these came from spores which were trapped in the air between the top of the soup and the cling film, and then settled on the surface of the soup. If you found colonies close to the edge of the container, they might have come from spores on the container itself, or in the water used to wash it out. There appear to be fungal spores all around and the atmosphere is an important means by which they are transported from one environment to another.

(b) You might have chosen to answer this by stating the difference between the numbers, which in the results above would be 6. Or you might have chosen to say how many times greater the number of colonies was in Container 2 than Container 1, which here would be 2.5 times. Either way is acceptable, as long as you explain your result clearly. There were more colonies in Container 2 because there was extra time for spores to settle out onto the surface of the soup.

(c) There were two different types of colony in Container 1 and four in Container 2. Their colour and shape were used to identify them. However, it was not always easy to see whether some of the larger more well-developed colonies were simply older versions of some of the smaller ones. Some of the larger colonies may be older colonies, but the same species as some smaller colonies, possibly reflecting different rates of division. If you exposed the soup in Container 2 to the outside air, you might have found some different colonies from the types which were indoors.

Now return to the activity.

Activity 4.1

Table 4.2 is the completed version of Table 4.1.

Table 4.2 Equations for the energy-producing processes of microbes (completed Table 4.1).

Process	Word equation and balanced molecular equation	Equation number
aerobic respiration	glucose + oxygen $\longrightarrow$ carbon dioxide + water + energy $C_6H_{12}O_6 + 6O_2 \longrightarrow 6CO_2 + 6H_2O$ + energy	1.1 4.4
alcohol fermentation	glucose $\longrightarrow$ carbon dioxide + alcohol + energy $C_6H_{12}O_6 \longrightarrow 2CO_2 + 2CH_2CH_3OH$ + energy	4.1 4.3
production of vinegar by *Acetobacter*	alcohol + oxygen $\longrightarrow$ acetic acid + water + energy $CH_3CH_2OH + O_2 \longrightarrow CH_3COOH + H_2O$ + energy	4.5 4.6
production of lactic acid by *Leuconostoc*	glucose $\longrightarrow$ lactic acid + energy $C_6H_{12}O_6 \longrightarrow 2CH_3CHOHCOOH$ + energy	4.7 4.8
production of lactic acid in cheesemaking	lactose + water $\longrightarrow$ lactic acid + energy $C_{12}H_{22}O_{11} + H_2O \longrightarrow 4CH_3CHOHCOOH$ + energy	4.9 4.10
breakdown of lactic acid by *Propionibacter*	lactic acid + oxygen $\longrightarrow$ carbon dioxide + water + energy $CH_3CHOHCOOH + 3O_2 \longrightarrow 3CO_2 + 3H_2O$ + energy	– 4.11
photosynthesis	carbon dioxide + water + energy $\longrightarrow$ glucose + oxygen $6CO_2 + 6H_2O$ + energy from Sun $\longrightarrow C_6H_{12}O_6 + 6O_2$	1.4 4.12

Activity 5.1

(a) The microbiologist would need to use aseptic techniques to ensure that the sample was not contaminated by any other microbes from the surrounding environment.

(b) There are so many microbes in the human gut that dilution of the sample would almost certainly be needed, so that they were not all growing on top of one another and the number of colonies in the Petri dish could be counted. Serial ten-fold dilutions could be used, using buffer solution to dilute the sample, and mixing well at each stage. Separate cultures could then be grown from each dilution until a culture with a reasonable number of colonies was found, i.e. one in which the colonies do not overlap and so can be counted.

(c) There is not a lot of oxygen in the contents of the human gut, though some will be taken in with the food. So there are likely to be microbes in the gut that are capable of respiring anaerobically, as well as others that are capable of aerobic respiration. If both spread plates and pour plates were made, then both types of microbe would be cultured, though there is a risk of double-counting, with some microbes able to grow in both aerobic and anaerobic conditions.

(d) Samples could be taken, diluted and spread on plates. Then the amount of dilution would need to be taken into account. So, if there were 15 colonies growing after 5 ten-fold dilutions, then there would have been

$15 \times 10 \times 10 \times 10 \times 10 \times 10$ microbes = 1 500 000 microbes, in the original sample before dilution. To calculate the density, the volume of the original sample would be needed, and then the number of microbes in 1 cm³ could be calculated.

(e) In Activity 2.1 you learned that looking at the morphology (shape and external appearance) of microbes under a microscope is not always a good way to identify different species, since many look very similar. Examination of the differences in their DNA and RNA is a much better method, though extracting and sequencing DNA is not something that would routinely be done in most hospital microbiology labs. You will learn more about the range of bacteria in the gut in Section 5.2.1.

Activity 5.2

(a) Humans need bacteria to help digest their food. Prior to this study, it had been thought that everyone would have a common group of bacterial species in their gut, but this generally turned out not to be the case. There was a range of species, but whatever the mixture of an individual human's microbial species, between them the microbes carried all the genes needed for helping the digestive process. So there can be a 'mix' of bacteria as long as between them, their genes 'match' together to give a complete set of those needed to digest the food.

(b) The other points reported were, firstly, that obese people had a bacterial mix containing more genes for digesting all the main nutrients (fat, protein and carbohydrates) than did lean people. This may mean that they digest food more efficiently and therefore extract more nutrients, which may be one factor in causing them to be obese. If this is true, then it may lead to new ways to treat obesity. Secondly, the researchers found that people who were closely related did have similar bacterial species in their gut.

Activity 5.3

(a) The word bug refers to a group of insects (Section 1.1). So microbes should not be referred to as 'bugs', although the term is often used in the popular media.

(b) The missing word is 'toxin'. The actively dividing bacteria produce a toxin (see Sections 1.2 and 5.4), and it is this toxin which is detected in the test.

(c) (i) A false positive is when a test gives a result suggesting that there is a particular infection, when such an infection does not exist.

A false negative is when the test indicates that there is no infection when, in fact, one is present.

(ii) A false negative result could be very dangerous since it would mean that a patient with the disease would be given the all-clear, when in fact, they might need admission to, or a continued stay in, hospital and urgent medical treatment. They could also risk passing on the infection to other people.

(iii) A false positive could result in a person being admitted to hospital, and treated with antibiotics, which could cause adverse effects on other aspects of the microbial populations in their gut.

(d) A carrier is someone who has the microbe in their body and is not showing symptoms of the disease.

(e) Here is a possible answer, though there are many ways of expressing the same information. When you compare it with yours, you should check that you have included most of the same facts that are included in this example.

MRSA is a microbe that has resistance to many antibiotics that are normally used to treat microbes. The name is short for methicillin-resistant *Staphylococcus aureus*, a reference to one antibiotic, methicillin, to which it is resistant. The microbe is found naturally in some people, but becomes a source of infection when the natural microbial balance in the body is disrupted, which is often the case in hospitalised patients. The microbe, like many others, probably gained its resistance by taking up small fragments of genetic material called plasmids. These small fragments of genetic material, which can contain genes for antibiotic resistance, can be passed from one microbe to another, which is how the resistance is spread around. Microbiologists have a constant struggle to keep up with its changing patterns of resistance to the available drugs.

Activity 6.1

Here is a possible answer, though there are many ways of expressing the same points, so your answer is bound to be different.

All cells need enzymes as catalysts for the reactions necessary for life. Enzymes are proteins and when they are heated the weak bonds holding them into the correct shape are broken. However, those microbes which grow at high temperatures, known as thermophiles, have enzymes which are less affected by heat than those of microbes which live at more normal temperatures, and so the enzymes continue to function and the microbes can survive.

Plasma membranes contain fat (phospholipids) in their structure and it is important that the membranes are neither too stiff nor too soft and flexible. The amount of stiffness is determined by whether the carbon chains in the tails of the fat molecules are saturated (they contain the full number of hydrogen atoms) or unsaturated (some hydrogen atoms are missing). Saturated chains pack together very closely and so membranes made from them tend to be stiffer than those made with unsaturated chains, which cannot pack as neatly due to kinks in the chains. So that their membranes are not too flexible at high temperatures, thermophiles have membranes which contain many more saturated chains than there would be in those microbes which live at normal temperatures.

(*177 words*)

Activity 7.1

There are no comments on this activity.

Activity 7.2

(a) Since the tree symbol represents all photosynthesising organisms on land, arrow A is the one which includes the photosynthesis by microbes on land.

(b) Arrow B would include the various types of microbial respiration on land, as well as the respiration of other photosynthesising organisms.

(c) Arrow D represents the breakdown by microbes of organic matter in the soil, releasing carbon dioxide back into the atmosphere.

(d) (i) Arrow F represents the uptake of carbon dioxide into the surface waters which is then taken in by photosynthetic microbes and converted into their organic compounds. (ii) Arrow E represents the release of carbon dioxide from the surface waters of the oceans, due to the respiration of microbes and other organisms living there.

(e) Arrow I (later in the alphabet than H) shows particles which are the remains of microbes falling towards the bottom of the ocean.

(f) Arrow J shows those particles collecting on the ocean floor (ocean sediment).

(g) The microbes will need to be those that can survive in deep water, the barophiles and barotolerant microbes (Section 6.4). They will break down the organic compounds in respiration to obtain their energy. This is indicated by arrow K.

(h) The calcium carbonate particles can form limestone or chalk. The organic compounds could be converted into gas or oil.

(i) Here is a possible answer, to compare with yours. There are some alternative routes, which are just as acceptable.

A carbon atom enters the leaf in a carbon dioxide molecule from the atmosphere. By the process of photosynthesis, it is incorporated into a sugar (carbohydrate) molecule in the leaf and may then find itself in another organic compound inside the leaf. When the leaf falls to the ground, it can be broken down by microbes in the soil, as they use the sugars and other molecules in the leaf for food. By the process of respiration, the carbon atom is then released to the atmosphere again in a molecule of carbon dioxide. By air movements, the carbon dioxide molecule is then carried out over the sea where it dissolves in the surface water. It is then taken in by a microbe in the plankton, one of the species of photosynthetic phytoplankton where it is again incorporated into a sugar molecule and then possibly into another organic compound. The phytoplankton is then eaten by another microbe, this time a member of the zooplankton, for example, a foraminiferan. These microbes make calcium carbonate skeletons (shells), so the carbon atom is incorporated into a calcium carbonate molecule. When the foraminiferan dies, the calcium carbonate sinks to the bottom of the sea and eventually it accumulates to form a calcium carbonate sediment (which could in time produce a limestone rock).

Finally, Table 7.6 lists all the arrows, the processes represented by them and the carbon transformations that take place in the carbon cycle.

Table 7.6 The processes in the carbon cycle of Figure 7.7.

Arrow	Process	Carbon transformation
A	photosynthesis	CO_2 in the atmosphere is converted by photosynthesis into organic carbon in plants and microbes with chlorophyll
B	respiration	respiration is the process by which organic carbon in living plants and microbes (and animals) is converted into CO_2 releasing stored energy
C	leaf fall and death	this is the process by which living organic matter becomes dead organic matter in the soil, either directly or via consumption by animals
D	decomposition	in decomposition, organic carbon in dead animal and plant material is converted into CO_2 in the atmosphere by respiration, mostly of microbes, but also of worms, etc. which break down larger pieces
E	CO_2 release	dissolved CO_2 which has been given out by respiration of organisms in the surface waters of the oceans is released back into the atmosphere
F	CO_2 dissolution	atmospheric CO_2 dissolves in the surface waters and is converted into organic carbon by photosynthetic organisms, many of which are microbes
G	upwelling	dissolved CO_2 in the ocean is transferred back towards the surface by the movement of ocean currents; upwelling occurs in some equatorial regions and in the Antarctic Ocean
H	sinking	dissolved CO_2 is moved down as cold ocean water sinks, mainly in polar regions
I	biological 'pump'	carbon containing particles, both organic matter and carbonate skeleton material, sink into the deep ocean
J	sedimentation	carbon particles are converted into organic and carbonate sediments
K	dissolution and respiration in sediment	carbonate sediments can dissolve in sea water below a certain depth (dissolution) and deep-sea microbes can break down organic sediments by respiration
L	rock formation (ocean)	carbonate sediments and organic carbon can be converted into rocks
M	rock formation (land)	deeply buried organic carbon from undecomposed vegetation can be converted into rock (possibly coal in the right conditions)
N	weathering	weathering is the process by which organic-rich and carbonate rocks are broken down, eroded by water and the carbon is transported to the oceans
O	volcanism	organic and carbonate carbon stored in rocks can be released into the atmosphere as CO_2 via volcanoes.
P	fossil fuel burning	the burning of fossil fuels to produce energy for human use releases CO_2 into the atmosphere
Q	burning of forests	the clearing and burning of forests by humans releases carbon stored as organic compounds into the air as CO_2

Acknowledgements

Grateful acknowledgement is made to the following sources:

Front Cover

Front cover image copyright Dennis Kunkel Microscopy, Inc.

Text

Extract 5.1: 'Bacterial mix and match is the key to good digestion', *New Scientist*. 6 December 2008, Vol. 199, issue 2685. Reed Business Information Ltd; *Extract 5.2*: BBC News (2008) 'C.diff. testing is often wrong', http://news.bbc.co.uk.

Figures

Fig. 1.1a: CNRI/Science Photo Library; *Fig. 1.1b*: Dr Dennis Kunkel/Getty Images; *Fig. 1.2*: Pasieka/Science Photo Library; *Fig. 1.3*: http://microbewiki. kenyon.edu; *Fig. 1.4*: Dr. Heide Schulz-Vogt, Max Planck Institute for Marine Microbiology; *Fig. 1.5*: Tessa Watson/Flickr Photo Sharing; *Figs. 1.7 & 2.4b*: John Durham/Science Photo Library; *Fig. 1.13a*: Jason Maehl/iStock Photo; *Fig. 1.13b*: NASA Ames Research Center; *Figs. 2.1a, 2.1b* left, *2.1c* left & *2.1d* left: © PhotoDisc Europe; *Fig. 2.1b* right: Andrew Gray/Flickr Photo Sharing; *Fig. 2.1c* right: Thomas Becker/Flickr Photo Sharing; *Fig. 2.1d* right: Sergio Caruso/Flickr Photo Sharing; *Fig. 2.1e* left: pannamoo/Flickr Photo Sharing; *Fig. 2.1e* right: Jon Hurd/Flickr Photo Sharing; *Fig. 2.4a*: Crown Copyright/ Health & Safety Laboratory/Science Photo Library; *Fig. 2.5*: Madigan, M.T., Martinko, J.M. & Parker, J. (eds) *Brock Biology of Microorganisms*, 9th edn, Prentice Hall Inc; *Fig. 2.6*: Dr Linda Stannard, UCT/Science Photo Library; *Figs. 2.9b*: London, J. & Cohen-Bazire, G. (1995) in Stanier, R. et al. (eds) *General Microbiology*, 5th ed. Macmillan; *Fig. 2.10*: Eye of Science/ Science Photo Library; *Fig. 2.13*: NSF Microbial Observatorory at Montana State University; *Figs. 2.15 & 7.2b*: Steve Gschmeissner/Science Photo Library; *Fig. 3.1*: Courtesy of Rijksmuseum van Oudheden; *Fig. 3.4*: Biophoto Associates/Science Photo Library; *Fig. 3.5*: Dr Jeremy Byrgess/Science Photo Library; *Fig. 3.8a*: Christian Guthier/Flickr Photo Sharing; *Fig. 3.8b*: Norm Thomas/Science Photo Library; *Fig 3.9a*: Horne, R. W. (1995) in Stanier, R., Ingraham, J., Wheelis, M. and Painter, R. (eds) *General Microbiology*, 5th edn, Macmillan; *Fig. 3.9b*: Kaiser, D. (2000) in Madigan, M. T., Martinko, J. M. & Parker, J. (eds) *Brock Biology of Microorganisms*, 9th edn. Prentice Hall Inc; *Figs. 3.9c & d*: CDC/Dr Fred Murphy; *Fig. 3.10*: Bettmann/Corbis; *Fig. 3.11*: CDC; *Fig. 3.12*: Science Source/Science Photo Library; *Fig. 3.13*: Eli Lilly & Co.; *Fig. 4.2*: SCIMAT/Science Photo Library; *Fig. 4.4b*: Joseph Heintz, University of Wisconsin; *Fig. 4.6*: Juergen Berger/Science Photo Library; *Fig. 4.8c*: Kyle Laughlin/Flickr Photo Sharing; *Fig. 4.10*: Professor David R Benson, University of Connecticut; *Fig. 5.3*: National Cancer Institute/Science Photo Library; *Fig. 5.4*: Volker Brinkmann; *Fig. 5.7*: CDC/Janice Carr & Jeff

Hageman; *Fig. 5.8*: Janice Carr/CDC; *Fig. 5.9b*: Dr L Caro/Science Photo Library; *Fig. 5.11*: Cynthia Goldsmith; *Fig. 5.13*: Kaplan, M.M. & Wester, R.G. (1977) 'The epidemiology of influenza', *Scientific American*, Vol. 237, no 6 December 1977, Scientific American Inc., © Bunji Tagawa; *Fig. 5.15*: Eye of Science/Science Photo Library; *Fig. 6.4a*: J Brew/Flickr Photo Sharing; *Fig. 6.4b*: Culture Collection of Autotrophic Organisms (CCALA) Institute of Botany, Academy of Sciences of the Czech Republic; *Fig. 6.9a*: U.S. National Oceanic & Atmospheric Administration/University of Washington; *Fig. 6.10*: Carol Stoker, NASA Ames Research Center; *Fig. 6.13*: Stephan Hoerold/ iStockphoto; *Fig. 6.14*: Dr Michael Daly/USAF; *Fig. 6.15*: Bob Andersen & DJ Patterson, MBL micro*scope; *Fig. 7.1*: NASA/Goddard Space Flight Center; *Fig. 7.2a*: Norman T Nicoll-Natural Visions; *Fig. 7.3a*: Peter Parks/ imagequest3d.com; *Fig. 7.3b*: Micro*scope; *Fig. 7.4*: OSU Laboratory for the Isolation of Novel Species; *Fig. 7.6*: Maryland Astrobiology Consortium, NASA & STScI; *Fig. 7.9a*: Dr Jeremy Burgess/Science Photo Library; *Fig. 7.9b*: Claude Nuridsany & Marie Perennou/Science Photo Library; *Fig. 7.11*: Ruth E. Blake, Depts. of Geology & Geophysics & Environmental Engineering, Yale University, *Fig. 8.1a*: Professor Andrew Knoll; *Fig. 8.1b*: Sinclair Stammers/Science Photo Library; *Fig. 8.2*: JW Schopf; *Figs. 8.4 & 8.8*: NASA; *Figs. 8.5 & 8.6*: ESA/DLR/FU Berlin (G. Neukum); *Fig. 8.9*: Source unknown; *Figs. 8.10, 8.11 & 8.12*: NASA/JPL-Caltech.

Every effort has been made to contact the copyright holders. If any have been inadvertently overlooked, the publishers will be pleased to make the necessary arrangements at the first opportunity.

Index

Page numbers in *italics* refer to entries in figures whilst those in **bold** refer to entries in tables.